P9-DGF-808

Long Distance Please

13019

Long Distance Please
The Story of The TransCanada
Telephone System

E. B. Ogle

Collins Publishers
Toronto

THE ONTARIO HISTORICAL SOCIETY

First published 1979
by Collins Publishers
100 Lesmill Road, Don Mills, Ontario

© 1979
Alberta Government Telephones
Bell Canada
British Columbia Telephone Company
The Island Telephone Company Limited
Manitoba Telephone System
Maritime Telegraph and Telephone Company Limited
The Newfoundland Telephone Company Limited
The New Brunswick Telephone Company, Limited
Saskatchewan Telecommunications
Telesat Canada

All rights reserved. No part of this publication may be reproduced, stored in a retrieval system, or transmitted in any form or by any means, electronic, mechanical, photocopying, recording or otherwise without the prior written permission of the publisher.

Canadian Cataloguing in Publication Data

Ogle, E.B.
    Long distance please

Bibliography: p
Includes index.

ISBN 0-00-216167-2

1. TransCanada Telephone System — History.
2. Telephone — Canada — History. 3. Telecommunication
— Canada — History. I. Title.

HE8870.T75035   384.6'065'71   C79-094917-2

Printed and bound in Canada
by T. H. Best Printing Company Ltd.

This book is dedicated to those in the telephone business who have kept alive the spirit of service and the standard of excellence that marked the pioneers in the industry.

Ed Ogle

Contents

Acknowledgements

I could not possibly have undertaken this work without the co-operation of literally hundreds of men and women who are involved in the telecommunications industry across Canada. Their assistance and support was freely and generously given and, indeed, to give full credit to everyone, this "telephone book" would require a yellow pages section.

Some people, however, made special contributions and they deserve my special thanks. These are the historians of telephony in Canada — Tony Cashman of AGT, Robert Spencer (retired) and Betty Geraghty of Bell Canada, Furber Marshall of Maritime Tel & Tel, and Elfleda Wilkinson (retired) and Tony Farr of B.C. Tel.

Others who helped particularly to shape this volume with their time, reminiscences and knowledge include: Gordon Ades, Don Archibald, Gordon Archibald, Walter Auld, Tony Brait, Bob Chinnick, Kenneth Cox, Thomas Eadie, Duncan Edmonds, Bob Genno, Ed Graham, Terry Heenan, Oscar Hierlihy, Hank Krupski, Vern Leworthy, Dr. Murray Mackay, Andrew McMahon, Norm Millidge, Norm Phemister, Struan Robertson and Gordon Thompson.

I am indebted to Ron Coulson, Joel Levesque and Sandra Noseworthy for their invaluable research assistance and to Lynda Leonard who did a terrific job searching out photographs. I am also grateful to Susan Lamarre, Janice Stevenson, Elaine Beehler and Sharon Henderson for their diligence and unfailing good humour in typing the various drafts of the manuscript.

Finally, to Eunice Thorne and Ed Matheson of Ampersand, my special thanks and gratitude for their editorial guidance and tireless support. Without them there truly would have been no book.

Ed Ogle

PROLOGUE

Big Talk
Consider the Bumblebee

*The planning of the communications future for a society
may be the most important activity in the realization of that
society's future.*
Moloch or Aquarius? by Gordon Thompson (1977)

As everyone knows, the bumblebee is a large, hairy, black and yellow bee of the genus Bombus which makes a loud humming sound in flight. Engineers can prove mathematically that the bumblebee cannot get off the ground. "Aerodynamically," they explain, "it is impossible for the bumblebee to fly." And that's that. Fortunately, the bumblebee doesn't know it, so it flies — and very well, indeed!

The TransCanada Telephone System (TCTS) is the bumblebee of communications. Like the sceptical engineers, many argue that TCTS cannot work. Fortunately, TCTS doesn't seem to know that, so it confounds critic and friend alike by working — and very well, indeed!

Norm Millidge, director of administration and secretary of TCTS, recently described the TransCanada Telephone System as: *a functional, collaborative alliance of the principal providers of telecommunications services in their respective operating areas, with its members sharing common purposes in operating, technical, marketing and revenue-sharing functions. . . . Its purpose is to provide an effective medium for the interfacing and integration of the telecommunications facilities of its members in order to meet the needs of their customers for telecommunications services extending beyond each member company's serving area.*

Translated, that means the TransCanada Telephone System is an organization of the principal Canadian telephone companies, which provides long distance telephone service — and some other services — to Canadians.

Sounds simple enough, but descriptions are deceptive; it's not nearly as neat and tidy as it sounds.

There are 10 companies in TCTS. Three of them, Alberta Government Telephones, Manitoba Telephone System and Saskatchewan Telecommunications, are provincial Crown corporations, owned and regulated by provincial governments. The four companies on the Atlantic seaboard — The New Brunswick Telephone Company, Limited, Maritime Telegraph and Telephone Co. Ltd., The Island Telephone Company Limited and Newfoundland Telephone Company Limited — are investor-owned and *provincially* regulated. Bell Canada and British Columbia Telephone Company are investor-owned but *federally* regulated — by the Canadian Radio-television and Telecommunications Commission (CRTC). Telesat, the newest member and the tenth company to join TCTS, is owned jointly by the federal government and by the approved telecommunications carriers* under The Telesat Canada Act. Telesat is federally regulated. Just to complicate matters further, B.C. Tel is controlled by U.S. interests. Regulatory bodies, too, have differing philosophies concerning public utilities.
utilities.

Obviously, TCTS membership is a mishmash of private enterprise, government ownership and foreign ownership — and a mismatch of large and small. Bell Canada, for example is one of the nations's largest utility companies controlling well over half the telephones in the country. The Island Telephone Company (on Prince Edward Island) is no bigger than some of Bell's small districts.

Although it may be a matter of stating the obvious, it must be said — at least once. *TCTS is not a trade association.* It is not a group of companies which have combined merely to act as a pressure group or speak for an industry with a single voice. Moreover, TCTS is not a corporation. It owns no stock, has no plant and has only one employee — its president. All other employees on the TCTS staff are on loan from member companies. It is a voluntary association, a consortium.

The TCTS Board of Management, chaired by the president, and consisting of one senior officer from each of the 10 member companies, directs the System. All matters coming before the Board must have the *unanimous* agreement of the members. Any single member, large or small, has the power to veto any decision.

And Canada's political leaders think they have problems with Confedera-

*The approved telecommunications carriers include the nine member companies of TCTS plus CN Telecommunications, CP Telecommunications, Québec Tel and Ontario Northland Communications.

tion! As a matter of fact, all the problems inherent in Canadian Confederation reside in the TCTS setup: language, awkward geography, the often contradictory aspirations of different regions and interest groups. . . . It's all there.

The TransCanada Telephone System has been the unifying force behind long distance telephone service in Canada since 1931. The fact that the name does not ring any bells with most Canadians does not alter the fact that in one way or another TCTS touches their lives every day.

The original terms of reference for this book called simply for a "history" of the TransCanada Telephone System. There was no such organization before 1931, so one might expect our story to begin there. (The term story is used advisedly because that's how I prefer to think of this work.) However, irrespective of the label, no account such as this can be complete without some examination of the roots of what is being considered. To appreciate the present-day ease of direct-dialling someone in London or Paris, one should have a sense of distance and a respect for the technology that has overcome it. It is also in order to trace some of the difficulties and acknowledge a few of the achievements of the people who have contributed to the wealth of communications facilities we take for granted today.

Nonetheless, my view of the TransCanada Telephone System is a personal one and it follows, therefore, that my version of its history is equally personal. No account can possibly cover all the events, give full credit to everyone involved in them or interrelate them to everyone's satisfaction. I hope, however, that this account contains all the significant events and provides a fair description of their impact.

In describing the events leading up to the establishment of TCTS in 1931, I have tried to provide as broad a base as seemed necessary to give reasonable perspective to the events and developments which followed thereafter. In quoting specific individuals, I have also tried to include points of view and descriptions which bear directly on the subject matter at hand.

In no sense is my story to be considered a statement of policy by the TransCanada Telephone System. The views and opinions expressed are entirely my own.

As a working journalist I have had both reason and occasion to become familiar with the state of communications in many parts of the world, and I know full well that an uncommunicated story is like an unobserved tree falling in a forest. No one hears it.

To examine Canada's long distance system is to appreciate why it is as good as it is — and how it got that way. That is the purpose of this work.

In my search for information and ferreting for facts, no company book has been closed to me, no request for an interview — be it with a company president or the newest trainee — has been denied. Therefore, I am satisfied that the working thesis is correct and I submit that any mistakes of fact or interpretation are mine and mine alone.

PART ONE
Setting the Stage

1

Champions of Chat
From Point Pelee to the Pole

*The exchange of information and ideas is the life-blood of
modern society. To an ever-increasing degree this exchange is
accomplished by telecommunications.*
Telecommunication Journal, Vol. 44 (1977)

It is fitting that the first long distance telephone call in history, in 1876, was a
Canadian event. Since 1921, when they achieved the distinction for the first time,
Canadians have been "Champions of Chat" more often than any other people in
the world. The distinction is, of course, a questionable one and it carries no prize,
but it does reflect a true situation based on reliable statistics published each year in
*The World's Telephones.**

Like it or not, Canadians are among the most talkative people in the world.

Why do Canadians talk so much? Vancouver psychologist Tibor Bezeredi
suggests that this Canadian predisposition may be influenced by our environment
— a natural outgrowth of the vastness of the country and its loneliness — creating
a psychological need to talk. "It could be worse," he points out. "If it were not for
the telephone, many Canadians might very well be talking to themselves."

Others suggest that it is the excellence of the Canadian communications
system which may account for the phenomenon. The flat monthly rate for the use
of a telephone rather than a charge for each call, as is common in other countries,
is almost certainly a contributing factor. But Vernon Leworthy, a retired Trans-
Canada Telephone System executive, sees nothing odd in it at all. "All people like

*Figures are compiled by AT&T Long Lines.

to talk," he says. "The telephone has merely made neighbours of us all."

Using 1978 figures, Canada is ranked eighth in the world with its 14.5 million telephones in actual use. The United States, as might be expected, is the runaway leader with over 162.1 million instruments. Japan stands second with 50.6 million, the United Kingdom third with 23.2 million, and West Germany fourth with 22.9 million. The USSR has 19.6 million, France has 17.5 million and Italy has 16.1 million. Spain follows Canada with 9.5 million telephones.

In terms of telephones in relation to population, Canada stands fourth in the world with 63.3 telephones for every 100 people in the country. (In 1928 Canada had 14 phones per 100 population, in 1951 the figure was up to 31, and in 1965 the figure had increased to 37.)

The United States with 74.4 telephones per 100 people leads the world, with Sweden second at 71.7 and Switzerland third at 65.9. The Soviet Union has only seven telephones for every 100 of its population.

Perhaps that poor showing in part explains why the Soviet News Agency, TASS, not long ago considered it necessary to claim the invention of the telephone in 1832 for Russia, some 40-odd years ahead of Alexander Graham Bell. The TASS story, however, failed to explain why this great Russian invention was not developed, and why there were no telephones in Russia until the International Bell Telephone Company made installations in Moscow and Leningrad (then St. Petersburg) early in the 1880s.

Like their Russian comrades, the Chinese have also laid claim to the invention of the telephone. They credit a philosopher named Kung Foo Whing, who apparently whipped one up around 968 A.D. Some Chinese, however, believe that Emperor Hsi Huang Ti made the first use of a form a telephony by shouting through long brass tubes extending between guard stations along China's 1,500-mile Great Wall.

In statistical terms, Edmonton tops the list of Canadian cities with 79.4, telephones for every 100 residents. Calgary follows with 78.3, then Ottawa with 78.2 and Toronto with 77.8. The figures for some other Canadian cities — telephones per 100 people — are:

Lethbridge	− 77.2	Saskatoon	− 71.0
Montreal	− 76.8	Winnipeg	− 67.7
Fredericton	− 74.8	Charlottetown	− 62.3
Quebec City	− 72.7	Halifax	− 61.8
Regina	− 72.5	Saint John	− 61.5
Victoria	− 72.5	St. John's	− 56.1

16

In world terms, Washington, D.C., has virtually a telephone and a half for each of its inhabitants — 149.5 per 100! A place called Southfield in Michigan has 142.9, and Stockholm in Sweden is third with 118.5. San Francisco has 111.2, Paris has 111.0 and Zurich has 107.7. Kansas City Mo. has exactly one telephone for each person living there.

Among the things Canadians talk about from time to time is the high cost of their telephone service, but they are miles ahead of their friends in other lands. It takes a Canadian worker only one and three-quarter hours of labour a month to pay for his basic telephone charges. His European counterpart works from five to 12 hours for the same service. It is also noteworthy that American wage-earners must work a shade longer than Canadians, and that the Japanese work about three times as long to pay for the same basic service.

However, the really big difference is in *what* the Canadian gets for his money — a whale of a lot better service!

The French government recently launched a multi-billion-dollar programme to provide everyone who wants one with a telephone by the end of 1980. In the meantime the waiting list for telephones is over a million, and it costs $220 to get a telephone installed. The average wait is still three to four years and some Parisians have been waiting for over 10 years! The standing joke is that half of France is waiting to get a telephone while the other half is waiting to get a dial tone. This led a French quipster to remark that by 1980, when everybody has a phone, all the lines will probably be busy.

Canadians are spoiled. They take their telephones for granted. In most Canadian cities, if you want to call Cousin Joe in London (England or Ontario) or Auntie Marie in Paris (France or Ontario), there's nothing more strenuous involved than dialing the appropriate number. But it's not so convenient in most of the rest of the world.

Cairo with only 250,000 lines to serve eight million people has the well-deserved repktation for the worst telephone service of any major city in the world. The system is virtually useless during business hours, and some businessmen fly to Greece to place international calls from the better-served hotels in Athens.

Neither Cairo nor Tehran has a telephone directory.

In Oman, businessmen hire young boys to sit at a telephone all day in the hope of getting a line. If they are lucky enough to get one they spend the rest of the day dialing numbers over and over again, in an effort to complete a few calls.

In Lebanon the telephones are under control of the government post office. Users have their calls routed through New York to reach neighbouring Jordan or Saudi Arabia!

In Argentina it is said that the only thing worse than not having a telephone is having one. Getting a dial tone often takes over an hour. Of the 2.5 million telephones in the country more than 70,000 are permanently out of order. There are over a million hopeful Argentinians on the waiting list.

Canadians can make use of all sorts of special "instant" services by dialing the appropriate sequence of numbers — the time, a prayer, a weather report, a joke and many other such gimmicks. In France, however, by dialing a certain number in Paris callers can hear a sensuous female voice give a detailed physical description of herself — including her vital measurements, "spécialties," address, hours of availability . . . and rates. In this respect, perhaps, France is one up on Canada — at least if one is a male chauvinist.

Everybody has heard about the so-called "hot-line" connections between world leaders: a brilliant red phone in Jimmy Carter's office in Washington with a twin in Leonid Brezhnev's office in the Kremlin — just in case. And then there is the story of Lester B. Pearson's hot-line telephone, which was installed in his East Block office on Parliament Hill. To Pearson's consternation one day it started ringing shrilly, but it couldn't immediately be located. Eventually, it was found on the floor behind some draperies. The call turned out to be a wrong number.

Another small body of telephone lore has it that Canada's first red telephone was a hot-line of another sort — installed fittingly in a house of ill-repute in Calgary.

Many Canadian calls overseas or to the North are routed by satellite. Because such signals have to travel 22,300 miles each way, there is a very slight time lag on these calls. Telephone engineers are well aware of this phenomenon even if most telephone users are not. Now and then, however, a double satellite call becomes necessary, perhaps from overseas to a place in the Arctic such as Inuvik; then, the lag becomes very noticeable and a caller may easily find himself talking out of phase with his party. Long distance switching systems try to avoid such routings.

In the Yukon a few years ago a local service was installed for the Loucheux Indians of Old Crow, a small settlement high above the Arctic Circle. The Indians loved the service; it saved them having to struggle into heavy parkas and mukluks and walk several blocks through subzero weather when they wanted to chat with a neighbour. The following year the service was hooked into long distance and the Indians were delighted with that, too. They quickly discovered they could call friends in Inuvik, Whitehorse, Edmonton and even Ottawa (if anyone had a friend there). Trouble came with the first bills after the installation of the long distance service. A worried chief hopped a plane to Whitehorse to complain to Jimmy Smith, the Yukon Commissioner. The unhappy chief showed Commissioner

Smith a bill for nearly $600. Smith studied it . . . calls to Inuvik, Arctic Red River, Fort McPherson, Dawson City, Whitehorse, Edmonton and Ottawa along with sundry other toll charges. "Looks about right," he observed. "Nonsense!" snorted the chief. "We didn't talk any more last month than we did the month before when the bill was only $17." Eventually, the telephone company excused that first month's charges and sent a man in to explain the facts of long distance calling and billing to the settlement.

In Victoria a few years ago a lady complained that she couldn't hear her telephone ring but that oddly enough, her dog could. The only way she knew when to answer the telephone was when her poodle howled. A somewhat mystified repairman showed up to discover that the lady possessed an early magneto telephone. Her dog was chained to the lead-in line to the house, and every time someone called, the poor poodle got a sharp electrical jolt. Naturally, he howled — and the lady hurried to answer the phone. A new phone was installed, different arrangements were made to restrain Fido and both mistress and hound were much happier with the subsequent service.

One of these days a hardy mountaineer will be the first man to climb a certain rugged peak in the St. Elias range in the Yukon, not far from Mount Kennedy. As he clambers over the final ledge, flushed with pride, the first thing he will see is an old-time crank telephone mounted on a post. It was set there years ago by a prank-loving helicopter pilot who doesn't mind waiting a while for his laughs.

Then there is the story of Alphonso Cotticelli (as told by Mark Goldman of *Weekend* Magazine), which points up the efficacy of the Canadian telephone system.

Alphonso, an Italian immigrant eager to try one of the modern conveniences he had seen before only in movies, dialed room service in a Winnipeg hotel to order a sandwich. The hotel operator, not understanding what he wanted, connected him to a Winnipeg operator, gave her his room number for time and charges and then hung up. The Winnipeg operator assumed he wanted to call home and connected him to an overseas operator in Montreal. The Montreal operator, not understanding Italian, connected him to a Rome operator. The Rome operator asked what he wanted. Alphonso said a toasted pepperoni sandwich with lettuce and a coke. . . .

Despite the fact that most trans-Canada calls today are channelled by microwave or satellite, there is still enough cable and conventional wire line in use to span a distance equal to 121 return trips to the moon or to circle the earth at the equator 2,333 times! In addition, TCTS furnishes over 34,000 miles of coast-to-coast, high-quality television circuits for the CBC and CTV.

Greeting calls on Christmas Day jam the lines more than on any other single occasion, with around one million calls — including yours — placed in Canada on that day.

The organization that makes it all work is the 10-member TransCanada Telephone System. But the whole thing started with a Scottish immigrant named Alexander Graham Bell.

2

In the Beginning
Mr. Watson, come here, I want you.

The inventor is a man who looks around upon the world and is not content with things as they are. He wants to improve whatever he sees. He wants to benefit the world; he is haunted by an idea. The spirit of invention possesses him, seeking materialization.
Alexander Graham Bell (1908)

The nineteenth century was a century of invention — inventions that changed forever the face of the earth and the way we live. Transportation, communication, food processing and production methods were affected in almost every line of human endeavour. From matches to skyscrapers — including the telegraph (harnessed lightning), the steamboat, the reaper, the incandescent lamp, the automobile, half-tone reproduction, the phonograph, the airplane — scores of ideas were spawned in an era of ferment. Perhaps leading all was the telephone with its overwhelming influence, revolutionizing first the business world, then that of society and leisure. Nothing so annihilated space as the telephone.

From the beginning of time nearly every pagan pantheon included a messenger god with winged feet. Clearly, early Man, realizing the importance of quick communication, devised a variety of ingenious systems to conquer his greatest enemy, distance. Early Greek marathon runners, carrier pigeons, American Indian smoke signals, the stagecoach, and the romantic pony express of the American West — as well as the Canadian pony express, which speeded news dispatches brought from Europe by trans-Atlantic liner to New York newspapers — all had one purpose: greater speed of communication.

For about 10 months between 1849 and 1850, couriers organized by New York newspapers, competing to be the first with the latest European news, picked up dispatches from trans-Atlantic liners as they entered Halifax harbour. These were raced by pony express across Nova Scotia, then by boat across the Bay of Fundy to Saint John; from here the news was flashed to New York City by telegraph. This curious race continued until telegraph lines were erected across Nova Scotia, so ending the need for the express riders.

In 1796 a German named Hutch, promoting a system of passing shouted messages through trumpets six miles apart, coined the word "telephone." The word derives from Greek roots "tele," meaning far off, and "phone," meaning sound or voice.

As is usual with inventions whose time has come, several men in different countries — including the United States, Canada, England and Germany — were experimenting with the idea of reproducing sound over distance. The break in telephone history came quietly on June 2, 1875, and was made by Alexander Graham Bell, a Scottish immigrant and teacher of the deaf, while he was working in the garret of an electrical shop in Boston.

Bell was working on his "harmonic telegraph," which he hoped would transmit several telegraph messages simultaneously over a single wire. (Bell thought this might perhaps be achieved by transmitting signals using different frequencies — hence the name, harmonic telegraph.) He and his assistant, a young electrician named Thomas A. Watson, were in different rooms, using turning reeds as they experimented with the device. Plucking at a reed screwed down too tightly, Watson produced a twanging sound. At the other end of the wire Bell heard the twang, which was quite different from the normal hum made by the vibrating transmitter. He ran quickly into the next room to see what Watson had done. The reed, tightened against the pole of its electro-magnet, had acted as a diaphragm. After an hour or so experimenting with it, Bell gave Watson instructions for making the first Bell telephone. The next day the crude instrument transmitted the sound of Bell's voice to Watson. Although Bell's words were not discernible, what Watson heard was definitely the sound of a voice.

Bell's backers had a clear understanding of telegraphs and the financial implications of being able to transmit several messages simultaneously over a single wire. The importance and implications of Bell's telephone discovery did not impress them at the time, and they were not at all happy with the prospect of Bell veering off in another experimental direction. Nonetheless, Bell and Watson continued to work on the instrument. On returning to his parents' home in Brantford, Ontario, that September, the young inventor wrote up the specifica-

Alexander Graham Bell was born in Edinburgh, Scotland on March 3, 1847. This photo was taken two years after he invented the telephone in 1874.

Alexander Melville Bell, the inventor's father, was principally responsible for promoting the telephone in Canada.

tions for his first telephone patent, calling it "The Electric Speaking Telephone" — a cumbersome title which the world soon shortened to "telephone."

On March 7, 1876, on his twenty-ninth birthday, Bell received U.S. patent number 174,465. (He obtained his Canadian patent number, 7,789, on August 24, 1877.) American social historian Mitchell Wilson describes it as "the most valuable single patent ever issued by the government." Three days later, Bell and Watson were again working in separate rooms in their shop in Boston. Watson was astonished to hear Bell's voice saying, "Mr. Watson, come here, I want you." Watson rushed down the hall into Bell's room shouting, "Mr. Bell, I heard every word you said — distinctly!"

Bell's place as Canada's greatest inventor is unchallenged. In terms of the size of the industry his invention produced and the social significance of its development, the telephone is Bell's most important invention — and one of the most important inventions in modern history.

The invention and development of the telephone has been accompanied by a certain amount of romance. Indeed, several of the myths surrounding the early days of the telephone have persisted, occasionally to the point of obscuring what really happened. Such a myth is the frequently told tale of Joshua Coopersmith.

In 1867, the story has it, a Boston newspaper noted that: "A man about 45 years of age, giving the name of Joshua Coopersmith, has been arrested in New York for attempting to extort funds from ignorant and superstitious people by exhibiting a device which he says will convey the human voice over metallic wires so that it will be heard by the listener at the other end. He calls the instrument a telephone which is obviously intended to imitate the word 'telegraph' and win the confidence of those who know of the success of the latter instrument without understanding the principles on which it is based. Well informed people know that it is impossible to transmit the human voice over wires, as may be done with dots, dashes, and signals of the Morse code, and that, were it possible to do so, the thing would be of no practical value. The authorities who apprehended this criminal are to be congratulated and it is hoped that his punishment will be prompt and fitting that it may serve as an example to other conscienceless schemers who would enrich themselves at the expense of their fellow creatures."

The purported newspaper article has never been produced, nor, for that matter, has Joshua. But tall tales about heroes do grow in profusion.

Another of the more persistent ones insists that Alexander Graham Bell tried vainly from time to time to sell telephone stock for absurdly low prices, as low as one dollar per share. (The storyteller then asks his listeners to consider how rich

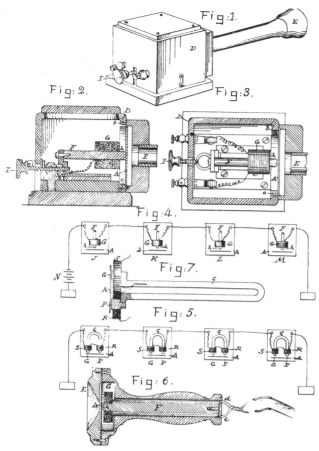

The drawing that accompanied the specifications.
Patent issued to A.G. Bell telephone on August 24, 1877.

they might be today if only one of their great-grandparents had grabbed that opportunity.) The reality is that Alexander Graham Bell wasn't involved or interested in that side of the business. He never sold a single share of stock, nor was there any need for him to do so.

Few people realized the importance of Bell's invention in the beginning. Early reaction to the very idea of telephony wavered between fear of the supernatural and ridicule of the impractical. Hearing voices out of nowhere? Black magic! Recognizable voices travelling miles between cities? Silly notion! Virtually no one understood how it worked. The simplest explanation was offered by a mechanic who noted logically that there was a hole down the middle of the wire.

In 1917 Alexander Graham Bell and his wife, Mabel Hubbard Bell, attended
the unveiling of the Bell Memorial at Brantford, Ontario.

Early models resembled a large box camera with a round projection pro-
truding from one end, somewhat like a lens. What appeared to be the lens was, in
fact, the mouthpiece — and the earpiece, and the transmitter and the receiver.
Some fairly agile manoeuvring was required to carry on a conversation. First a
caller had to speak into the "mouthpiece," then quickly put his ear to it to catch
the return message. Bruised lips and bashed ears were not uncommon and one set
of instructions exhorted: "Do not talk with your ear and listen with your mouth."

Many people who talked into a telephone for the first time experienced a sort
of stage fright and felt foolish shouting at the top of their voices. Bankers
suggested that telephones might be useful to grocers but they were certainly of no
value to them. Conversely, grocers could see a phone being used by a banker, but
— how could it help them?

One editor called it "Salem witchcraft." The New York *Herald* proclaimed,
"The effect is weird and almost supernatural." The Bostom *Times,* poking fun,
complained: ". . . the most serious aspect of this invention is the awful and
irresponsible power it will give the average mother-in-law who will be able to send
her voice around the globe." Humorist Mark Twain quipped that if Bell had
invented a muffler or a gag he might have done the world a real service. The

London *Times* dismissed it as, "the latest American humbug." When several Japanese students in Boston demonstrated the device, people were amazed to discover "the thing even spoke Japanese."

Lawyers objected to an imagined lack of privacy. One solicitor had his telephone installed in a vault, where he narrowly escaped suffocation. Doctors worried that they might not be able to charge for professional advice given over the instrument. Preachers, at first delighted with the prospect of delivering Sunday sermons by telephone, were less enchanted when it occurred to them that parishioners might thus escape the collection box.

Things moved slowly. In early 1877 a man named Emery drifted into the Boston office of Gardiner Greene Hubbard (a very successful Boston lawyer and Alexander Graham Bell's father-in-law-to-be), and leased two telephone sets for 20 dollars the pair. This was the first money ever paid for a telephone.

Against strong pressures from most of his associates (mainly because of an urgent need for immediate capital), and at a time when sales would undoubtedly have produced more income than leases, Gardiner Hubbard insisted that the leasing principle was wiser and better for the development of telephone business. It was Hubbard, therefore, who was responsible for the adoption of what became a fundamental principle of telephone service — the leasing and licensing system — establishing the foundation for the future success of the Bell Telephone Company.

The first permanent outdoor line ever built for telephone service was put up for an electrical manufacturer named Charles Williams, Jr. It extended from his shop at 109 Court Street, Boston (where all of Bell's apparatus for his telephone experiments and the first commercial telephones were made) to his residence in Somerville, approximately two and a half miles away. It was put into service on April 4, 1877. On May 1, that year, the first telephone was rented for business — a private line connecting the Boston office of two young lawyers to the Somerville home of one of them.

The first telephone exchange was opened early in 1878 in New Haven, Connecticut, and the first exchange in Canada (and the British Empire) was opened in Hamilton, Ontario, shortly thereafter. That same year the first telephone lines went up along Albert and Osgoode Streets in Toronto, between Osgoode Hall and the offices of three law firms.

The first commercial lease in Canada was signed by Henry Cossart Baker, a young entrepreneur in Hamilton who had a hand in virtually everything in that city. But Alexander Melville Bell, the inventor's father to whom Canadian rights had been assigned, had a keen sense of public relations and insisted that the first lease be to the federal Government — to connect the office of the prime minister with the residence of the Governor-General. This historic lease was executed on November 9, 1877, but was backdated to indicate that the rental period began on September 21. It was a printed form executed by Alexander Melville Bell, of Brantford, Ontario, as party of the first part, and the Honourable Alexander Mackenzie (the Prime Minister) in his capacity as Minister of Public Works in Canada, lessee, party of the second part. It leased two hand telephones numbered 18 and 19 and two box telephones numbered 25 and 26 with two call-bell instruments. The rent was $42.50 per annum, payable annually in advance on the twenty-first day of September in each year. Later, exasperated when the telephone sometimes ceased functioning in the midst of a conversation, Mackenzie ordered it repaired or taken out. But Lady Dufferin, already fascinated by her new toy, appealed to her husband, the Governor-General, and the Prime Minister was overruled.

Apart from the hookup between the Governor-General and the Prime Minister in 1877, nothing much else went particularly well. Bell, his father, and Thomas Watson — Bell's staunch assistant — ranged the seaboard demonstrating the machine. They put on a good show, which was greatly enjoyed by nearly all who

In August 1870, the Bell family arrived in Canada and purchased this house in Brantford, Ontario. This was their home until 1881. It was here the telephone was invented.

George Brown, the fiery editor of the Toronto *Globe,* and his brother, J.G. Brown, were offered a half interest in all the Bell telephone patents outside of the United States for the amazing sum of $25 each a month for six months — but they failed to carry the agreement through! In retrospect, it was probably one of the most expensive blunders in financial history. Asked to secure the patents in England, Brown just didn't get around to it.

The Dominion Telegraph Co. in Toronto was offered all Canadian rights but the manager didn't even bother to acknowledge Melville Bell's letter.

Even the Canadian Government did its discouraging best, slapping a heavy duty on imported telephone equipment and putting Melville Bell in the position of being unable to supply his subscribers with transmitters and receivers at prices previously contracted for.

saw it. Their entertainment was replete with patriotic songs and opera selections sung over the telephone. They also provided opportunities for everyone to try the new gadget. But Canadians didn't seem to catch on that this was more than an edifying toy. Canadian businessmen and financial wizards with their usual perspicacity wanted nothing to do with it. Investors avoided it like the plague.

Bell returned to Brantford in 1906 for a reunion with the builders of the first telephone line. He is flanked by E. McIntyre (left) and Thomas Brooks (right).

When the inventor returned from his honeymoon trip in England, he could report a highly successful demonstration to Queen Victoria herself, but no luck whatever in terms of interesting any British investors. Not only that, he was broke and in need of a thousand dollars to meet some pressing debts. Discouraged and sick, he declared: "Thousands of telephones are now in operation in all parts of the country, yet I have not received one cent from my invention. On the contrary, I am largely out of pocket by my researches, as the mere value of the profession that I have sacrificed during my three years' work amounting to $12,000."

Bell's backers — Gardiner Hubbard, and Thomas Sanders, a Boston leather merchant — weren't in much better shape. Much of the $100,000 Sanders had put into Bell's invention had been borrowed; he now faced bankruptcy. Hubbard was also very close to the line. At one stage they offered American rights to Western Union for a paltry $100,000. President William Orton of the already gigantic American telecommunications company turned it down flat. His powerful company had no use for an "electrical toy."

Finally, by the end of 1879 the National Bell Telephone Co. came to the rescue and at the Bell family's insistence took over Canadian as well as American rights to the business. In 1880 they sent a Boston businessman and retired sea captain, Charles Fleetford Sise, to Montreal to organize The Bell Telephone Company of Canada — a development Canadians can hardly point to with pride.

For nearly 17 months, while the struggling U.S. and Canadian Bell companies and Bell's backers sought to stay out of the poorhouse, Bell's claim to the invention remained unchallenged. As long as the telephone appeared to be just another whimsical oddity of science, a toy, no one cared. But when repeated Bell demonstrations attracted more and more attention, and hundreds of articles appeared in magazines and newspapers, and telephones began to sell across the country, all sorts of claims began to pop out of the woodwork. As the potential of the telephone began to be appreciated, lawsuits challenging the Bell patent began to swarm like flies to a garbage truck. There were over 600 in the next 11 years.

Meanwhile Western Union, the U.S. giant, had suddenly seen the light and brought its big guns to bear on the little Bell company. Certainly the most powerful electrical company in the world at the time and perhaps the largest corporation of its day, Western Union incorporated its own telephone company, corralled a trio of top inventors including Thomas Alva Edison, started buying up Bell exchanges, sued Bell for infringement of Western Union patents and generally did its best to run roughshod over the Bell people.

Bell fought back. In 1878, a new manager named Theodore N. Vail took over and, with a trio of determined lawyers, fought Western Union to a standstill in the

U.S. courts. (Later it was said that although Bell invented the telephone, Vail invented the telephone business.) After two costly years the Goliath surrendered to the David when Western Union's own lawyers advised them that the Bell patent could not be displaced. The decision turned things around for Bell: its stock quickly soared from $50 to $1,000 a share, and within five months the company was reorganized and renamed the American Bell Telephone Company. The next year (1881) 1,200 new towns and cities were marked on the telephone map, and the following year even more were added. The great North American romance with the telephone was under way. The boom was on. Bell's original backers became wealthy and, almost overnight, the Bell family itself was catapulted into the millionaire class.

By any standard the impact of Bell's telephone has been massive. In Canada alone his invention today provides employment for over 100,000 people across a telephone network linking more than 14.5 million telephones.

For over 45 years after the invention of the telephone, Bell, who has been described as a man who might have invented anything and everything given the time, lived an active, creative life, much of it at his summer home, Beinn Bhreagh (Beautiful Mountain) on Cape Breton Island, near Baddeck, Nova Scotia. Canadians have preserved Bell's memory with imposing memorials at Baddeck and Brantford. A statue of the inventor by Canadian sculptor Cleve Horne, commissioned by the Telephone Pioneeers of America, stands in the portico of the Brantford telephone exchange.

At Tutelo Heights near Brantford the public can also see for themselves what the world was like at the time of the invention. There, the Bell homestead is kept as a Bell family museum, maintained jointly by the city of Brantford, the township of Brantford, Brant County, Bell Canada and the Telephone Pioneers of America. Most of the rooms in the Homestead have been restored precisely as they were when Bell lived and worked and dreamed in Brantford during the days of the early work on the telephone. The Homestead was marked as a national historic site in 1953 by the Government of Canada.

Although Bell was born in Scotland and died a U.S. citizen, his life and life-work were closely associated with Canada. Bell arrived in Canada in 1870 and in 1871 went to Boston to take up a post as a teacher of the deaf. From then until 1880, when he took up permanent residence in the United States, he spent his vacations with his parents at Brantford. From 1887 until his death in 1922, he spent from six to 10 months each year at his summer home in Cape Breton. It was in Brantford in 1874 that he first disclosed his telephone idea to his father. It was in Brantford in 1875 that he wrote the patent specifications for the telephone. And it was in Brantford in 1876 that he made many tests of the telephone, including the world's first long distance call.

In the Nova Scotia village of Baddeck the Canadian Government has built the Alexander Graham Bell Museum, which has been open to the public since 1956. While the memorial at Brantford is dedicated primarily to the telephone, the Baddeck museum is concerned mainly with Bell as an inventor. The displays include enlarged photographs, documents, sketches and models of equipment invented or developed by Bell during his lifetime of experimentation and discovery.

Just as Bell had forseen its invention, he also anticipated the development of telephony — "It is conceivable," he wrote, "that cables of telephone wires could be laid underground or suspended overhead, communicating by branch wires with private dwellings, counting houses, shops, manufactories . . . uniting them through the main cable with a central office where wires could be connected as desired, establishing direct communication between any two places in the city. Such a plan as this will, I firmly believe, be the outcome of the introduction of the telephone to the public. Not only so, but I believe that in the future wires will unite

Bell built Beinn Breagh in 1893. It was the site of many of his experiments with heavier-than-air machines and hydrofoils.

32

the head offices of the telephone company in different cities and a man in one part of the country may communicate by word of mouth with another in a distant place."

This extraordinary pioneer, whose legacy has shaped the whole pattern of modern life, died at Beinn Bhreagh in August 1922 and was buried on his beloved Cape Breton hillside overlooking the Bras d'Or Lakes.

3

The Formative Years
Transcontinental Dreams

As a telephone man I hope the day will come when, instead of only a band of steel from coast to coast and a one hundred and twenty hour journey linking the furthest east and furthest west provinces, a band of copper and a few hours will bind them still closer.

J.H. Winfield
general manager of Maritime Telegraph & Telephone Company Limited
(1921)

It was Alexander Graham Bell who laid the foundation for dreamers like Theodore N. Vail, the first general manager of the American Bell Telephone Company. Vail was also one of the first people to understand the really revolutionary implications of the telephone and its potential to conquer distance. "I saw that if the telephone could talk one mile today, it would be talking a hundred miles tomorrow," he said, persisting in the then-wild notion that the telephone was destined to connect cities and nations as well as neighbours. Vail dreamed big dreams — what he saw was a national telephone system.

Within one week in August 1876, Bell performed a series of critical experiments relating to the use of wire over long distances. Early in the month, after carrying out several tests over short distances in the Brantford area, Bell decided to set up a demonstration which would prove once and for all that long distance was not an obstacle for the telephone.

To conduct his test he required the use of a suitable long distance telegraph line, so he contacted a lusty young Toronto company — Dominion Telegraph. Bell wrote directly to Dominion's manager, a British ex-railwayman named Thomas Swinyard who promptly sniffed at the letter and told an assistant to chuck it into the wastepaper basket. "Another one of those cranks," he huffed. But Swinyard's helper, a young telegrapher named Lewis McFarlane who was interested in the strange new gadget, persuaded Swinyard to allow Bell to use the lines.

On August 10, Bell set up a receiver in Robert White's boot and shoe store in Paris, Ontario, and a transmitter approximately eight miles away in Brantford. At first only explosive sounds like the booms of distant artillery could be heard. Bell telegraphed an assistant to make certain adjustments, and voices could then be heard clearly — including one that was not supposed to be there. Bell hastily sent another telegram (the setup permitted only one-way transmission), and reply confirmed that his father was on the other end of the line — his voice recognizable on the world's first long distance call. Bell recorded that although the transmitter was located in Brantford, and the receiver (which was an improved form of the old Centennial iron-box receiver) was located in Paris, eight miles away, the battery which powered the line was in Toronto — over 60 miles away. "So we actually had a circuit of somewhere between 60 and 70 miles."

That was the first time human speech was transmitted over a distance of several miles. In effect, it was the first long distance call.

In New York, meanwhile, Vail was also pushing the long distance concept. He persuaded Charles J. Glidden (who was to become famous as the organizer of the first round-the-world motor tour) to build the first intercity telephone line between Boston and Lowell, Massachusetts. But Vail was by no means satisfied with that. He wanted a line between Boston and Providence, Rhode Island! His associates at Bell, however, refused to support him. Undaunted, Vail formed a separate company and built the line himself. Initially, it appeared that his colleagues had been right because the line was virtually unusable; there was a serious induction problem, caused by a nearby high-speed telegraph line. Vail's line promptly earned the derisive tile, "Vail's Folly." But when one of Vail's bright young engineers came up with the idea of "metallicking" the double line (which effectively established a closed or complete circuit without relying on the conventional practice of grounding) it worked beautifully.

Having seen the light, Vail's associates at Bell took over the new line and promptly began stringing double wire from Boston to New York — a courageous and costly project for those times. The line required 10,000 poles, and the new kind of copper wire was used for the first time. The project cost $70,000, which sounds like peanuts today but was caviar then. Despite the investment, one Bell official is known to have muttered, "I wouldn't take that line as a gift." He was a

Toll lead for western Ontario leaving Toronto from the vicinity of Terauley and Albert streets. This toll lead was one of the heaviest in Bell Canada territory.

silly man. The line was a winner from the beginning and swept away any notion that the telephone would never be anything more than a neighborhood affair. "It was the salvation of the business," declared Edward J. Hill, the railroad tycoon.

Allthough the first commercial Bell Telephone Company long distance line in Canada had connected Hamilton and nearby Dundas in 1879, the first metallic circuit line connected Hamilton and Toronto in 1888.

In 1877, *Scientific American* published a special article which provided precise instructions on how to make a telephone. For literally decades thereafter it seemed that everyone who read the article sooner or later took a stab at making a cigar-box phone. Some do-it-yourselfers on the Canadian Prairies even went so far, in the early years of the new century, to string up wire any old way, even using barbed-wire fences. They had to contend with everything from bears, who mistook the hum of the singing wires for the hum of honey bees, to passers-by who could easily find other uses for a length or two of good wire. And across the continent, not surprisingly, there was not a marksman anywhere who could resist a target as tempting as a glass insulator on a pole.

In the late nineteenth century the telephone business took off like a twentieth century rocket. In the U.S., the American Bell Telephone Company of Boston, which also controlled The Bell Telephone Company of Canada, secured its first million dollars in capital in 1879. It recorded its first million of earnings in 1881, paid its first million in dividends in 1884 and accumulated its first million of surplus in 1885. By 1886 the company had also paid its first million in legal expenses and by 1888 was handling a million calls a day. Bell installed its millionth telephone by 1898. By 1892 the "thousand-mile talk" was no longer a fairy-tale, nor was it even particularly surprising. There was no apparent let-up in the craze for telephones.

In eastern cities the numbers of wires swelled from a few strands here and there to veritable mazes with lines crisscrossing in the air over the streets much like webs spun by huge insane mechanical spiders. Poles rose in height from 50, to 60 then to 70 and 80 feet, often with more than 25 cross-arms. Topping them all was a pole line along West Street in New York City — where every pole was a Norway pine towering 90 feet into the sky — carrying 30 cross-arms and 300 wires. In New York City alone wires were scattered over 11,000 buildings and rooftops. It was impossible to keep roofs in repair; chimney smoke, the fierce enemy of iron wire, rusted lines to threads within a couple of years. Telephone men literally ran out of space and had no place to run the thousands of miles of new wire that would-be customers were demanding.

Of course, what made all this possible was the timely technological develop-

The first telephone pole on Ridout Street, in London, Ontario, was erected in 1893.

ment of the switchboard. Without switchboards there would be telephones, but no telephone system. It is very easy to connect 5,000 people to one another through a switchboard: you simply run a wire from each of their phones to the central switchboard, then connect everyone, as required, at that point. This is traditionally the function of the switchboard operator. Without a switchboard, it would take 12,497,500 wires to connect each of the 5,000 customers to each other — 4,999 wires for each phone!

The telephone people were eventually forced to go underground. There was simply nowhere else to go. The first underground cable was a hundred strands of wire twisted into a single cable, insulated with cotton or paper, soaked in oil, set inside iron pipes (or concrete boxes filled with sand), topped with creosoted wood and buried in asphalt. Moisture proved the deadly enemy underground, and by 1890 paper-wrapped cables sheathed in a tight lead casing were being tested in Philadelphia. Within six years 200,000 miles of such cable were buried under the streets of North American cities.

Wire itself also had to be improved. Early galvanized iron wire was cheap, but it had a limited range of commercial transmission because it was a poor conductor

Boy operators at a No. 1 Standard Magneto switchboard in Sherbrooke, Quebec, 1895.

of electricity. Steel was preferred because it was stronger, but researchers soon found that silver or copper performed best. Silver was out of the question because of its cost, and copper was too soft. Further research developed an improved copper wire called hard-drawn copper. It was at least four times better than iron or steel as a conductor and nearly as strong. However, it was also about four times as expensive.

The true conquest of distance had to await the inventions of the Pupin coil (named for its inventor, Michael J. Pupin), which greatly reduced transmission loss, the vacuum tube (invented by Lee DeForest) and the telephone repeater, which restored the vigour and crispness of a fading message. The invention of the vacuum tube made telephone repeaters possible. The Pupin coil also enabled linemen to use much thinner wire, thus reducing both weight and cost.

Meanwhile, Vail was busily engaged in merging a half-dozen small manufacturers of telephone equipment and components into one highly efficient and productive unit, Western Electric, which assured the booming telephone company of a steady supply of equipment. He also went on, in 1890, to create the operating arm of the American Bell Telephone Company called Long Lines, which was responsible for all the interstate and national (i.e., long distance) activities of the still-scattered regional Bell companies. Long Lines subsequently became the American Telephone and Telegraph Company: the *owner* of all long distance lines in the U.S., the custodian and protector of all patents, and the headquarters of invention, information, capital and legal aid for the entire federation of Bell companies. Indeed, AT&T went so far as to become the parent of them all!

Vail's dream of a great telephone system included Canada. His marching orders for AT&T were: ". . . to connect one or more points in each and every city, town or place in the State of New York with one or more points in each and every other city, town or place in said State and in each and every other State of the United States and in Canada and Mexico; and each and every of said cities, towns or places in said States and countries and also by cable and other appropriate means with the rest of the world."

Charles Fleetford Sise, Sr.

To promote the idea of "long distance," a long distance salon was outfitted in New York City to encourage people to make long distance calls and to talk to other cities. Cabs were dispatched for customers. On arrival, a caller was escorted over Oriental rugs to a gilded booth draped with silken curtains where the call was made. The salon became famous as "Room nine."

In the United States, President William Howard Taft gave long distance a boost by making a point of having a long distance talk with his family every evening he was away from home.

Charles Fleetford Sise was a central figure in the success of Bell Canada. Soon after the National Bell Telephone Company of Boston took over Canadian rights to the telephone in 1879, they sent Sise to Montreal to get things moving. Sise, a no-nonsense Boston shipping magnate who had sailed the seven seas in his own ship, was a one-time neighbour of President Jefferson Davis of the Confederate States of America, and a successful insurance company executive. Until 1880 he had not spent a minute in the telephone business. Nevertheless, he moved swiftly and surely.

By the time Sise arrived in Montreal, scores of telephone companies had sprung up across Canada, but none had the commanding leadership or the financial backing to dominate the field. Sise merged with some, swallowed up others and laid down policy lines for Bell Canada which set a pace of success no one else could match. It was Sise who determined that: 1) the quality of service provided would, in the long-run, be more effective than the level of rates in eliminating competition; 2) rates were nevertheless important and must be kept as low as consistent with the company's obligation to earn a reasonable return for its shareholders; 3) an extension of long distance lines, even at some financial loss, would strongly fortify the company's position; and 4) the goodwill of phone subscribers could not be overvalued and should be won by all fair means that opportunity should offer. Sise's emphasis on long distance matched that of Vail to the south.

Like Theodore Vail, Sise had a grand dream of a Canadian national network. His idea was to extend the Bell empire into every province except British Columbia. It was not that he had anything against the Pacific province, it merely seemed to him unlikely that it would ever pay to haul poles and equipment over the mountain barriers. So Sise limited his dream of empire to the region between the Atlantic Ocean and the Rockies. But a shortage of investment funds shifted the winds of fortune for the one-time ship captain, and he had to trim the sails of his ambitions a bit.

By 1888 The Bell Telephone Company of Canada found it expedient to combine with local interests in Nova Scotia, New Brunswick and Prince Edward Island to form local companies in each of those eastern provinces. Bell sold its holdings, including its plant and properties, retaining only a small stock interest in each of the new companies.

Prairie winds blew just as adversely, and by 1908, first Manitoba and then Alberta and Saskatchewan opted for government-owned systems and bought Bell out.

In 1915 the first transcontinental telephone hookup was made between New York and San Francisco. Vail was by then president of AT&T and he could easily have been the first man to talk from coast to coast. However, he deferred to the inventor and accorded the honour to Alexander Graham Bell. The occasion was timed to coincide with and publicize the Panama Pacific Exposition held in San Francisco that year. In New York Alexander Graham Bell opened the first transcontinental line to the public by repeating the first intelligible words ever heard over a telephone, "Mr. Watson, come here, I want you." From San Francisco, Mr. Watson responded that it would take him a week to do that now.

The official opening of transcontinental service in the U.S. was the prelude to a series of demonstrations that continued for over a year and which linked San Francisco with a score of eastern cities for special occasions.

Such early service over the first transcontinental line was limited. The only calls accepted unconditionally were between San Francisco and New York, Boston or Washington. To determine whether or not it was possible to talk to another point, a bureau was established at the New York long distance office where the transmission characteristics of the proposed connection were tested. Only a certain range of frequencies could be transmitted (about one-third that handled by modern equipment) and the result was that the voices one heard sounded much like those on an early phonograph record. Changes in the weather — and there was always crummy weather somewhere along the 3,400 miles of line — caused wide fluctuations in the efficiency of the circuit. There was also a definite limit to the volume (audio) that could be achieved at the end of the line because any increase in amplification beyond a critical point caused a fearful howling in the repeaters.

In the beginning, the number of cross-country calls hardly warranted a direct circuit. A call from New York City to San Francisco was completed by patching together several separate circuits. Intermediate connections on the first transcontinental line were made at Chicago, Denver and Salt Lake City, making four separate pieces of line; if the call involved a point beyond either New York or San Francisco, there were five. The significance of this is simply that before a connec-

Two early telephones. The 1878 model at the left was used as both transmitter and receiver by moving it from mouth to ear.

tion could be made, there had to be at least one idle circuit in each segment, and delays therefore, were inevitable. The average connection took about an hour to set up, and a three-minute call cost $20.70. Compare that with the cost today!

By 1913, AT&T had expanded its long line network (the company's trans-continental network in the United States — then and now) as far as Denver. At that time, however, AT&T was being threatened with anti-trust action, and to ward it off, the company made its famous Kingsbury Commitment whereby it promised to: 1) dispose of all its Western Union Stock 2) discontinue its policy of acquiring independent telephone companies and 3) permit other telephone companies to obtain toll service over the lines of the Bell System. The significance of the Kingsbury Commitment for Canada was that until 1913 when AT&T took this position, Canadian companies, with the exception of Bell Canada, did not have access to U.S. long distance facilities. It was because of AT&T's new policy that other Canadian companies where permitted to route their long distance traffic through the U.S.

In the U.S. all long distance lines are owned by AT&T whereas in Canada the long distance lines are owned by the regional independents. This represents a fundamental difference between the two operating systems.

Montreal was linked to San Francisco for the first time on May 11, 1915.

The first Montreal-Vancouver call was made before many witnesses on February 14, 1916. One end of the call was the crowded banquet room of Montreal's Ritz-Carlton Hotel; the other was Vancouver's Globe Theatre. Connections were made through Buffalo, Omaha, Salt Lake City and Portland, Oregon — a circuit of 4,227 miles. As VIPs from the East spoke with VIPs from the West, guests listened in on earphones set up at each table.

Next day both Vancouver newspapers, the *Province* and the *Sun*, gave the item front-page coverage. The *Province* headlined its story: "Hello Montreal! Vancouver is speaking," followed by "Citizens in Globe Theatre Hear 4,000 Mile Chat," and, "Tonight and Tomorrow Night B.C. Telephone Co. Invites You to the Globe."

The story read in part: "Science has placed at naught time and distance and the human voice is wafted from ocean to ocean across thousands of miles of hills and plains; the East and West have met, have joined and are as one.... Last night in the Globe Theatre hundreds of residents of Vancouver sat and listened to conversations carried on between Vancouver and Montreal, and some few were privileged to converse with friends in the Eastern Metropolis recognizing each other's voices and exchanging greetings with the same ease and facility which features their daily use of the telephone.

"It was a dramatic moment when Mr. F.W. Peters [general superintendent for the CPR in Vancouver] stepped on the stage at the theatre last night and picked up the receiver to speak to Lord Shaughnessy, president of the CPR at Montreal. Each guest at the official demonstration was connected by means of a miniature receiver with the telephone on the stage and quite distinctly came back the voice of the Canadian baron over the wire to answer Mr. Peters' greeting. The seemingly impossible had been accomplished even as it had when the rails of the transcontinental, the president and western official of which were speaking, had slowly pushed their way through the almost impenetrable barriers of the Rockies and joined the then far-flung Western province with a band of steel to the Eastern portion of the Dominion."

The following week *Telephone Talk*, B.C. Tel's house organ, described the connection as "the latest record of the long distance telephone, 4,300 miles." Eight public demonstrations were held and *Telephone Talk* recorded that 4,556 people attended the demonstrations.

After the original call, the line was switched from Vancouver to San Francisco where gramophone records were played of Harry Lauder singing, and a comic vaudeville recitation of "Cohen on the Telephone."

Under the watchful eye of Alexander Graham Bell, dignitaries listen in on the first
Montreal to Vancouver link-up on February 15, 1916. Head table guests included
C. F. Sise , L. B. McFarlane and Lord Shaugnessy.

The first regular commercial call from Montreal to Vancouver was made the
following day. The Montreal *Star* reported that the connection was made in a few
minutes and that the conversation over 4,000 miles of line was very clear.

At the time, the long distance service of the Bell Telephone Company of
Canada was available only between communities in Ontario and Quebec and to
centres in the United States within a radius of about 2,000 miles from Toronto and
Montreal. Regular commercial service to the Atlantic provinces did not open until
1919. It was not until 1925 that a telephone user could call anywhere in Canada or
the United States, and even then service between the Atlantic provinces and
Quebec, between Ontario and the Prairies and between the Prairies and British
Columbia was possible only by using lines through the United States. In those
days, the elapsed time between requesting a long distance connection and the
completion of a call was from 14 to 15 minutes.

In the company's annual report for 1920 the directors of The Bell Telephone
Company said: "During the past year many important improvements were made
to our plant and we are now in a position to give universal long distance service to

our subscribers. Even at our smaller offices, subscribers have been connected to very distant points, in both Canada and the United States and those at our larger offices demand long-haul connections daily. For example, Montreal, Toronto, Ottawa and Hamilton subscribers have had satisfactory commercial conversations with cities in Florida, California, Manitoba, British Columbia and the Maritimes."

Actually, the service was not quite universal. It was not yet possible to talk to places in Alberta or Saskatchewan or for people in those provinces to call points in Ontario and Quebec. Still, the emphasis was squarely on toll calls (or long distance calls, as we know them today) and these were recognized even then as the cream of telephone revenue.

The first call linking Ottawa with Vancouver came on January 15, 1920. The call was routed through New York, Chicago, Denver, Salt Lake City, San Francisco and Seattle. It took four hours to set up the connection and the cost for three minutes was $16.15. Today you can make the same three-minute call for as little as $1.18 (40¢ for the first minute and 39¢ for each of the two minutes following) by dialing direct, or at most for $6.75 if you make a person-to-person, operator-assisted call.

By the 1920s the quality of transcontinental telephony was comparable to a conversation between two persons shouting back and forth across a distance of 70 or 80 feet in an open field, with little outside noise to interfere. The time required to make the connections for an average long distance call was about 15 minutes and it involved at least five switching points and operators. Calls which completely spanned the continent usually took longer because of the larger number of switching points involved. One man put in a call for a distant point from a public phone in a drug store and sat down to enjoy an ice-cream soda. He was astonished and delighted to have the call come through before he had finished his ice cream. "Some service, I'll say." he declared.

The possibility of a transcontinental telephone network was given additional support when, on July 1, 1927, Canada celebrated her diamond jubilee with a nation-wide radio broadcast. (It is a little known fact that the nation's first coast-to-coast "all-Canadian" routed broadcast was a project undertaken by the telephone companies involved.) The effort was the talk of the land, but in real terms it was more of a flash-in-the-pan performance than a commercial arrangement. Still, the success of the broadcast did much to stir individual Canadian companies to greater effort, and it had a significant impact on decisions which were subsequently made at Minaki in 1928.

HOW TO BUILD RURAL TELEPHONE LINES

As a stop gap measure to assist rural customers demanding phone service, the Northern Electric Company Ltd., issued this booklet in 1909 outlining how to "do-it-yourself".

On August 7, 1928, service was established between Winnipeg and points in Ontario and Quebec over a direct Canadian circuit from Sudbury to Winnipeg via the twin cities of Fort William and Port Arthur (now Thunder Bay, Ontario).

In December 1928, the gap between Quebec City and Saint John, New Brunswick, was bridged by a new pole line.

These links provided for all-Canadian interprovincial traffic but long-haul calls still had to be routed through the United States. Although a connection between Halifax and Vancouver over purely Canadian lines was possible, it would have involved seven switching points. Unfortunately, the technology of the day was not yet sufficiently advanced to enable the telephone customers to use that route.

And so the stage was set.

PART TWO
The Unifying Force

1

Closing the Gaps
Not One Cent of Government Help

*The invention of the telephone has been one of the most
significant events in the march of civilization and culture.
Man's development and the growth of civilization have
depended in the main on progress in a few activities — the
discovery of fire, domestication of animals, invention of the
wheel, but above all, in the evolution of the means to
transmit, receive, communicate and to record knowledge and
information. The invention of the telephone has truly
revolutionized our means of communicating information.*

Thanks A Hundred, Mr. Bell
(Pamphlet — Brantford, 1974)

The service provided by the TransCanada Telephone System is a triumph of
national purpose over regionalism. The System itself, however, really developed
from the failure of a single company in Canada to establish a nation-wide
telephone network comparable to the one developed by the American Telephone
and Telegraph Company in the United States. The Bell Telephone Company of
Canada, which early established itself as the giant of Canadian telephony, tried. It
was defeated, however, by shortages of investment capital at crucial times and its
inability or unwillingness to manage and operate systems located thousands of
miles from its head office.

In its adolescence Canadian telephony was thus characterized by a sort of
regional clumping. Central Canada — Quebec and Ontario — became the core
base for the Bell Telephone Company of Canada. The Atlantic provinces de-

veloped their own systems with a strong assist from Bell people. Even more isolated on the west coast, the British Columbia Telephone Company (whose development, surprisingly, followed right on the heels of Bell in central Canada), took its own path, eventually becoming the only major Canadian system under U.S. control. Manitoba, Saskatchewan and Alberta developed parallel systems under provincial government control. Propinquity, as much as anything else, contributed to the regional grouping and natural development of the Prairie companies.

The awkward geography of Canada, combined with sporadic regional settlement and development, worked against East-West lines of communications for many years. The gaps between the four main developing regions were barriers to cross-Canada communications. Natural barriers, such as the chains of mountains, cut off British Columbia from the rest of Canada. Difficult terrain, distance and low population density in many areas made telephony a poor proposition between Canada's central and prairie regions. Similar considerations and conditions prevented central and eastern Canadian links from developing.

Immigration to Canada combined with railway access to the West produced a surge of population growth first across the Prairies and then over the mountains into British Columbia. Hundreds of millions of dollars of public money were poured into CPR's band of steel to bind the nation together. However, no similar offer of help to further link the East and West with strands of copper was ever made. Incredibly, the telephone companies of Canada would accomplish by themselves the feat that the railways managed only with vast federal help. The federal Government poured hundreds of millions of taxpayer dollars into the railway project but did not provide one cent of cash, subsidy or help of any other kind with the building of the coast-to-coast telephone lines.

Encouraged by market developments and advancing technology, more and more Canadian telephone men began to dream of a cross-country telephone hookup that would be national in scope. The action formally began at a regional meeting in Winnipeg in October 1920, which quite unexpectedly became national in outlook.

Invited by Manitoba's Minister of Telephones, the heads of the telephone companies for the four Western provinces met to consider technical matters and to discuss the possibility of a western network. Bell people had been invited to assist at the meeting. Although not on the agenda, discussion leaped to a national level and from that meeting emerged the Telephone Association of Canada (TAC),*

*The Telephone Association of Canada became the Canadian Telecommunications Carriers Association (CTCA) on February 8, 1972.

and the beginnings of a jointly expressed interest in an all-Canadian continental toll line.

Initially, the new organization concerned itself mainly with technical questions and the development of uniform practices and procedures which would provide a consistent standard as well as a higher level of service across Canada.

The TAC's first formal meetings were convened in Vancouver between August 22 and 27, 1921. At those meetings George H. Halse, vice-president and general manager of the British Columbia Telephone Company, expressed the hope that the delegates would go on record as favouring the establishment of a trans-Canada telephone line, irrespective of the consideration that perhaps the need for it was felt more in the East than in the West. Citing the fact that the telephone business of the Kootenay and Boundary districts of British Columbia was handled by Spokane, Washington, because of the lack of facilities and connections directly between those districts and Vancouver, Halse suggested it was a matter of national importance to have such business stay in Canada. Every delegate at the convention could point to similar anomalies in his own region.

J.H. Winfield, general manager of the Maritime Telegraph and Telephone Company Limited, speaking on behalf of the east coast provinces, immediately supported the idea and drew a parallel between the ribbon of steel — the CPR, which was so vital in bringing together the Canadian East and West — and the new band of copper that would further unify the strung-out country.

John E. Lowry, then commissioner of the Manitoba Telephone System, made it official business with a motion that the question of the practicality of a trans-Canada telephone line be submitted to a committee already set up to deal with standardized regulations.

From the beginning, the all-Canadian line was labelled the "All-Red" line because on maps of the day, the British Empire was always shown in red.

For the next several years, while cross-Canada calls and revenues continued to be channelled through the U.S., the results of engineering and other studies were dutifully presented to delegates gathered for the annual meetings of the TAC. Two key elements dominated these reports. First, thinly settled areas (such as between Saint John and Quebec City, Sudbury and Winnipeg, and Calgary and Vancouver) simply would not pay for themselves. The cost of linking such centres, therefore, simply could not be justified in terms of the potential volume of business that would be generated between them. Secondly, the reports raised the question of whether or not the railway companies would be willing to lease their telegraph circuits to a rival in the communications business.

Aside from these inevitably discouraging reports, nothing more was done for several years. Meanwhile, the gaps of economic feasibility were slowly being closed, thereby making the final assault on the problem areas easier.

The 1920s marked a period of network expansion in the various regions. Adjacent connections were made: the Atlantic provinces to Central Canada, the Prairie systems — Alberta, Saskatchewan and Manitoba — to one another, and British Columbia to Alberta.

When the Telephone Association of Canada met in Edmonton, on August 28, 1923, delegates were told that the three Prairie provinces were now interconnected; ceremonies took place simultaneously in Edmonton, Regina and Winnipeg to celebrate the occasion. Two years later, Alberta — which had been gradually extending its connections with British Columbia, Saskatchewan and Montana — achieved "universal" connections with British Columbia and Saskatchewan. Through its Montana tie-in (which was part of AT&T's Northern Transcontinental Line) Alberta also achieved universal connections with the rest of North America.

The opening of the Northern Transcontinental Line in the United States had a substantial impact on the British Columbia Telephone Company. Until then (1925) a call from Vancouver to Calgary involved switching at Seattle and Spokane, Washington; Missoula, Helena, Great Falls, and Shelby, Montana; and Lethbridge. This was always time-consuming and only occasionally satisfactory.

On May 5, 1926, Winnipeg connected with Fort William, Ontario, for the first time, using the Canadian Pacific Telegraph line. This was a significant development because it was the first tacit indication given by the railway company that it was prepared to lease its lines for telephone purposes. About the same time Winnipeg made its first direct connection with Chicago. Commissioner Lowry announced that Winnipeg "now can reach directly, not only Chicago, but practically every other important city in the United States with only a single switching point at Chicago."

Early in 1927 a Winnipeg man made a 53-minute call to New York at a cost of $137.80. "This is the longest and most costly talk that has been carried on over Winnipeg telephones but it is also an indication that the people of Winnipeg talk more than they used to," Lowry commented.

The new northern United States line also made it possible for Saskatchewan to be linked, as Alberta had been previously, to the continental network. The annual report of the Saskatchewan Department of Telephones for the year ending April 30, 1928, noted that there were 1,451 long distance messages originating in the province destined for North American points outside the Prairie provinces.

By the end of the 1920s most Canadians could talk to one another and to much of the rest of the world by long distance telephone, but in order to do so they still had to route most of the connections through the United States. It was theoretically possible to make a coast-to-coast call using strictly Canadian facilities, by connecting circuits from region to region. The reality, however, was that while the connecting circuits between adjacent regions were workable for short distance calls, they could not provide the level of quality required for a successful transcontinental conversation.

An important boost for the idea of a trans-Canada network was given by the nationwide radio broadcasting network when it was set up for the diamond jubilee of Confederation celebration on July 1, 1927. The facilities used linked 10,525 miles of two-wire telephone circuit and 8,965 miles of telegraph line which had to be harmonized by telephone engineers to provide the quality necessary for the Halifax to Vancouver network. Although the facilities along the route from Sudbury to Winnipeg were provided by AT&T, this was the nation's first "all-Canadian" coast-to-coast broadcast. It was also a red-letter day because it represented one of the first public displays of co-operation between the telegraph and telephone companies. Thousands of miles of telegraph and telephone lines were hooked into the first "sea to sea" broadcast of the jubilee events on Parliament Hill.

The broadcast included the ringing of the Peace Tower carillon, and speeches by the Governor-General, Viscount Willingdon, and the Prime Minister, W. Lyon Mackenzie King. Ironically, in view of conditions today, the Prime Minister said: "In the confederation debate in the Legislature of United Canada in 1865, the Hon. Christopher Duskin drew attention to what, at the time, seemed an inevitable impediment to national consciousness on the part of the citizens of Canada. He said: 'We have a large class whose national feelings turn toward London, whose very heart is there; another large class whose sympathies centre here at Quebec, or in a sentimental way may have some reference to France; another large class whose memories are of the Emerald Isle, and yet another whose comparisons are rather with Washington; but have we any class of people who are attracted, or whose feelings are going to be directed with any earnestness to the city of Ottawa, the centre of the new nationality that is to be created?' After many years this doubt has been dispelled, and the question has been answered by the voice of the Canadian people united in the celebration of the diamond jubilee of Confederation."

Promoters of the broadcast were more than pleased, summing it up as "a

The microphone used in the diamond jubilee broadcast of 1927 became a treasured momento for Thomas Ahearn. But organizing the coast-to-coast broadcast was only one of his major achievements. Called the number one pioneer of the electrical industry, Ahearn operated the first telephone exchange in Ottawa. He was responsible for building the first long distance line from Ottawa to Pembroke Ontario. He also founded the Chaudiere Electric Light and Power Company (later to become the Ottawa Light, Heat and Power Company) and the Ottawa Electric Rail Company.

wholesome stimulation of the patriotic impulse from ocean to ocean, a unique commemoration of an historic occasion that will survive in the memory of thousands for years to come. . . ."

W.H. Stubbs of Bashaw, Alberta wrote: "It was one of the best receptions we have ever had and we did not miss a word of it. There were five of us listening in here and we took the telephone receiver down so that any of the people on this rural line might listen in, which many did."

There was only one mechanical mishap. Because of the summer heat, wires expanded at several points along the line, and the short-circuits they caused were not uncommon. As a matter of record, one such short-circuit threatened just west of Pembroke, Ontario, during the great broadcast. The lineman on the job was ordered in eloquent language by his chief to "stay up on the pole and hold up the wire until the broadcast was finished!" Although the record does not go so far as to tell us how long the poor lineman had to endure the Dominion Day sun, no short-circuit occurred to mar the celebration.

The coast-to-coast success of the national hookup so stirred the Telephone Association of Canada that when the eighth annual convention met at Minaki, Ontario, in 1928 the Bell Telephone Company was requested to undertake an engineering and feasibility study into what was then called the "Trans-Canada Toll System." The study was to include cost estimates relating to construction and new or upgraded facilities as might be required and was to recommend a method of operation. Although it was acknowledged that the amount of business might be limited there was a strong feeling that the availability of direct circuits, which would facilitate faster and more efficient service, would stimulate business.

James Hamilton of the British Columbia Telephone Company rose at that meeting and characteristically challenged the engineering committee to "wake up." R.V. Macaulay, then chief engineer of Bell and chairman of the TAC engineering committee, acknowledged the challenge by replying that, "Hamilton has made the point. It is time we got busy and set up a cross-Canada telephone system."

The Bell report was presented to another meeting of the Telephone Association, held in Jasper, Alberta in August the next year (1929). The study and its recommendations were quickly adopted and a new engineering and plant committee, under the chairmanship of R.V. Macaulay, was set up to co-ordinate the construction and engineering of a trans-Canada system.

In 1930, a meeting was held by the following seven companies: Maritime Telegraph and Telephone Company Limited; The New Brunswick Telephone Company, Limited; Bell Telephone Company of Canada; Manitoba Telephone System; Saskatchewan Government Telephones; Alberta Government Telephones and British Columbia Telephone Company. At that meeting, it was agreed in principle that each of these companies would connect its respective toll lines with the systems of the other companies in adjoining territories in order to establish a through system of toll lines extending from Halifax to Vancouver. The network so established would be used by the participating companies for the interchange of telecommunications services between the systems. It was estimated that $5 million worth of new line and upgraded facilities would have to be installed, and it was agreed that each member company would assume the responsibility for and bear the cost of the work in its own territory.

On May 13, 1931, a clearing house for trans-Canada business was set up under a manager, J.C. Garbutt, of Bell. He quickly organized and issued a bulletin covering settlement summaries for TransCanada Telephone System toll revenues. In August that year the member companies signed a formal agreement on operations, management, and division of revenues. Bell Canada standard operating practices and routing instructions were adopted along with standard maintenance practices. The engineering committee became formally responsible for new circuits, changes in existing circuits, transmission design and standards, the scheduling of construction work and the preparation of studies (depending upon special requirements).

The joint objectives of the members were also spelled out:

Provide telecommunications users with effective national, international and intercontinental telecommunications services through the planning, designing, construction and operation of a national telecommunications system, by co-ordinating the activities of each member, and the establishment and effective marketing of a variety of modern, high-quality, reliable telecommunications services that will:

Meet the growing and changing service needs of the public.

Meet the particular requirements of Canada's defence and national emergency operations.

Facilitate the exchange of telecommunications traffic to and from other Canadian and international carriers.

Encourage the fullest possible use of Canadian telecommunications facilities for the transfer of information.

Generate revenue through the effective marketing of such services.

Establish a fair and equitable revenue settlements system to distribute jointly-earned revenues to the member companies, and

Develop and maintain required technical and operating standards.

The agreement also covered the establishment of an administrative staff and organizational structure necessary to transact TCTS business.

And so, the business of building the TransCanada Telephone System got under way.

It was obvious from the beginning that an organization of some kind would be required to supervise and co-ordinate the work of building, maintaining and operating the trans-Canada system. At a meeting of the Executive committee of the Telephone Association in 1931 a TCTS Management committee was formed made up of top executives from each member company. To this day, that group is the central authority of TCTS. Subsequently, several additional committees were created responsible to the chairman of the Management committee. These committees maintain contact with all branches of telephone operation: engineering, traffic, marketing, public relations, advertising and so forth.

In 1931, the seven companies who were party to the original TCTS agreement had a total investment of approximately $265,120,000 in plant and facilities, and an estimated combined total of 1,166,823 subscribers. In 1932, 41,000 long distance calls originated with these companies.

The net revenues divided among the members at the end of 1931 totalled $63,703. For 1932, the first full year of TCTS operation, revenues totalled $165,490.

At the elaborate official ceremonies on January 25, 1932, the Earl of Bessborough, Governor-General of Canada, declared the facilities of the Trans-Canada Telephone System open to the Canadian public. From that day on the facilities have been extended and improved as the demand has increased.

Three more members have joined TCTS since its establishment: the Newfoundland Telephone Company Limited, in 1957; The Island Telephone Company Limited, in 1975; and Telesat Canada in 1977.

Today's TCTS network consists of open-wire, cable, medium- and high-frequency radio links, microwave, a domestic satellite system and a variety of other transmission facilities. The system includes nearly 12 million miles of circuitry within Canadian borders and is growing constantly. Links with the United States are provided at many points and overseas connections to and from the network are made through Teleglobe Canada, a Crown corporation, the nation's overseas carrier. TCTS companies (not including Telesat) have a combined investment in plant and facilities of over $11.2 billion. There are almost 13 million telephones in the network and the number of long distance calls during 1976 was well over one billion.

The network is available to every telephone system in the land,* and it provides Canadian telephone users with what amounts to a single high-quality, nation-wide and world service at a reasonable cost. Through Teleglobe, customers of TCTS companies can obtain telephone, telegraph, teleprinter, video and data transmission services to virtually any place on the globe.

Within the borders of Canada, TCTS operates one of the world's longest single microwave systems carrying telephone conversations, radio and television programmes and computer data from coast to coast. Among the other TCTS

---

*Although TCTS has only 10 members today, these are by no means the *only* telephone companies operating in Canada today. The 1976 Statistics Canada report lists 806 separate Canadian telephone companies.

Long distance operators were the "repeaters" in the early days. The introduction of repeaters at intervals along long distance lines from 1915 improved the quality of long distance communications. This is a long distance operator of 1928.

services offered are advanced data communication services including a wide selection of low-, medium- and high-speed facilities.

The geography of Canada — over 4,000 miles east and west and nearly 3,000 miles from the United States border to the North Pole — points up the need for efficient telecommunications to bind together a far-flung people. At the same time that vastness presents formidable obstacles to the achievement of telecommunications excellence.

In 1973, Albin R. Meir, technical editorial director of the U.S. trade magazine, *Telephony: The Journal of the Telephone Industry*, wrote: "In an effort to prevent an erosion of Canadian businesses and services in favor of American capabilities, Canada has been making an extraordinary effort to create and maintain a business environment that favors Canadian enterprise — and excellent communications, particularly telephony, has been long recognized as one of the most vital elements in such a policy. Accordingly, Canadian efforts to develop better communications services have resulted in dramatic progress and some of the best communications found anywhere in the world."

As a matter of fact, in at least two areas — digital transmission and domestic geostationary communications satellites — Canadians can confidently claim to be the world leader.

This enormous and amazing network has evolved from the original TCTS concept of an open-wire pole line stretching from the Atlantic to the Pacific to provide Canada with its own all-Canadian, All-Red toll circuit. The thread which holds it together is the *voluntary* undertaking of the individual members of TCTS that they will provide and maintain the plant and equipment required in their territory.

TCTS goals have always been clear enough. The difficulty has been how to meld seven (later 10) disparate organizations into a single working unit.

2

Masterpiece of Pragmatism
The Bottom Line

Time after time we came back to the basic problem of how or what is the most economical way of providing the best possible telephone service at the lowest possible cost consistent with fair treatment for the employees and the investors.

T.W. Eadie (1969)

Happily for everyone there have always been believers in bumblebees. Fortunately for the Canadian telephone industry the people who believed the TransCanada Telephone System would work have always outnumbered those who were equally convinced that it wouldn't. And for all the pressures which have been applied that might have caused it to fail, TCTS members have always put forward strong counter-initiatives to make it succeed.

TCTS was born literally at the beginning of the Depression in the dirty thirties. The engineers and administrators who were its original architects were meticulous planners, and as such they went to great lengths to provide for contingencies and other unexpected developments. But there was one thing they didn't take into account, and that was the Depression. With it the young communications organization was put to a severe test.

On the positive side, all of the member companies had good — albeit parochial — reasons for wanting TCTS to succeed. A case in point was recalled by Gordon Farrell, retired president of B.C. Tel. "I suppose British Columbia's main reason for supporting the trans-Canada wire line," he said, "was to get away from having to use United States lines. When the trans-Canada proposal came up we had only recently been taken over by our U.S. cousins [the Theodore Gary interests of Kansas City, Missouri] and they were in a bit of financial difficulty themselves, so they couldn't help us out with any money. We wanted to get our own lines because we had only 25 miles* [of line] to the U.S. border and we were spending a lot of time arguing with the American Telegraph & Telephone Company about what B.C. Tel was entitled to for originating a call . . . and those AT&T boys were pretty tough."

On the negative side, while the rest of Canada was hurting, the Prairie provinces were really suffering. Farmers stood at the edge of their fields and watched their lives blow away in swirling clouds of dust. There were wry, dry jokes about gophers digging their holes three feet off the ground. Tractors and combines were repossessed or left to rust in farmyards. Wheat brave enough to grow didn't produce heads and even if it did the price made it hardly worth the effort to reap a crop. Fleeing to the cities, farmers merely traded hopelessness for despair.

Provincial governments were as broke as the farmers, and the Prairie governments found themselves running "broke" telephone systems. In the Prairie provinces particularly, the telphone systems had counted heavily on revenues from the emerging new field of radio broadcasting to provide the much needed money to cover the costs of installing the new TCTS circuits. Instead, the federal Government agency responsible for radio broadcasting handed the bulk of the radio contracts to the telephone companies' arch-rivals — the Canadian National and Canadian Pacific telegraph systems. The shocked and disappointed Prairie companies, in search of a scapegoat, pointed accusing fingers at Bell. Paul A. McFarlane, at the time a Bell vice-president and the first chairman of TCTS, was aware from the beginning that the Government favoured the railway telegraph companies and he was prepared to settle for the best percentage he could get, deeming that to be better than nothing. But the Prairie people felt they had been kicked in the slats and they suspected that Bell had helped lace up the boot.

TCTS might well have foundered on that issue alone. And there were others as well.

Financial pressures on the private companies, notably in the Atlantic provinces, forced cutbacks and economies that were almost crippling. Bell too was

*Before 1932, B.C. Tel's long distance revenues were derived largely from the use of those 25 miles of line. Revenue sharing on the basis of the amount of line used (mileage), therefore, always worked against B.C. For example, on a 250-mile call routed through the U.S., B.C. Tel would get only 10 per cent of the toll revenues; on a 1,000-mile call, B.C. Tel's share would be only 2.5 per cent of the total.

hard-pressed to meet both its financial and service obligations. The pressures of the times were for companies to "hold the line" and to cut back if they couldn't. It was a time when there was a great deal of pressure to "think regional." Certainly it was not a time to take on additional obligations or carry unnecessary burdens.

The fact that TCTS did not founder is also testimony to the great care that was taken by its original architects in planning the organization. They had a clear understanding of the purposes and objectives of the new organization and the roles and motivations for the member companies — but they had no precedents to follow. They wanted TCTS to work, but more than that, they wanted it to last. From the beginning, therefore, they recognized that TCTS would survive only if its members were convinced that the advantages of their association far outweighed any disadvantages, and that as members they could be certain of fair treatment. It was these considerations that influenced the adoption of its operating principles and the essential design of the organization.

Probably the most important operating principle is that of requiring unanimous agreement on operating matters by the members. Closely related to it is the veto principle, which entitles any member to withhold its support from *any* TCTS project, and thereby stall indefinitely or kill that project. Together, the application of these operating principles guarantees fair treatment for every member of TCTS.

Norm Phemister, retired TCTS director of Government Relations, explained how the veto works: "To outsiders it might appear that the power of veto would make it impossible to operate the organization, but it is a fundamental aspect of TransCanada. Even the smallest company (which has fewer telephones than Bell has in one of its average districts) has the power to veto *any* project. But what happens if there is a veto, if complete agreement — consensus — on some project cannot be reached? Everyone doesn't give up on it or try to pressure the holdout. The chairman simply says, 'All right gentlemen, please go back to your own companies and think about this matter and we'll go back to our drawing boards and review the problem, then we'll bring it back to the Board of Management for reconsideration.' The requirement for unanimity makes it impossible for a majority to impose its will on a reluctant minority."

There are differences of opinion as to precisely what constitutes the mechanism by which agreements are reached at TCTS.

According to Jack Carlile, former president of TCTS and a vice-president of British Columbia Telephone Company: "Canada, by its very nature, is a compromise. And compromise is the name of the TransCanada Telephone System game. TCTS is 10 companies each with the power of veto. We've got to compromise!"

G.E. Brice, of AGT's Public Relations department, has another view: "TCTS achieves unanimity through a process of 'integration,' not compromise. This process involves the establishment of basic telecommunications goals and needs which are common to all members. With such basic concepts as the starting point there has never been any serious difficulty in working out the plans which have led to the level of high quality of telecommunications in Canada."

The architects of TCTS also recognized that they needed some kind of permanent organization — a central committee of sorts — to attend to the complicated technical, administrative and financial matters that would necessarily require attention. And so, the basic committee structure was adopted which, with only minor adjustment over the years, has survived until now. As can be seen from the chart on page (000), the TransCanada Telephone System is directed by a *Board of Management,* which is made up of one senior officer from each of the 10 member companies.

The president of TCTS acts as the chairman of the Board of Management and also directs the activities of the System through a *Management committee,* made up of a senior official from each member company and the directors of each of five operational groups. The president serves as chairman of both the Board of Management and the Management committee.

The Management committee provides general direction and supervision of programmes undertaken by TCTS functional committees and staff groups, and ensures that the most efficient means are employed to determine TCTS policies and achieve TCTS objectives.

Central staff groups are made up of selected qualified personnel on loan from the various member companies. Functional committees, also made up of representatives of member companies, meet periodically to perform specific co-ordinating and development functions.

The five organizational groups — Administration, Business Development, Carrier Relations and Settlements, Operations and the Computer Communications group — are each headed by a director appointed by the Board of Management.

The *director of Administration (and secretary)* is responsible for the general administration of the System headquarters operation, public relations, advertising and promotion, personnel, the clearing house, all accounting functions and all EDP information system used by TCTS.

The *director of Business Development* co-ordinates the development and marketing of new services; as chairman of the Business Development committee, the Marketing committee and the Rates committee, he is responsible for most of the business-oriented activities of TCTS.

The *director of Carrier Relations and Settlements* is responsible for the co-ordination of traffic interchange and settlement agreements with other organizations and for all associated methods and implementation processes within and by TCTS. As chairman of the Settlements committee he is also concerned with policy formulation and implementation of the Revenue Settlement Plan (RSP) across the System.

The *director of the Computer Communications Group* is responsible for the planning and co-ordination of all System computer communications matters.

The *director of Operations* is responsible for the planning and day-to-day operations of TCTS networks. He directs the activities of the Engineering and Plant committee and the Traffic committee (each with its own chairman and each made up of company representatives experienced in those respective areas).

In addition to the directors of the five organizational groups who are members of the Management committee, there are two others which report directly to the president. The *Accounting committee* provides a continuing forum through which members can discuss and review general accounting questions; and the *director — Government Relations* is responsible for maintaining close relationships with government officials and agencies whose plans and policies affect the telecommunications industries.

The TCTS committee structure is not unlike the organization chart of any individual member company. Major projects progress through the committee structure to the management level to be brought before the Board of Management for executive decision whenever necessary.

Each committee member is responsible, within his own company, for liaison with his own company counterparts on other committees.

Probably the most compelling reason underlying the formation of TCTS had to do with money matters. Obviously, increased long distance usage meant increased toll revenues. But the question of 'who was to be paid how much for what' required agreement among the parties from the outset. These and other financial questions were extremely complicated. It should come as no surprise, therefore, that throughout the history of TCTS most of the really serious problems have centred on money matters — the bottom line.

The fundamental objective of the TCTS settlement process remains, as it has been from the beginning, to provide the most equitable method of distributing revenues derived from TCTS services. However straightforward that goal may seem, a high percentage of the disagreements within TCTS have revolved around the methods proposed to achieve it, and an equally high percentage of management's time has been devoted to providing answers to this all-important and complex question.

The original settlement plan in 1931 provided for a division of revenues based largely on connecting agreements in effect between the various companies before TCTS was established. The established pro-rating provisions and the standard commissions for calls were retained.

Each member received a set or agreed-upon commission for send-paid and received-collect calls in its territory. Any remaining long distance revenue was divided among the three or more members who combined to handle the call. The division of such revenues was based on the length of the toll lines provided by each member in relation to the total length of all toll lines involved in the call.

Connecting calls between any two adjacent companies were not included in the TCTS revenue-sharing arrangement but were settled between the two companies involved.

There followed a number of relatively minor changes and revisions until 1958 when the "full division plan" of settlement was adopted. Under the new plan each member company was reimbursed for the costs of its operations related to providing long distance service — in effect, the cost of doing TCTS business — and the remaining revenues were distributed among the members in the same proportions as the ratio of the capital devoted to TCTS by each member to the total capital of TCTS. This provision was intended to promote capital investment by the individual members and to compensate for extraordinary expenditures, such as those incurred by SASK TEL with the installation in Regina of one of the country's two major direct-dialing switching centres. Saskatchewan undoubtedly would have felt that its system could never bear the expense of such a major installation, whose benefits accrued to all members, without the compensating factors of increased revenues keyed to the extra expense.

Because of continually evolving conditions a new Revenue Settlement Plan (RSP) was adopted in 1977. Norm Millidge, director of Administration (and secretary) of TCTS, explained that the revision was a response to strong indications that the settlement arrangement at the time was not distributing money across the system in a manner that accurately reflected participation in the system. "We couldn't go on modifying the old settlement plan to meet changes in technol-

66

The TransCanada Telephone System was created in 1931 at the annual meeting of the Telephone Association of Canada. Executives from across the country in a group photo at Minaki Lodge, near Kenora, Ontario.

ogy. It wasn't enough; we couldn't keep pace. We needed a new plan."

Briefly, in adopting the new plan the Board of Management agreed that the TCTS settlement programme should include the TCTS revenues derived from toll services which originate and terminate within Canada and make use of the facilities of three or more TCTS members. In addition, the settlement includes the TCTS share of revenues from the Canada-United States and Canada-overseas settlements. Other non-basic services that are developed and marketed by TCTS members — such as Dataroute, television, TWX rents and radio broadcasting — are also classified as TCTS items for settlement purposes, regardless of the number of members involved.

Among the basic principles of settlement agreed upon by the TCTS Board of Management are:

The settlement plan should be demonstrably equitable to each member; it should be as simple and economical as possible to operate;

it should have a high degree of predictability and stability with respect to revenues derived from the system;

it should be such that a member's ownership — public or private — neither benefits nor adversely affects its participation;

it should recognize the impact of cost on each member's operation;

it should provide that identifiable TCTS toll costs — recoverable assigned costs — should be the first costs claimed against system revenues; and

the plan should recognize connecting company contributions within a member's territory.

Precise formulas were provided for determination of costs and other claims to revenue participation, and a 10-year period was set to phase in the new revenue distribution system.

Norm Millidge has observed that: "TCTS by its very nature is involved in problems. If there weren't any, we wouldn't be needed and we wouldn't exist as an organization. Sometimes, problems stem quite simply from pride in one's own company; the assurance people have that whatever their own company does is best. But problems are also a matter of degree . . . and I can think of no more than a couple of cases when companies have indicated that they were seriously considering withdrawing from TCTS. . . . In both those cases the threat was used as a pressure tactic. However, when a situation is *really* serious, when it really matters, everyone knows it and threats aren't necessary."

The mix of state-owned and private enterprise systems has, of course, been responsible for a fair share of headaches. Sometimes this has meant nothing more serious than delaying the approval of a proposal while the representative of a provincial government telephone company goes home to sell an idea to his appropriate Minister or department. Occasionally, a decision has been coloured by ideology.

James F. (Jim) Mills, recently retired chairman and general manager of the Manitoba Telephone System, recalled an occasion when the Treasurer of Manitoba was attending a meeting in Saskatoon. At one point he was taken aside by Clarence Fines, Saskatchewan's provincial Treasurer and a doctrinaire socialist. Fines had a well-developed distrust of big business and most things Eastern, and was also highly suspicious of his non-Prairie TCTS colleagues. Fines confided to his Manitoba counterpart that "TransCanada is fiddling the government-owned companies." It was inevitable that political thinking should rear its ugly head now and then.

Stuart Muirhead, former head of Saskatchewan Government Telephones, recalled: "The Board of Directors and the government seemed to think that because Saskatchewan was a socialist province and we were associating with big business, we were bound to get cheated. In 1957, I was chairing a TransCanada meeting in Victoria at which we were considering changes in the Revenue Settlement Plan. Late in the day I was asked to make reservations for two of the members of the Saskatchewan Telephone Board of Directors. The government wanted them there, apparently because it was afraid I might be duped by the big bad capitalistic boys.

"As I recall they didn't have much to say. A few of the TransCanada people were put out but there was never any real threat of a showdown or a split. Whenever there has been any sign of a serious confrontation, our people have always buckled down and have resolved their problems. It has always been that way in TransCanada."

Another executive recalls: "A few years back we had a problem in Manitoba. The general manager was making speeches about the tremendous efficiency of the Manitoba Telephone System, claiming that this was the reason for their low rates compared to Bell Canada. Well, of course the reason for their low rates was that they weren't paying federal taxes,* which accounted for virtually half of the Bell rate. But the manager ignored little points like that. Bell rather pointedly made it clear they didn't care much for the Manitoban's performance but the reply was, 'Sorry but we have to live with political reality here and we're doing this for political reasons.'"

Obviously, TCTS members do a lot of thinking and put a great deal of effort into making the System work. This effort is essential; without it TCTS would soon fall apart. The fact that this has become routine is brought sharply into focus by an observation made by former TCTS chairman Z.H. (Hank) Krupski: "If you understand everybody else's problems, and they understand yours then it is surprisingly easy for you to come up with solutions everyone can live with. Trust serves as the basis of confidence and enables all members to cope with revenue settlements, new technologies, problems of competition or whatever. That's the way TCTS works."

According to Gordon Archibald, chairman of the Board of Directors of MT&T: "It's like a marriage. You know compromises will be necessary; you're willing to make them to make the marriage work. There is a feeling that it must work, it has to work. There is a sense of kinship."

Dr. A. Murray MacKay, retired chairman of the Board of Maritime Telegraph and Telephone, observed: "One reason it works is because all the top

---

*As provincially-owned Crown corporations, the three Prairie telephone companies do not pay federal taxes.

69

people get along so well; they have respect for each other both as persons and as telephone people. They understand each other's problems."

In the opinion of A.A. Brait, president and general manager of Newfoundland Telephone Company Limited: "The cement that in the long run holds TCTS together is the mutual recognition by all the member companies that all must work together or none will work at all."

In a study of federal regulation of telecommunications in Canada commissioned by Bell Canada and undertaken by John McManus in the early seventies, McManus observed that, "Bell Canada is clearly the technical and administrative leader of TCTS," and he went on to point out that the first six chairmen of the TCTS Management committee were all executives of Bell Canada.

Tom Eadie, himself the third chairman and a Bell executive, claimed that the organization has been strengthened in recent years by the ability of TCTS to draw on other member companies to fill that position. Jack Carlile of B.C. Tel was the first non-Bell chairman of the TCTS Board of Management, from 1971 to 1973. He was followed by Eldon Thompson of NBTel from 1974 to 1977 and the current president, Terence F. (Terry) Heenan of B.C. Tel.

McManus's study further suggested to him that TCTS has generally been able to cope more easily with technical innovations than with rate changes, pricing of new services and modifications of the Revenue Settlement Plan. With the long distance kitty to be divided among members now nudging the billion-dollar mark, compromises are getting tougher every day.

B.C. Tel's Carlile put it this way: "We've always had to compromise. That's the name of the game. But it seems to me that recently our ability to compromise is itself being compromised.

"The problems associated with dividing revenues is partly to blame. It was fairly easy to agree in principle and work out mechanics afterwards when amounts were small. It wasn't even difficult to tell someone that he was going to lose two or three hundred thousand dollars as a result of a new settlement. But today, we're talking about hundreds of millions of dollars and people are looking past principles to bucks."

Carlile went on to say: "When the federal Government moved to bring total telecommunications together its effect was to institutionalize confrontation instead of compromise. People are now more likely to stick to their guns and to be less flexible. The business of compromise today is not only complicated, it has become enormously risky. Considering Bell in relation to these problmes it is easy to understand why that company has become less willing to take the lead and provide the resources. Now, TCTS must take the lead.

"Looking ahead I sometimes wonder if our structure is adequate. All our committees are made up of people with two loyalties: to their own company and to TCTS. It has worked wonderfully well so far. I wonder, can it go on indefinitely?"

Terry Heenan, who took office as president of TCTS on January 1, 1978, readily acknowledges that there are problems, but he also sees them as challenges and opportunities.

"The TransCanada Telephone System has been evolving for a good many years," he points out, "and there has always existed a need to tighten it up and develop the administrative part of the operation. There are many issues that will require members of the System to work even more closely together. For example, Telesat Canada has to be integrated into the system. They have to get to know us, learn how we operate, and we have to get to know them. Our mutual objective is the integration of satellite technology into the network in the most efficient way.

"Other matters to be dealt with include changing markets, new or increased competitive forces, new rating concepts that will expand the voice interexchange market (involving upward of half a billion dollars), CNCP's attempt to get interconnection, the question of our relationship with Bell's manufacturing arm — Northern Telecom — and that company's need for a market base to justify the investment required to ensure that technology is available when needed, and evolution of the network into digital technology both in terms of transmission and switching. There is plenty to do."

Little wonder that a French journalist studying the Canadian telecommunications setup quite simply called TCTS "a masterpiece of pragmatism."

3

The Pole Line
Rattlesnakes to Hoarfrost

The poles of this huge communications fence across Canada averaged 30 feet in height, but some in British Columbia towered to 112 feet, and on B.C.'s Lulu Island, one radio-telephone pole reached 130 feet. Each pole supported from one to six cross-arms and carried from two to 60 wires, exclusive of cable.
Telephone Talk (1931)

Telephone poles, more than 185,000 of them, in as straight a line as possible, stretching in single file from cranberry bogs on eastern shores, along the rivers of Quebec, through the rocky bush country of northern Ontario, across the wheat fields of the Prairies and over the mountains of British Columbia — that was the new TransCanada Telephone System pole line. From the Atlantic to the Pacific, a span of 4,263 miles, poles bearing on their shoulders (or cross-arms for the less poetic) magic strands of copper on which words went winging across the continent in a thirtieth of a second.

The TransCanada Telephone System's cross-continent circuit allowed voices to traverse the nation for the first time without dipping into the United States. The year was 1931. The cost, slightly over five million dollars.

In the 1920s there were three major gaps in East-West telephony. In western Canada, the massive ranges of mountains represented barriers hundreds of miles long which, it seemed, were almost impossible to span with poles and wires. Between the western and central regions lay a thousand-mile stretch of rocky country extending from Winnipeg to Sudbury, which was sparsely settled and difficult to build across. As in the mountain region, the only practical solution seemed to be the use of railway company telegraph wires. The third section was between Saint John and Quebec. It involved a further 400-mile stretch that was thinly populated, non-productive in terms of revenue and extremely difficult country for pole construction.

By the time the members of the Telephone Association of Canada received the report from its engineering committee in 1929, providing key data on the Trans-Canada requirements, these three major gaps had been bridged. But the short-line circuits, now available between adjacent systems right across Canada, were not adequate for the sort of long distance use anticipated for the TransCanada Telephone System line.

In order to provide a suitable grade of transmission across the entire system, particularly where very long connections were required, circuits with high inherent transmission stability and good transmission quality were necessary. The routes followed by existing circuits between adjacent provinces were useful as starting points. If they were not suitable themselves, they generally could be made so more economically than any other route. Although complete rebuilding was required in many places and major changes were necessary at other points, the choice of any alternative route would have involved entirely new, longer and more expensive lines. The existing routes would generally be followed, but two major adjustments had to be made.

In the case of the route through British Columbia, it was decided to establish a new route rather than use the CPR line along which the first interprovincial route was established in 1928. There were two good reasons for this. The new route, 150 miles to the south through the Kettle and Coquihalla Valleys and the Crows-nest Pass, did not require long lengths of cable through the railway tunnels, such as at Rogers Pass, which were responsible for transmission problems from the beginning. The new route also passed through settled areas, which meant it was not only accessible for maintenance, but could also be used to accommodate intermediate circuits along the way.

The other exception was a 200-mile stretch between Brandon and Winnipeg, where it was deemed desirable to stay away from the existing main line. The new circuit was about 40 miles longer as a result, but it eliminated all the problems associated with rebuilding the old line, a large part of which featured poles with as many as eight cross-arms. It also avoided a long power parallel near Winnipeg, thus preventing possible interference. (A power parallel occurs when a telephone line runs alongside a high-tension power line.)

Syd Bonneville, the Bell engineer responsible for the fundamental engineering on the new line, noted: "The transmission requirements for the TransCanada circuits were engineered on the basis of meeting the limits recommended for the general toll switching plan. In view of the length of the system's circuits, many difficult but interesting transmission problems arose which are not normally encountered in designing shorter haul facilities. Transmission design requirements with respect to noise, cross-talk* and distortion for both direct and switched connections were instrumental in restricting the length of the voice frequency circuits and using carrier systems for the longer circuits."

Ultimately, nearly two-thirds of the TCTS circuit mileage was carrier circuit. The carrier system made it possible for several conversations to be transmitted over the same pair of wires at the same time because each conversation was on a different frequency. They no more interfered with one another than one radio station interferes with a second broadcasting at a different point on the dial. "C" carrier was a three-channel system used on the trans-Canada voice highway to provide *four* voice paths on one pair of wires, three by means of the carrier system and one through the regular voice frequency path.

Originally, 12 TCTS circuits were planned but the cutbacks forced by the Depression reduced these to seven. Each basic circuit utilized a three-channel "C" carrier to ensure satisfactory transmission over the 4,200-mile span. To boost the signals, repeater stations were established at 22 points along the line.

Because of the importance of the new trans-Canada network — and its vulnerability, because of the absence of alternate routes across three-quarters of its length — careful consideration was given to open-wire facilities. The use of number 165 copper line wire (about 1/6 inch in diameter), compared with lighter-gauge wires, offered the advantages of greater mechanical strength and less risk from storm damage and other circuit troubles.

The original line between Sudbury and Winnipeg had combined telephone wires of lighter gauges with the Canadian Pacific's 114 wire. Now, 165-gauge wire was strung over its entire route.

For troublesome heavy storm areas the pole line was built to Class I requirements. This specifies the highest grade of pole line normally used for telephone purposes. For the new construction or reconstruction work, western cedar poles were used west of Winnipeg, creosoted pine in the east.

---

*If two sets of wires remain parallel over a long distance and conversations are carried over each pair simultaneously, the two conversations spill over into each other, although the wires never touch each other. This is caused by "induction," and is commonly known as cross-talk. To avoid this interference the positions of the wires in relation to each other are altered at regular intervals. The left-hand wire of a pair switches over to become the right-hand wire, and vice versa. This is called transposition.

The "All-Red" line stretched from sea to sea for more than 4,000 miles. This section was located near Strathmore, east of Calgary, Alberta.

A new type Pyrex insulator was used but it didn't work well in the extremes of the British Columbia climate. Pyrex becomes brittle in cold weather, extremely so when it is mounted on steel pins. In cold weather, the copper contracted and snapped off the tops of the insulators. Eventually, another high-grade glass had to be substituted.

A different standard of transposition to prevent cross-talk was also engineered into the line. The transposing on the cross-Canada line was engineered to occur at every second pole and was designed to permit, ultimately, the use of carrier circuits. This meant, of course, that extensive alterations had to be made to the pole arrangement and even the spacing between existing poles had to be altered to provide for the new transposition arrangement. Altogether, some 2,000 miles of existing line, largely in the Prairie provinces, was completely rebuilt. Pole work to retranspose an additional 1,500 miles was carried out.

Bell engineer Bonneville recalls checking the transposition system, travelling along the line on a motor-scooter. In classic understatement, Syd described his trip as "quite an experience."

In talking about the rigid specifications for transposition sections laid down by the transmission engineers, Frank Wolokoff, a foreman with a B.C. Tel at the time, remembers: ". . . They were fussy about the lengths of the transposition sections. You couldn't just end a section anywhere. When we built to the Alberta border at Crowsnest Lake, we didn't stop right at the border. We went six to 10 poles into Alberta for an exact matchup with the Alberta line. A funny thing

Eugene P. LaBelle, general superintendent of plant for B.C. Tel surveys a right of way clearing for the trans-Canada line around 1931.

happened later on. There was some highway construction on the Alberta side of the Crowsnest, which shortened the pole line. So at the end they simply ran the pole line part way up a hill and back down again to make it come out even at our end of the section."

In preparation for the TCTS hookup Bell built its most expensive open-wire line (designated line 236) from Oshawa to North Bay, where it connected with the existing line to Sudbury. Tom Eadie, who was to become president and chairman of the Board of Bell and also chairman of TCTS, recalled 40 years later: "If line 236 were to be built in 1970 it would probably have cost 10 times the $1.5 million we spent on it in 1930. The line was taken down in 1970 and we recovered 1.1 million pounds of copper. It was worth $550,000 at that time."

In Alberta's Turner Valley area, scene of the province's first oil and gas fields, corrosion problems with open-wire copper conductors were experienced. Finally, the use of an expensive non-corrosive substitute had to be sanctioned. It was either that or replace the copper lines every few years.

Saskatchewan's Stuart R. Muirhead, then chief engineer of Saskatchewan Government Telephones, remembers the building of that province's share of the TransCanada Telephone System during the Depression: "We were hit pretty hard by the Depression and we didn't have much money to work with, but on the other hand everything was cheaper because of the hard times and we got it built for a lot less money."

Saskatchewan linemen were grateful for the work then, although they recall having to pay as much as 25 to 30 cents for meals when they were on the road, a substantial part of a day's wages.

Muirhead reveals that Saskatchewan was able to save a good deal of money because the province had squirrelled away some used wire for possible future use. "The TCTS specifications called for 165 copper wire line and we had a lot of it on hand which we had rolled up from another job. We improvised a device which enabled us to test the used wire to see how much pull it would take. It soon became clear that most of our wire was good enough to reuse."

Jack Johnstone, a lineman working in Saskatchewan, relates: "We had this fixed idea that we had to keep the wire dead level. When we came to a gully we'd have to get 50- and 60-foot poles. If you were used to climbing a 30-foot pole, climbing a 40- or 50-footer seemed 10 times as high. Later we were told that a line which follows the contour of the ground is better.

"Hoarfrost gave us the most trouble. Regina is in the basin of an old lake bottom and when conditions are right the hoarfrost builds up pretty heavy between Regina and McLean. We tried everything. We even had men going along whacking the wires with bamboo sticks. Years later we even tried helicopters. Nothing worked." (The problem still exists today.)

G. Gordon Milne and some of his fellow workers had some fun one July night testing the newly-installed carrier circuits in Saskatchewan. Lining up the circuit between Regina and Yorkton, the testers decided to "announce" a make-believe sportscast of a hockey game. They were so convincing that when the phony broadcast inadvertently got onto a local circuit, people phoned in to find out where the hockey game was being played in July.

The TCTS line was the biggest telephone construction job undertaken in British Columbia up to that time. The cost to B.C. Tel was close to $1.25 million. It required 35,000 new poles and 1.2 million pounds of copper wire, created two new circuits (four wires) and covered a distance of approximately 680 miles, from Vancouver to Crowsnest on the Alberta boundary.

In the Pacific province the line traversed four mountain ranges. The section within 50 miles of the coast, however, proved to be by far the most difficult for the maintenance men. Heavy snowfalls, snow slides, heavy rains, floods, high water, trees, high winds and forest fires were only a few problems from the catalogue of catastrophes that caused line failures.

B.C. Tel's Frank Wolokoff tells about surveying and staking the route for a new section of the TCTS line in the Coquihalla Valley. "We encountered everything from bears to rattlesnakes. Several of the boys had narrow escapes and in that section alone they killed eight rattlers."

Walter Jones, superintendent of maintenance for B.C. Tel, and a couple of fellow field workers were sent to the Coquihalla Pass area to look for a shorter route. "It was a long day — July 19, 1929. We had a guide and a packer to handle the horses. We drove west from Princeton to Coalmount. Then we took the horses as far as the Tulameen River crossing. There the packer left the horses and we had to scramble the last 10 miles on foot. The distance wasn't all that great, but it was all up and down. We went down some of the slopes awfully fast. If the guide and packer hadn't been with us we'd still be there! There was no way we could build there. Even in June ravines were still plugged with snow. So we built along the CPR right-of-way and the TCTS line opened in February 1932. We promptly had a series of snowslides that buried the line for months."

A tough but genial construction man named Al Strachan was in charge of building a 180-mile section of the line in British Columbia. Strachan has never fogotten that job.

"In the summer of 1931 we built from Crowsnest Lake on the Alberta-British Columbia border, to Kuskanook on Kootenay Lake. Our first camp was at Jaffery, from which we worked west. Then we came back to Fernie and worked to the border at Crowsnest Lake.

"On our second leg we had to completely rebuild seven miles near Wardner. A forest fire had swept through there and played the devil with it. Most of the poles were still standing but the heavy copper — it was number eight wire — had heated up and stretched right down to the ground.

"I had about 50 men working in several crews. First there was the brushing crew that went through to clear the path. We started with one brush crew. The men were equipped with six-foot saws but between Yahk and Creston the cedars were so big we had to send for seven-foot saws. The foreman was Frank Belanger, the ex-train robber. He was the last of the Bill Miner* gang, the outfit that pulled off the last train robbery in British Columbia. Frank stood six foot two inches. His son, Frank, Jr., was on the crew, too. He stood six-foot-four. When I needed a second brush crew, I put Frank Junior in charge.

"The digging crew went in after the brush crews. Then came the pole-haulers,

*Bill Miner was a notorious train robber who operated in the American southwest. He was convicted of robbing a CPR train at Ducks, B.C., in 1906. Belanger was reputed to be Louis Colqhoun, one of Miner's accomplices.

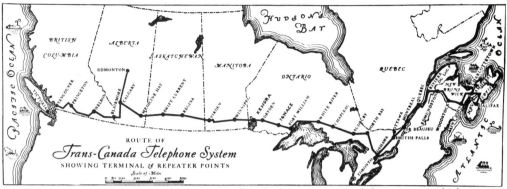

This map illustrates the 4,260 mile TransCanada Telephone System and the points at which repeater stations were established.

and in some places like the Moyie Bluffs, above Moyie Lake, they had to set them down carefully behind trees or they would slide down the hill and land on the highway or on the railroad track. On parts of the route the blasters had to make the holes. The diggers couldn't get through the solid rock. Joe Stevenson, who did the blasting, was good at cleaning out the holes. There were two teams in the crew making holes — each with one man turning the rod and two swinging sledges. Then the pole setters came along. We had to set a pole every 140 feet and that took a lot of dynamite in some places.

"Emil Aube travelled just ahead of the pole-setters. Emil was our framer. He framed the tops of the pole.

"They really charged for everything up there, even though it was the depths of the Depression and eggs were a nickel a dozen. Emil went into a store one time where a sign said 'Fresh Eggs-Fresh Bread.' He ordered a dozen eggs and two loaves of bread and handed the lady a dollar bill expecting 85 cents change but she said, 'That's just right.'

"At the end the wire crew came along.

"Another great man I had was John Benache, the champion tie-maker of British Columbia. God, he was a wonder with an axe.

"We had two steel men. They cut the ends and made the pieces we needed. Albert Knobbs — we called him Knobby — was one of them. Knobby had quite a sense of humour. We think it was Knobby who salted some holes on the Moyie Bluffs. We didn't work Sundays. One Sunday, Knobby mixed some zinc balls with the dirt and covered them up. On Monday morning sure enough, some of the fellows came up with this shiny stuff. They thought for sure they'd hit a gold mine.

"The other steel man was a little guy named Yeager. He really was a prospector. He had a bottle half-full of gold nuggets and he could tell you exactly where he had found each one. He also had a bottle three-quarters full of dust. Yeager's son worked for us, too.

"Norman Kusab had some fun with the Yeagers when we finished at Crowsnest Lake. There were some old horses in a field nearby, and all the boys went to town to get drunk. Norman got one of the old horses and backed it into Yeager's tent and closed the flap. When the Yeagers came back and opened the flap there was the horse looking them right in the face. . . ."

And so it went from coast to coast across the country as boomer gangs, rock-hard bush crews, pole haulers, hard-rock blasting experts, pole setters, linemen — proud of their abilities, not satisfied until the job was done right, but full of fun and mischief once the work for the day was finished — put the Canadian voice on a path from sea to sea.

4

From Sea to Sea
A Link of Empire

*On Monday, January 25th, 1932, the striking of twelve noon
by the chimes in the Peace Tower at Ottawa marked the
opening of a brief ceremony inaugurating the TransCanada
Telephone System.*

A Link of Empire (1932)

After 10 years of preparation, study, analysis of the route, assessment of revenues, balancing of costs and intricate and innovative engineering, everything that had to be done before work could properly begin on an all-Canada, coast to coast toll line was finished. Then followed two years of rugged work, strengthening the weak provincial connections in the circuit from the Atlantic provinces to Quebec and through northern Ontario to Winnipeg, bridging the chasms and leaping the mountains of British Columbia. But the two years were well-spent, building thousands of miles of pole line to a standard never before achieved or attempted so that a voice in Nova Scotia might be heard in Victoria one-thirtieth of a second later.

The formation of the TransCanada Telephone System brought to fruition a project that must be classed as an outstanding example of co-operation in the public service, representing the united efforts of the seven major telephone systems of Canada at that time — British Columbia Telephone Company; Alberta Government Telephones; Department of Telephones, Saskatchewan; The Manitoba Telephone System; The Bell Telephone Company of Canada; The New Brunswick Telephone Company, Limited; and Maritime Telegraph and Telephone Company Limited.

When the chimes had sounded a master of ceremonies conducted a telephonic roll call of the nine provinces. When each announced itself ready, the Governor-General, His Excellency, the Earl of Bessborough, spoke on an open line to each provincial capital:

Those of us who are taking part in this ceremony today may justly congratulate one another and the provinces of this Dominion that, through vision and enterprise of Canadians, another link has been forged between component parts of the Empire. The completion of this link appears to me to be particularly opportune at this time when our statesmen the world over are giving their most serious consideration to projects designed to create closer economic union between the British peoples.

In the pursuit of this laudable ambition, the TransCanada Telephone System from Halifax to Vancouver is an achievement of no mean significance. It binds more closely together provinces which less than 50 years ago were first united by the social and commercial ties made possible by railroad construction.

Today we open another route of communication. By it, the voice of business and friendship can traverse the four thousand miles from sea to sea in, I am told, one-thirtieth of a second.

This great accomplishment has been made possible through the painstaking development of the invention of a Scottish-Canadian who, seven years after Confederation, first demonstrated in this country the practicability of transmitting spoken words over wires.

Since the time of that invention by Alexander Graham Bell, the telephone has become an integral part of our social and commercial life. It has been provided for the peoples of the various provinces under government ownership in some places and through private enterprise in others.

It is a tribute alike to both public and private ownership that the seven participating organizations should have worked together in harmony over a period of some 10 years to overcome stupendous difficulties and bring about the consummation which we celebrate today.

The telephone line thus constructed is, I am given to understand, capable of almost limitless expansion to provide for the growing demands of this country in the years to come.

Nor is the usefulness of this . . . telephone system confined to this country. It may be linked with trans-oceanic telephone systems which, in ever-widening circles, reach out to bind the human race together as never before in the history of mankind.

The Earl of Bessborough, Governor-General of Canada, inaugurates the TransCanada Telephone System on January 25, 1932.

I am sure I am only expressing a sentiment common to all of us when I say that I sincerely trust that this TransCanada Telephone System will play a significant part in increasing and strengthening the existing good will and esteem between the inhabitants of every part of this Dominion, rendering its vast distance no longer a barrier to communication between citizens though they may be separated from one another by hundreds of leagues within this continent.

Let us also express the further and wider hope that this system will serve to unite in even closer bands of fellowship the citizens of our whole Empire though they be separated by the oceans lying between us and our sister nations within the British Commonwealth.

One of a series of advertisements used in the subsequent promotion of the new TransCanada Telephone System was headed, "The Shortest Distance Between Two Points." The copy referred in glowing terms to the 4,000 miles of wire which stretched from coast to coast providing an *all-Canadian* telephone service ". . . linking up every intermediate city, town and hamlet. . . ." Even then, the promotion of the System was directed to business users. The "instantaneous communication from anywhere to anywhere in the Dominion" was considered to be especially attractive to businessmen who now had at their disposal "a system surpassed nowhere in the world in accuracy, convenience and economy."

Then followed the first of nine switches to provincial capitals and the Honourable W.H. Covert, Lieutenant-Governor of Nova Scotia, responded:

Your Excellency, it is most fitting that the first voice to span this far-flung continent, so loyal to the Crown and traditions of the British Empire, should be that of your Excellency, and I feel especially honoured at being privileged to participate in these ceremonies on behalf of this old province of Nova Scotia.

We have become so accustomed to using the telephone at any and every hour of the day and night, that we feel aggrieved if, within the limits of our own company's system, there is any difficulty in hearing distinctly; but there is still wonder and amazement that the voice when the initial carrying force is tired and spent, can, as the passenger was assisted by the relay horses in the olden days, be rushed forward by the wizard-like mechanism called the repeater, to the end of any proposed journey.

Voices have been carried from Nova Scotia to British Columbia to Nova Scotia before today, but only by borrowing a portion of the passage over our neighbour's lines. Now we are glad and proud to say that, through the enterprise and skill of our own people, we are able to proceed at any distance wholly through our own country. East and West may meet at any moment without any difficulty whatever. . . .

The repeaters referred to by Lieutenant-Governor Covert were amplifying devices, without which cross-continent calls would have been impossible. On the earliest long distance lines the limit to which the human voice could be carried without fading out was approximately 200 miles. Improvements in equipment had increased the range, but not until the invention of the vacuum tube amplifier — leading to the development of the telephone repeater around 1914 — were cross-continent calls possible. Twenty-two repeaters were built into the Trans-Canada line to aid transmission.

The Honourable Charles Dalton, Lieutenant-Governor, replying for Prince Edward Island, then said:

. . . Prince Edward Island has long been concerned with the problem of communication. It was between this Island and New Brunswick that the world's first submarine telegraphic cable was laid in 1852. . . . It was here in this city of Charlottetown that the seed of this great Dominion germinated, and we look forward to this new link in our communication to bind the widely separated parts of our Dominion closer together.

Allan D. Nickerson, who joined Maritime Tel & Tel in 1919 as its first transmission engineer, recalls: "I was sent over to Charlottetown. I sat in a minor room in the Governor's office and had free access to the tea which was served to all the dignitaries. I spent a couple of days talking to Ottawa, testing the line. I was sort of Lieutenant-Governor for a couple days you might say. We didn't have to worry about any signalling or anything like that. It was all set up. When you get to be Lieutenant-Governor you don't have to worry about turning the crank. You just come in and things are all set for you. The quality of the transmission on the circuit for the official opening was the best there had ever been."

The line was next switched to The Honourable Sir John Douglas Hazen, Administrator, who spoke for New Brunswick:

This is an age of connection, and in the language of His Excellency the Governor-General, another link 'has been forged' between the provinces of Canada and the far-flung parts of the Empire. . . . It will rank with other great undertakings which have contributed to civilization and friendly relations by abridging distance and obliterating time and space. . . . It is gratifying to know that the usefulness of the TransCanada Telphone System and the benefit which will flow from it will not be confined to Canada alone, as I

Telephone executives and dignitaries participating in the TransCanada Telephone System inaugural call in Saint John.

understand arrangements have been made for extending it beyond our borders and linking it with trans-oceanic telephone systems as Canada grows in wealth and population. In this way it will serve to connect the human race as it is claimed no other agency has done since the beginning of time. . . .

Each of the seven companies constructed and maintained the facilities required within its own territory and thus bore its share of the total cost, which was estimated to be about $5 million. Altogether some 2,000 miles of existing line were completely rebuilt. By province the line mileage worked out at Nova Scotia 142, New Brunswick 385, Ontario and Quebec (Bell) 1,952, Manitoba 242, Saskatchewan 465, Alberta 418, and British Columbia 659.

The Honourable Henry George Carroll, Lieutenant-Governor, spoke for Quebec: *

Je suis heureux de me joindre à vous et aux Honorables Lieutenants-Gouverneurs des provinces canadiennes, et de féliciter la Cie de Téléphone Bell du service qu'elle inaugure en ce moment.

Elle prouve aujourd'hui à la population du Dominion les avantages d'un réseau exclusivement canadien qui relie ensemble toutes les parties du pays.

Par un fil tendu d'un océan à l'autre le téléphone associe des volontés des collaborations et des intérêts. Il réalise ce que l'on croyait une chimère par laquelle l'homme peut être instantanément présent partout où il veut échanger des idées et des sentiments.

Il convient, je crois, en cette occasion, que les paroles transmises à travers toutes les provinces expriment les sentiments de cordiale fraternité qui les unissent.

A cet instant c'est la voix de Québec qui salue en vous le Représentant du Roi au Canada et offre ses meilleurs voeux d'amitié aux provinces soeurs.

Elle leur apporte l'assurance que le pacte fédéral qui nous unit à elles n'est pas conçu dans cette province comme une fiction constitutionnelle, mais

---

*I am happy to be here with you and the Honourable Lieutenant-Governors of the Canadian provinces to compliment the Bell Telephone Company and acknowledge the service which it is now inaugurating.

Today, the company can demonstrate to the people of the Dominion the benefits of an exclusively Canadian network which links together all parts of the country.

By means of a wire strung from one ocean to the other, the telephone now brings together (national) goals, collaborations and interests. It makes real what was previously thought to be a mere dream; that in an instant man can be present wherever he wishes to exchange ideas and impressions.

It is appropriate on this occasion, I believe, that the words being transmitted across the

comme un accord des intelligences et des coeurs dans l'accomplissement des desinées nationales. Et comme la vaste étendue du pays pourrait être un obstacle à notre cohésion et à notre entente, il y a lieux de nous féliciter de nous sentir plus rapprochés les uns des autres, et de voir si bien facilités maintenant les communications et les rapports qui sont les besoins de la vie des affairs, comme elles sont la force des amitiés durables.

The system actually went into operation on August 1, 1931. Six weeks later the first reports covering August business were received. The reports advised that revenues of $11,426 derived from 2,152 calls were to be apportioned.

The Honourable Sir William Mulock, Administrator replying for Ontario, said:

... In the ordinary course of life, families and friends become scattered, perhaps never to meet again. What a thrill of joy to a fond parent to hear over the telephone the actual voice of a long-absent child; or a child to hear direct from a parent's lips, words of sympathy and love; or to separated brothers and sisters to talk to each other of the memories of home and youth.

There are moments in everyone's life when his thoughts turn toward his home and the friends of his youth and the heart yearns for the touch of a vanished hand and the sound of the voice that is still. What a comfort at such a moment that the living may now over the telephone, enjoy such spiritual reunions, exchanging words of love and sympathy and giving encouragement and strength to each to bear his cross.

Rendering such a unique service — if for no other reason — I regard the telephone as a blessed agency for the good of mankind.

The final report of the Engineering committee, presented to the Executive committee of the Telephone Association of Canada in August 1929, just before the stock-market crash, estimated 1932 revenues at $1,056,000. The actual amount for 1932 was $194,135.

---

provinces should express the cordial sentiment of brotherhood which unite them.

Now, in speaking for Quebec, I greet you — the representative of the King in Canada — and I offer (Quebec's) best wishes of friendship to the sister provinces.

These words carry the assurance that the federal pact which unites us is not in this province considered to be a constitutional fiction; rather (it is) an agreement of minds and hearts toward the achievement of our national destiny. The vastness of our country is such (its enormous size and the distance between its parts) that it can stand as an obstacle to national unity and understanding. It is fitting (therefore) that we should also congratulate ourselves that we now feel closer together (as a result of) having significantly improved a communications system which satisfies the needs of the business community and ensures the strength of lasting friendships.

Speaking for the Lieutenant-Governor of Manitoba who was ill, The Honourable W.J. Major, Attorney-General and Minister of Telephones, replied for Manitoba:

... Manitoba, the keystone province of the Dominion, the people of this province detached from the citizens of Eastern Canada by miles of sparsely settled territory, look upon the event of this morning as the creation of a link that will bind them in a spirit of greater comradeship to their compatriots in other sections of the Dominion.

It was therefore, with enthusiasm that the Manitoba Telephone System, owned and operated by our own citizens, made its contribution which has resulted in a project that will stand out in Canadian history as a striking illustration of Canadian unity and a striking illustration as well of the capacity of the Canadian people for co-operative and collective effort.

Jim Mills, who was general manager of the Manitoba Telephone System for 20 years, recalls: "There was an unusual arrangement in Manitoba. Bell owned all the equipment and facilities from the Ontario border to Winnipeg. That was a distance of 83 miles. Bell actually owned facilities right into our toll building in Winnipeg, and paid rent. The whole success of TransCanada is based on mutual trust. We agreed to agree. That's the only way it could work."

Lieutenant-Colonel the Honourable Hugh Edwin Munroe, Lieutenant-Governor, spoke for Saskatchewan:

... Saskatchewan is the third province of Canada in point of population. For many years it has been known as the banner wheat province of Canada and the granary of the Empire. Unfortunately, during the last three years we have had crop failure over a large area in the southern part of the province owing to drought conditions. Many of our best farmers, as a result, have found themselves without funds with which to support their families and without fodder for their stock. In these days of suffering and anxiety for very many of our people, kind friends in different parts of Canada, with generosity beyond all praise, and without distinction of race and creed, have, from their abundance, sent carload after carload of fruit, vegetables, preserves and clothing to those who were in need. On behalf of the government and people of Saskatchewan, I gratefully acknowledge to Your Excellency and to the Lieutenant-Governors of the Eastern provinces of Canada these many acts of kindness and good will which the people of Saskatchewan will never forget. These acts of sympathy and loving kindness have brought the East and West closer together.

At the inauguration of the TCTS pole line executives of all the member companies listened in all across the country. This is a group of managers from the Manitoba Telephone System.

The All-Red copper wire stretching across Canada from coast to coast adds but a physical tie to those invisible ties of affection already binding the East and West.

In Regina, the group taking part in the inaugural ceremonies was seated around the Confederation Table, a much-prized memento of Canada's Confederation period. The Fathers of Confederation were seated around that same table during the conference which opened at Charlottetown on October 10, 1864, and which led to the drafting of the British North America Act. After a period of service in the Privy Council Chambers at Ottawa, the table was moved to Battleford, then the seat of government of the Northwest Territories. It was subsequently shifted to Regina when that city became the capital of Saskatchewan.

Stuart R. Muirhead, who was chief engineer of Saskatchewan Government Telephones for 20 years, recalls: "We made the decision before the Depression really hit us. If the decision hadn't been made when it was, early in 1930, I doubt if we'd have gotten approval."

In Alberta, the Honourable W.L. Walsh, Lieutenant-Governor, spoke for his province:

   . . . we rejoice in the fact that the widely-scattered provinces of our far-flung

Dominion are now bound together by another method of communication built entirely upon Canadian soil, which makes it possible for every part of Canada to express to every other part its needs and ambitions and hopes through the finest of all mediums, the human voice.

In the West we sometimes think we are not properly understood by the East, and I fear that the East occasionally thinks that its aims are misinterpreted by the West. When individual misunderstandings exist they can be cleared up more effectively by personal contact than by all other methods. But when, as is often the case, a meeting face to face is impossible, there is no substitute for it comparable to a talk over the telephone.

May we hope that these new wires, which stretch from sea to sea may be freely utilized, not only to retain and restore good understanding between individuals, but to promote harmony in national affairs. This is the great opportunity which this new system presents. . . . These new telephone lines are one more tool in the hands of those who strive to weld Canada into one great nation with common ideals and common aims. . . .

Tony Cashman, author of *Singing Wires*, the lively history of the telephone in Alberta, notes: "The romance of the undertaking was largely lost on the crews who did the building, and the revenue was of passing interest if any, but the construction impressed them mightily. The TransCanada was *quality*, built with such strength as to almost physically bind Canada together."

Lieutenant-Governor J.W. Fordham Johnson of British Columbia completed the cross-Canada tour, declaring:

This new telephone line is more than a new means of commercial and social communication. This all-Canadian line will increase Canada's feeling of self-reliance. It will add something to her self-respect.

Even if it is considered merely as a line of poles from coast to coast, the size of this project from a construction standpoint is obvious. But the job was bigger than that. Telephone men despair when they try to tell me about all the intricacies of carrying the human voice a distance of more than 4,000 miles. They tell me that the current which goes out from here on its way to Halifax is only a few thousandths of the quantity required to operate an ordinary light in my house. They tell me about minute particles of coal in my telephone which make it possible for me to impress my voice on the delicate electric currents. It has given me a new conception of the problems involved in designing, building and operating this line.

It is doubtful whether anywhere else on this continent a stretch of pole line has been built across rougher country than that traversed by the Trans-Canada line in British Columbia.

During its journey across our province, particularly in the eastern section, the new line rises as high as a mile above sea level. It makes its way along the edge of canyons; it leaps across rivers; and it follows the right-of-way that has been cut through miles of standing timber. From the pictures that I have seen and the stories that I have heard, I have decided the trans-Canada line across British Columbia was an engineering and construction feat of great magnitude.

Now that the poles are up and the copper wires are laid upon their shoulders, it will be the business of the telephone men to keep the pathways of speech unbroken. They will watch over the new circuits. They will test them. They will keep an eye on strange metres. They will know when anything goes wrong. They will hurry out into the snows of the hills in search of trouble, and they will work in the cold and wet and sometimes in the darkness. They will do it partly for the money they earn, but partly, too, because of a loyalty which among the Anglo-Saxon people is called duty, and which has always been looked upon by them as of the highest importance. . . .

The cost to the British Columbia Telephone Company for the 625 miles of line from Vancouver to the Crowsnest Pass on the Alberta boundary was approximately $1.25 million. This was around $19,230 per mile and represented just about 25 per cent of the total cost of the line.

Someone calculated that field engineers working on the trans-Canada line in British Columbia alone walked over 2,000 miles. More than 2,700 miles of copper wire weighing more than 1.2 million pounds was used. One B.C. engineer drew a cartoon depicting an extraordinary landscape; it portrays a fantastic world gone mad with hanging mountains, bottomless chasms, aerial tramways, mountain goats and rattlesnakes — all sustained by the new telephone line. During one discussion of the route, someone suggested that wild animals in the mountainous regions might be a menace to service. Moose, for example, might get caught in the wires. "Hmph!" snorted A.H. Lemmon, chief engineer. "If the line is built as high in some places as proposed, angels will be getting caught in the wires!"

Gil Kennedy, who was hired by Jim Hamilton in 1923 to work for B.C. Tel, commented years later: "I always felt Jim didn't get the credit due him. He never became president of the company but he had a great deal to do with the development of B.C. Tel and I think he was the man who really conceived the idea of TransCanada in the first place. If you could have a picture of the 'fathers of TransCanada' like the 'fathers of Confederation,' Jim would have to be in it."

After Lieutenant-Governor Johnson's tribute to the builders of the line, the action was switched back to Ottawa where the Governor-General declared the TransCanada Telephone System "Open to the people of Canada."

In the world of make-believe everybody then "lived happily ever after." In reality, things haven't been quite that simple. . . .

In 1932, advertisements introducing TCTS to Canadians appeared in most major dailies.

PART THREE

The Ten Partners
First There Were Seven

1

The Bell
And a Man Named Sise

*Came the telephone with its insistent ring . . . the Victorian
household was never the same again.*
Charles Fleetford Sise
by R.C. Fetherstonehaugh (1944)

Today's generation has little idea of what Toronto and Montreal were like in
1880, the year the Bell Telephone Company of Canada was granted its charter.

In Montreal, St. Catherine Street west of Bleury was still residential. Stores
were only just beginning to intrude. A row of fine houses stood where Windsor
Station now stands. The horse trams went only as far as Guy Street and sleighs
were the rule in winter. Only a few streets in the city were paved and at night the
familiar figure of the lamplighter hurried from lamp-post to lamp-post.

Toronto had a population of fewer than 80,000. The city extended from the
Don River in the east to Dufferin Street in the west, and the sandy road of Bloor
Street bounded it on the north. Yonge Street was developing as a retail business
section, but few stores were more than three stories high. The Canadian National
Exhibition grounds — all of two years old — were a long way from the centre of
town.

The impact of the telephone and the changes it brought to the life and people
of Canada were enormous. Imagine the mid-Victorian atmosphere that prevailed
in the homes of well-to-do Montrealers and Torontonians in the pre-telephone
world of 1880. The style and order of the day were stuffy parlours, ornate and
uncomfortable furniture and heavy draperies which deepened the gloom of lamp-

lit rooms. Whatnots in the corners of hundreds of parlours contained seashells, glass-enclosed flowers and treasured family photographs. By the dim light of prismed hanging lamps people read the latest parliamentary debates on the Canadian Pacific Railway contract, or about Peter Redpath's gift of a museum to McGill University, or, with proper shock, about the assassination of George Brown. Now introduce the telephone into this picture with its insistent ring, its demands, and its amazing ability to move people to get things done. The Victorian household was never to be the same.

Commercially, the telephone became a reality in Canada in 1877 when the Canadian patent was issued and Alexander Graham Bell, the inventor, assigned most of the Canadian rights to his father, Alexander Melville Bell. Father Bell was an enthusiast and a good public relations man, but he was not really much of a businessman. After trying in vain to find a Canadian buyer for the patent rights, he sold them to the National Bell Telephone Company of Boston.

Meanwhile, ruinous competition had sprung up in Canada in the telephone business. Rival telegraph companies fighting one another used the telephone as a lure for new customers. One telegraph company went so far as to offer three months' free service to get new subscribers. Its rival countered with free installation. In some places the companies provided extra signal bells on the subscriber's line for wake-up calls. In others the companies handled grocery orders for subscribers and even summoned doctors in cases of accident.

Telephone use was growing rapidly in both the United States and Canada. To bring some order out of the competitive chaos in Canada, in 1880 the parent company in Boston, the National Bell Telephone Company, dispatched to Canada Charles Fleetford Sise — an insurance executive, master mariner, and one-time Confederate agent. A Montreal businessman named Andrew Robertson was named the first president of the new Bell Telephone Company of Canada, but it was the tough and wordly-wise Sise as vice-president and general manager who ran the show. Like his American counterpart, Theodore N. Vail, Sise immediately set out to turn his dream of a national telephone network into reality. The company's first prospectus claimed 2,000 customers and exchanges or agencies in 32 communities across Canada.

Sise was a meticulous, tightly disciplined and well-organized man with a keen sense of business priorities. He therefore moved quickly to pick up such competitors as Montreal Telegraph, Dominion Telegraph, and the Hamilton and Windsor exchanges, along with most of the larger companies. Because Canadian investors were unwilling to invest capital in such "speculative" adventures, the American Bell Telephone Company had to put up approximately 25 per cent of

An operator's work in the early days of the telephone was much more physical than it is today. She connected and disconnected local and long distance calls manually, gave listing information, provided time of day service and handled practically all emergency calls. The automation of the Traffic Operator Position System (TOPS) has relieved operators of the physical work of yesteryear.

the required capital.* (In 1881 the U.S. company changed its name from the National Bell Telephone Company to the American Bell Telephone Company.)

Reaching both east and west, Sise bought out exchanges in Saint John and Halifax and picked up Manitoba pioneer Horace McDougall's Winnipeg exchange. In Saskatchewan, by 1883, Bell had telephones in the Mounted Police Barracks in Regina as well as in the Lieutenant-Governor's residence, the Royal Hotel and a couple of other places, including the livery stable — a strategic location. In Newfoundland the Anglo-American Telegraph Company claimed exclusvie telephone rights dating back to its original deal with Cyrus Field and his telegraph in the early 1860s. However, the telegraph company's manager, Alexander MacKay, agreed to use Bell equipment on a royalty basis. And in Prince Edward Island Bell held rights until 1888 when, with the undercover help of a Bell agent, Islanders bought out those rights and started their own company.

But the fledgling Bell Telephone Company of Canada was in trouble. When Bell stock went on public sale in December 1880 at $100 per share, the rush for shares had all the excitement of watching cactus grow. For nearly a year the Bell in Canada survived only because Sise loaned the company money out of his own pocket.

It was only fitting that when the first convention of Bell telephone companies (licensed by the parent National Telephone Company) convened in Niagara Falls in September 1880, lapel buttons printed to promote the use of "Hello" instead of "Hoy Hoy" (as suggested by Melville Bell) when answering the telephone got messed up — and some came out reading "OHell."

Two crises threatened, and were surmounted, in 1885.

That year the Minister of Agriculture, then in charge of Communications, voided Bell's Canadian telephone patent. The Canadian Patent Act specified that any person should be permitted to obtain a patent on an article upon application and that after a stipulated time from the date of the patent the patented article could not be imported into Canada. To the Minister that apparently meant public sale of telephones and not rental. He also charged that the rubber handles for Bell's telephones were being imported. As far as he was concerned, therefore, two aspects of the Patent Act were being contravened — so he voided the patent, and there was no appeal to his ruling!

*Until 1930 the American Bell Telephone Company and its successor, AT&T, gradually acquired additional shares of the Bell Telephone Company of Canada — which at that point represented 25.1 per cent of the fully paid shares outstanding. No further shares were acquired after 1930. By 1974, AT&T's share holdings represented only 2.0 per cent of the total B.T. Co. shares outstanding. In 1975, AT&T sold all of its Bell Canada common shares to Canadian buyers.

Many thought that this unexpected dictum would open the field to cut-throat competition, which would mean the end of Bell. Sise never panicked. He merely noted in his Log Book: "Decision against us at Ottawa." He was confident that Bell's head start and better service would make it impossible for any brash new competitor to threaten them seriously, and he was right.

That same year a smallpox epidemic raged in Montreal. Before the epidemic waned, 3,000 deaths had been recorded. A rumour to the effect that smallpox was transmitted over telephone wires began circulating and one night a mob with torches and axes headed for the telephone exchange. Sise armed men from his workshop with axe handles and prepared to defend the exchange. The chance arrival of a military unit averted the clash.

In the old days, when Sise was the master of a merchant ship, he religiously kept a ship's log, recording faithfully every event of any importance. He continued the practice in his new position when he joined The Bell Telephone Company of Canada. A random sampling from his Log Book not only charts accurately the progress of the company, but also shows the tremendous scope of telephone matters he attended to personally for more than 35 years.

From the Log Books now preserved in the archives of Bell Canada in Montreal:

September 16, 1880
Engaged Roberts as janitor of building in Hospital street at $8.00 per month.
April 15, 1881
Authorized purchase of Toronto company at $10,000 stock and $17,500 cash.
December, 1881
Letter from Toronto Ministerial Association requesting us to close Exchange on Sunday.
September 18, 1883
Montreal has 1000 subscribers.
April, 1886
Advised of destruction of Toronto exchange by fire.
October 9, 1887
The line from Ottawa to Montreal was opened yesterday and is working successfully, conversation being as distinct as local work in Montreal.
June 28, 1888
Women to be used for night operators, experimentally to see if service improves.
March 29, 1890
Mr. Andrew Robertson, president, died this morning.
September 2, 1893
Moose Jaw opened with 23 subscribers.

July 4, 1894

About 26th June a man called. Said he was the man who sent us $100 "conscience money" about May 2nd; that he had for years used a friend's telephone; thought he should pay us another sum in addition. This I declined to receive.

March 23, 1897

Earthquake between 6 and 7 p.m.

January 5, 1904

Told Blank that we declined to contribute toward election expenses of Blank or anyone else in opposition to the government as a favor. The Company has no funds for politics.

December 2, 1907

Hon. Robert Rogers called and proposed that the Province should purchase our plant in Manitoba.

August 4, 1914

War declared between Great Britain and Germany.

August 12, 1914

Positions of employees joining "the Militia" should be retained for them, and those whose families are dependent upon them and not otherwise provided for, should receive half pay during their absence in the field.

February 15, 1915

35th annual meeting. C.F. Sise appointed chairman of the board. L.B. McFarlane succeeding him as president.

Among Sise's early key moves, few surpassed in importance the setting up of the company's own mechanical department to build the equipment, particularly telephones, required by the company.

The production of telephone equipment began in Canada in 1878 when Alexander Graham Bell and his father arranged for James Cowherd, a brilliant young technician from Brantford, to study manufacturing techniques at Charles Williams' factory in Boston. Cowherd subsequently set up a factory in Brantford and until his untimely death in 1881, he supplied all the telephones used by the Bell Telephone Company of Canada. After trying several other manufacturers without success, Bell organized its own shop in Montreal in 1882.* Thirteen years later, in 1895, this became the Northern Electric & Manufacturing Company. In 1914 this company and another, Imperial Wire and Cable Company, combined to form the Northern Electric Company Limited, forerunner of today's Northern Telecom, the fourth largest manufacturer of communications equipment in the world.

Difficulties in raising much-needed capital, the sparse population across

*Developments triggered by Cowherd's death resulted in the manufacturing of Canadian telephone equipment being removed from Brantford and centred in Montreal.

Canada and the desire in some parts of the country to have the telephone business under provincial government ownership put a damper on Sise's original plans for a national network.

By 1888 the Atlantic provinces had set up their own companies with the Bell retaining a sizeable stock interest in all three.

On the Prairies it seemed no one appreciated what the Bell and Mr. Sise were doing or intended to do for the West. There was, instead, a general tendency to refer to the Bell as the "Octopus" and the telephone company was regarded with the same hostility as that other hated natural enemy of the prairie farmer, the Canadian Pacific Railway.

By the time Alberta and Saskatchewan became provinces in 1905, Manitoba was already talking about operating its own telephone system and running the Bell out. The new provinces wasted little time in picking up the same stick.

W.H. Cushing, Alberta's first Minister of Public Works, was a politician with an ear well-tuned to the rural addresses of most of the voters, if not to one of Mr. Sise's instruments. Cushing declared flatly that "the Bell Company has always been opposed to furnishing the farmers with service." Although this was an exaggeration his charge had a basis in fact. At the time only about 2,000 of Bell's 70,000 customers were rural dwellers. And Sise himself had determined company policy: "The Bell had only so much money to invest; therefore it was placed where it would bring the greatest return and serve the greatest number of people; and there wasn't much left for farm lines."

That made sense but it didn't sit well with folks out in the sticks who wanted nothing quite as much as someone to talk to. Western farmers, reared in an environment where the nearest neighbour could be a couple or more hours' walk "thataway," had a gut feeling that the telephone could revolutionize their lives. Because there was no one to help them if they didn't help themselves, the rural people worked together and, quite naturally, thought in co-operative terms, tending to favour co-operative and government ownership and to mistrust monopolies — particularly those headquartered in the East. Sise did his best to preserve Bell interests in the West, but by the end of 1909 the company was virtually forced to sell out to all three provincial governments, and its operations were confined to Ontario and Quebec.

The story of all telephone companies has one underlying, unifying theme from the early years right up to this minute: constant technical innovation. The use of batteries is a case in point. In the early 1880s, a battery was an essential part of every telephone set. It was a constant nuisance that began to disappear only after it was discovered that a powerful common battery in the central exchange office could serve all the telephones on a line. Long distance calling improved markedly and rapidly thereafter.

In 1890 it was possible, with favourable atmospheric conditions, to call as far away as 200 miles. With the development of the vacuum tube repeater in 1915, east-west transcontinental service became possible and by 1925, using mainly U.S. lines, calls could be made between almost any two points in Canada and the United States. The "All-Red" route, which was officially inaugurated in 1932 after seven months of operation, enabled Canadians to call from coast to coast without having to divert any part of the transmission through the United States.

Along with technical innovation, co-ordination and co-operation are the two key elements that have enabled Canada to maintain its position of leadership in telecommuncations. A long distance call from St. John's to Vancouver passes over the facilities of eight of Canada's major telephone companies. The user is aware of only one. The reason? All of the companies involved work together to create what is effectively a single, integrated, national telephone network.

The early years of the twentieth century were boom years for the industry. Advancing technology overtook manual switching systems with the result that operators in many parts of the country were soon replaced by automatic switching equipment and dial service. Many prairie cities went automatic before the first World War; Saskatoon went automatic as far back as 1907. It is noteworthy that in both Canada and the U.S. Bell lagged behind the industry in going automatic. Because of the sheer volume and cost of the equipment involved and its heavy commitment to a manufacturing organization (Northern Electric in Canada and Western Electric in the U.S.), Bell was slow to phase out its old common battery equipment and replace it with newer automatic equipment. Bell's first dial office was opened in Toronto in 1924. Its first electronic switching office was opened in Montreal in February 1967, to serve Expo '67.

Bell's 500,000th telephone was installed in 1924 as the boom swelled through the 1920s. Regular transatlantic radio-telephone service was established via New York in 1927, and direct transatlantic Montreal-London service in 1932. High capacity long distance quadded cables, with up to 450 pairs of wires, came into service (1,200 pair cables were for local, not long distance use) and "carrier" systems capable of squeezing several conversations onto one pair of wires were introduced shortly thereafter.

The Depression slowed down the industry temporarily. In 1931, for the first time in Bell's history, more telephones were removed than installed. But the second World War created a tremendous need for communications services and the network was strained to its limits to meet demands, handicapped by shortages of both men and materials. With the end of the war, the fantastic growth resumed at a redoubled pace.

In the decade following the war the number of telephones in service more than doubled, from one million to 2.3 million, with customers sometimes having to wait more than two years for an installation. Long distance calls, which had doubled during the war, doubled again. Long distance circuitry jumped from 165,000 to 700,000 miles and expenditures on new facilities soared from $18 million in 1945 to $100 million only 10 years later.

Fully automatic direct-distance dialing (DDD), introduced in Guelph, Ontario, in 1958, now extends to cover all Bell customers. The same year the 3,900-mile TransCanada microwave system, the longest single system in the world, was opened — making it possible to beam communications between the Atlantic and the Pacific coasts and provide nation-wide television for the first time.

Expansion pushed northward, too. The year 1958 saw one of the world's first tropospheric scatter systems (which bounce signals off the troposphere and receive them up to 200 miles away), providing service to many northern Canadian communities for the first time. In 1973, with the coming of *Anik,* Canada's own communications satellite, Bell could reach out more than 2,000 miles north to serve the little Inuit hamlet of Rea Point on Melville Island in the Northwest Territories. As of November 1978, Bell's most northerly Earth station at Griese Fjord on Ellesmere Island came into operation, only a few hundred miles from the North Pole itself.

The late 1950's also saw increased diversification of Bell's communications activities. Throughout the 1960s and the 1970s a steady stream of telephone and specialized telecommunications services was introduced.

Bell now transmits any information that can be translated into electrical signals, and there is very little information today that cannot be so dealt with. If it were possible to cut open a major trunk cable to see what it is carrying, out of it would flow network-type radio and television programming, enormous volumes of printed text, thousands of telephone conversations, perhaps an electrocardiogram of a heart attack victim, news photos, weather maps, handwritten messages and diagrams and the code-like babble of computer communication — machines talking to machines. Push-button phones have made potential computer users of everyone.

As do the other Canadian telephone companies, Bell provides special switchboard facilities and services for business. These special telephone facilities include internal direct-dialing systems, paging services, mobile telephones, conference call services, automatic answering equipment a host of others.

The industry also offers specialized telecommunications network facilities serving pipelines, electrical utilities, and service and facilities for private-line telephones and an increasingly sophisticated range of conveniences on the individual telephone. Dialing often-used or emergency numbers with a single touch of a button, or forwarding a call to wherever the desired party may be, are two examples.

Bell and Canada have taken the world lead with respect to data transmission. In conjunction with the other TransCanada Telephone System companies, Bell offers a packet of services including the Vucom series of visual display computer terminals that are seen in airline ticket offices, newspaper newsrooms and many other locations; the Datacom series of high-speed teletypewriters, the Dataroute; a nationwide digital data system; and Datapac, a universally available packet-switched data network that connects a growing number of users to many computers over a shared network.

The TCTS network, of which Bell is a part, has been called Canada's largest computer — spread over millions of square miles — with components in almost every home and office, constantly accepting, transmitting and delivering enormous amounts of information.

Although telephone service today continues to be the company's basic business, that service is part of a far larger picture. Bell is the senior partner in a group of companies comprising more than 50 subsidiaries and affiliates. The interests of these companies range world-wide and frequently take them far beyond the straightforward business of providing telecommunications services and products. Their activities extend into such diverse fields as data processing, publishing and printing.

Oldest and best-known of the Bell subsidiaries is Northern Telecom Limited, which grew from that little mechanical department set up by Sise in the 1880s to the largest manufacturer of telecommunications equipment in Canada.

Bell-Northern Research, jointly owned by Bell and Northern Telecom, is responsible for research and development in all phases of telecommunications.

In 1969, Bell invested $4.9 million in the stock of Telesat Canada. Owned jointly by the Government and the major Canadian telecommunications carriers, Telesat was founded to operate the *Anik* satellite system.

With the exception of Québec Téléphone, all major telecommunications companies in eastern Canada are members of the Bell group. Québec Téléphone is one of the nation's larger independent companies. Among the companies in which Bell has significant holdings are three of its fellow members of the TransCanada Telephone System: The New Brunswick Telephone Company, Limited; Maritime Telegraph and Telephone Company Limited; and Newfoundland Telephone

Company Limited. In addition, Bell has interests in Telontario, Inc., Northern Telephone Limited and Télébec Limitée.

Thirteen telephone organizations across Canada have service agreements with Bell Canada through which, for an annual fee, Bell provides them with technical and operating assistance. Bell, in effect, acts as a consultant to the smaller companies, as it is considered to be more economical to have one central organization doing research and development on behalf of all.

As with any giant corporation, people are the common denominator and it is the people who constitute its most vital element. The Bell group of companies in total employs more than 80,000 people. Bell Canada alone employs over 50,000 with just over half of them women, making the Bell the largest private employer of women in Canada. Employees come from all walks of life and contribute myriad skills. They include operators, installers, managers, computer programmers, engineers, accountants, sales personnel, statisticians, doctors, lawyers, economists, service representatives, secretaries and clerks — to name only a few. At present, the company spends over $22 million a year on education and training programmes for its employees.

Bell Canada has the largest corporate construction programme in Canada. It invests more than three-quarters of a billion dollars annually to expand and replace its existing facilities, to relocate service for today's highly mobile customers and to accommodate the widening spectrum of its customers' requirements.

Bell has more shareholders than any other Canadian corporation — nearly one-quarter of a million — and the majority of them are individuals living in Canada who have invested part of their savings in partial ownership of the company.

As do all members of the TransCanada Telephone System, Bell looks to the future, seeking to meet the growing needs of the people it serves. Gordon Thompson, the philosopher of Bell-Northern Research, says: "The challenge of the future lies not in the development of technology alone but in the development of technology that relates to Man — technology that will be Man's servant, not his master."

In the past Bell Canada was a major force in knitting together a far-flung people. Today, Bell's myriad communications facilities are a significant part of the foundation of the nation's economy. Tomorrow, as a major mover of information in this electronic age, the company expects to play an even more important role in shaping ideas and guiding decisions.

2

The Atlantic Region
The Slickest Little Company in Canada

There was weird competition. Men were going around selling sound boxes or acoustic telephones made out of cigar boxes connected with piano wire. . . . In many towns competitors who had infringed the patent were already doing business, and users could only with difficulty be convinced that the instruments offered were illegal.

Pioneering the Telephone in Canada
by William Patten (1928)

Like ink spilled on a blotter, telephony spread east and west.

Because of its strategic position between Europe and North America, Newfoundland played an early role in telecommunications. In July 1866, the first transatlantic telegraph cable was completed between Ireland and Newfoundland, terminating on the Newfoundland side at Heart's Content. Thirty-five years later, on Signal Hill, Guglielmo Marconi, flying a kite to support his antenna, received the first wireless telegraph signal ever transmitted across the Atlantic.

In 1878 John Delany, Postmaster General of Newfoundland in St. John's, a man who liked to tinker as well as keep track of mail to the island colony, carefully followed instructions published in *Scientific American* and built his own telephone with a magnet, a coil, a diaphragm and a case he had hammered together. He ran an iron wire over the house of John Higgins, a meteorologist friend, and they became the first people in Newfoundland to have a telephone conversation.

The Bell tried to get an exclusive franchise to provide telephone service for the entire island of Newfoundland, but the Anglo-American Company, which was granted a 50-year telegraph franchise by the government of Newfoundland, argued that its contract gave it a monopoly over all electrical communications on the Island. Alexander MacKay, who had been appointed manager of Anglo-American 30 years earlier by Cyrus Field himself, was one of the first telegraphers in British North America, but he knew practically nothing about telephones. He was convinced that Bell had discovered some way to talk directly across the Atlantic, which would, he feared, put the telegraph people out of business. (He was right — but about 50 years ahead of the fact; transatlantic telephony wasn't possible until 1927.) When the government ruled in favour of Anglo-American, Bell offered their patent rights to the telegraph company on a royalty basis and, in 1885, Anglo-American established the first public telephone exchange in St. John's.

In 1878, G.G. Flewwelling of Hampton, New Brunswick, a well-known manufacturer of wooden matches, leased the first two telephones in that province from Professor A. Melville Bell through G.S. Robinson, the agent for the telephone business in that province. A month later a Saint John, New Brunswick, hardware store owner, James McAvity, leased a pair of box telephones to connect his shop with the offices of his brass foundry. He strung some number nine iron wire on insulated brackets attached to chimneys and rooftops, but needed permission from the city fathers to cross the streets with his wires. The permission he secured made his the first municipally approved line ever erected, and the wording of his authorization was so broad that years later the New Brunswick Telephone Company, Limited granted him free telephone service for 10 years for the transfer of his city privileges to them.

On June 21, 1880, with the help of Louis McFarlane (the one-time Dominion Telegraph employee who helped Alexander Graham Bell obtain the use of the telegraph line for the first long distance call between Brantford and Paris, Ontario) C.F. Sise bought the Dominion Telegraph exchange in Saint John, New Brunswick for the Bell Telephone Company. On January 24, 1881, Sise also acquired the Western Union exchange in Saint John. Just prior to this latter acquisition, Lewis McFarlane and an associate pounded the wooden sidewalks of Saint John for two weeks before they got a single subscriber. But since it takes two to telephone as well as to tango, they had to let that one go. Years later, after McFarlane had become the third president of the Canadian Bell Telephone Company, he related the story to a Saint John *Telegraph Journal* reporter:

Romance by Telephone from a turn-of-the-century New Brunswick Telephone Company cartoon.

"Mr. Snider [P.W. Snider was the local agent for Dominion Telegraph] and myself started out at nine o'clock every morning along the wooden sidewalks and canvassed every business house and many homes. We kept at it for two weeks and we were very earnest about the matter but so doubtful was everyone about the utility and stability of the telephone that we secured only one subscriber. He was the manager of the old Dufferin Hotel. We could not sign him on at that time, however, for he would have had no one to talk to."

When McFarlane went to Fredericton to take charge of the newly-leased Bell plant, the city marshal appeared on the scene demanding a license fee, which was required to do business in that city. McFarlane happened to be demonstrating a new Bell transmitter to a prospective customer — the local collector of customs, a man who was known to be interested in telephone gadgets — at the time. When McFarlane mentioned its price, the marshal promptly arrested him for being unlicensed *and* trying to sell a telephone to a collector. In the bureaucratic confusion that followed, McFarlane was popped into the local lock-up. J.G. Byrne, Bell's Fredericton agent (who subsequently became manager of the Saint John office) got McFarlane out on bail, but when he left his lawyer's office the persistent marshal was waiting and nailed him again — this time with a fifteen dollar "assessment". In court the next day confusion was rampant, but in the end McFarlane got off with a two dollar fine which he promptly paid. He then hurried out of town on the next train.

When he returned to Saint John later he fared somewhat better. Finding both Dominion Telegraph and Western Union with already established exchanges, he located suitable office space for Bell and spent the weekend with assistants lugging all the necessary equipment up three flights of stairs so he could open the office on the following Monday morning. He discovered that Western Union was having trouble signing up customers because it took so long for them to get equipment from the United States, whereupon he scurried back to Toronto, rented an express car and loaded it with gear. Back in Saint John, he offered free service for two or three months, so capturing the lion's share of the business there.

In August 1877, Gardiner Greene Hubbard, Alexander Graham Bell's father-in-law, himself took the first two telephones to Nova Scotia. These were installed in the Caledonia colliery at Glace Bay, the first telephones to be used in a mine — anywhere. Nearly a half-century later the telephone was to play a vital role in a rescue drama at another Nova Scotia mine, at Moose River.

In Halifax, one February Sunday in 1880, an enterprising telephone hustler rigged up one of the granddaddies of church service broadcasts. A telephone was installed in St. Paul's Church, the oldest Anglican church in North America, and the canny local agent invited "a number of newspapermen and others, who were not noted for attending church" down to the telephone office to hear the sermon. They were duly impressed, if not with one service then surely with the other.

In the early days, the board of directors of a telephone company personally had to look after just about everything. When one Nova Scotia exchange was reopened after a fire, the telephone operator asked for an extra two dollars a month on the grounds that she was no longer living with her parents and she needed the extra money for board. The directors solemnly considered the request in the splendour of their board room, then passed the buck to the manager of the exchange with a strongly worded observation that twenty dollars a month seemed quite adequate.

By 1883 the first private lines had been strung on Prince Edward Island, and the Bell agent there, Rob Angus, was beating the potato patches for more customers. C.F. Sise, Bell's vice-president and general manager, already had Lewis B. McFarlane well-established in the eastern part of Canada enlisting agents and getting the building of the Bell empire underway in that part of the country. It was McFarlane who signed on the enterprising Angus, an insurance salesman who was confident he could sell a few telephones in his free time.

Bell had three basic priorities in a remote area like Prince Edward Island: get a

A congregation of New Brunswick Telephone Company linemen photographed in the linemen's room on Prince William Street in Saint John in 1908.

foothold; lease telephone instruments; and establish exchanges if business warranted it. Angus was hired to attend to these. However, the Islanders and their legislative representatives had a priority of their own — a system of rapid communication for the entire Island. They wanted a full-fledged facility and a company of their own. They were therefore unwilling to go along with someone who merely peddled telephones on the side. It didn't take Angus long to find out which way the wind was blowing, whereupon he decided to look after his own interests. With a thousand dollars of his own money (with which he secured 40 shares in the new company) and the support of six prominent Charlottetown businessmen, he left the Bell in the lurch and proceeded to form the Telephone Company of Prince Edward Island with himself as the secretary/manager.

Rather than fight Bell's right to the invention in Canada, the tiny new company negotiated a deal for the purchase of Bell's rights in P.E.I. And so, on July 8, 1888, the Telephone Company of Prince Edward Island signed an agreement with the Bell Telephone Company taking over all Bell rights and properties on the Island in return for fifteen hundred dollars in cash and 40 shares in the new company.

At first the new company's operations were confined to Charlottetown. There were only 11 telephones known to be in use on the Island, seven of which were in the offices of the P.E.I. Railway. Nonetheless, one of the first pieces of equipment ordered was a 50-line switchboard, and soon the public was informed that the new company was ready to transmit written and verbal messages from Charlottetown to Hunter River, County Line, Freetown, Kensington, Summerside and St. Eleanor's, and that "subscribers wishing to be called for early trains, etc., can be signalled at any hour desired. Special bells," it was noted, "may be had in bedrooms for a small rental." (In New Brunswick, operators also stood ready to provide information on boat and train arrivals and departures, the location of fires and other handy things.)

From its incorporation in 1885 the Telephone Company of Prince Edward Island gradually built up a system more or less covering the whole of the Island. The little company was barely holding its head above water when, on April 22, 1910 the Maritime Telegraph and Telephone Company was incorporated with a view to consolidating *all* the major Maritime companies. By consolidating, the directors of the new company hoped to bring all plant in eastern Canada up to a high standard and also establish long distance connections with the rest of the world.

They were only partly successful. They began by having their man W.H. Covert acquire a majority of the shares of the Telephone Company of P.E.I. from individual shareholders. They ended by buying the Nova Scotia Telephone Company in its entirety through the action of its shareholders in a special general meeting.

Maritime Telegraph and Telephone proposed to establish connections with P.E.I., connecting their metallic (two-wire) systems to the Islander's grounded (one-wire) system. They urged the Islanders to modernize their system, but the directors of the Island company knew they couldn't afford that sort of expense. They had been hurting financially since the advent of electric power and electric lighting in the 1890s. When the lights turned on the phones turned off and the only solution to that problem was to install costly metallic circuits. The Island company had managed this in the cities, but the cost of converting the widespread rural system was prohibitive.

A delegation from the Telephone Company of P.E.I. seeking federal subsidy for a telephone cable to the mainland told the Federal Works people in February 1907 that "Anglo-American Telegraph service reaches no points apart from the P.E.I. Railway," that it "reaches only three points in P.E.I. not at present reached by the telephone service, while the telephone service reaches 84 points not touched by the Anglo-American Telegraph Service." (According to Furber Marshall, historian for Maritime Tel & Tel, A.A.T. served 28 points and the Telephone Company of P.E.I. served 109 with 25 places enjoying the services of both companies.)

The point was that A.A.T. was strictly in the long distance message business,

110

A pole crew working at Buckley Point, P.E.I. around 1925.

having the ability to deliver messages by telephone to 84 points on the Island plus the advantage of off-Island connections.

MT&T, wanting to cut a couple of corners itself, also made a very clear proposal to the federal Government. They argued that under the terms of Confederation the Government had agreed to maintain telegraph communications with Prince Edward Island, and since the telephone was unknown at that time and was really only an extension of the word 'telegraph,' it was the *duty* of the federal Government to lay a telephone cable. The matter was discussed over a long period, and objected to by the Anglo-American Cable Company (the only telegraph company on the Island at the time) on the grounds that they had a perpetual and exclusive right to land submarine cables on Prince Edward Island. The Government finally told Maritime Tel & Tel to settle that claim first. The Maritime boys then pulled a fast one on Anglo-America. Claiming that the Anglo-American Company's perpetual exclusive right only applied to cables landing in Prince Edward Island from countries other than on the continent of North America, they laid a cable from Pictou to Wood Island at their own expense, then notified the Anglo people that if they had an objection they should take out an injunction. No action was taken by Anglo, and the federal Government was thus satisfied that Anglo had withdrawn its objections.

The cable laid by MT&T was only intended to accomplish a strategic purpose. It was not a regular telephone cable, and within a few months it failed and was abandoned. Thereafter negotiations were reopened with the federal Government, with the result that in 1918 two cables were laid — one from Island to Wood Island, and the other between Capes Tormentine and Caribou Travers.

MT&T now had its links with P.E.I., but its executives, knowing the Island's rundown plant would never provide satisfactory service until it was entirely rebuilt and modernized, offered to purchase the outstanding shares of the Prince Edward Island company.

The purchase of 2,705 out of 4,000 outstanding shares of Telephone Company of P.E.I. was the action of one Walter H. Covert, a Halifax barrister and the provisional president of MT&T from May 3 to November 6, 1910. The shares had a par value of $67,475 and Covert sold them to MT&T June 28, 1911, to be turned over not later than September 20, 1911. MT&T's holdings in the telephone company of P.E.I. did not vary until 1917, when the MT&T directors sold their shares, (causing a stockholders' revolt) and were forced to buy them back.

Why anyone subscribed in those days or why subscribers *continued* with early telephone service is something of a mystery. The public didn't seem to know exactly what to expect from the new invention, but the fact that it did work obviously offset the frequent failures and kept interest from flagging.

The congestion of open wires on house tops and poles caused lines to cross in every decent wind storm. The cotton-insulated wires grounded out with the slightest dampness and lines following the same route had more cross-talk than a hecklers' convention. Bells and transmitters were usually either out of adjustment or burned by lightning. The early magneto type telephones carried warnings against their use during electrical storms, injunctions which many telephone users followed religiously even years after the danger had been minimized or eliminated altogether. The manual switchboards of the day were awkward to manoeuvre and completion of calls was maddeningly slow. In Newfoundland service was so bad that some customers vented their frustration on the operators, which led the company to note acerbically in one of its first directories: "*Ladies* are employed as operators — kindly treat them as such."

The introduction of electric street lighting systems threw so much induction onto the ground lines (before the days of metallic circuits) that the telephones along the routes illuminated by the new carbon lamps went out of commission the moment the electric lights came on in the evening.

Electric streetcars also caused a serious problem for many telephone exchanges. When a streetcar passed the telephone office every mechanical signal (drop) on the switchboard came down. Operators were supplied with a yardstick to restore them en masse, including the legitimate drops.

Another hidden disaster caused by the street railways resulted from the heavy electric currents which were supposed to return through the tracks. Instead, they found an easier path through the lead coverings of underground telephone cable and gradually, by electrolysis, the lead decomposed and the telephone lines were exposed to troubles caused by dampness. These problems continued until metallic circuits were introduced.

Telephony appears to have been an enjoyable if not overly lucrative business in the Atlantic region in those days. However, it got very complicated at times.

By 1888, Bell, fighting to establish a firm financial foothold in Ontario and Quebec while building along the eastern and western fringes of its empire, found investment capital very hard to come by. Sise did the sensible thing; he cut back on the fringes.

He sold the Bell exchanges in New Brunswick and Nova Scotia to the newly-formed Nova Scotia Telephone Company. In the meantime, the New Brunswick Telephone Company had been incorporated in opposition to the Nova Scotia Telephone Company and in 1889 the New Brunswick Telephone Company acquired the exchanges in New Brunswick being operated by the Nova Scotia company. In negotiating this transaction, it developed that the Nova Scotia Telephone Company was so controlled by the Bell that the acquisition had to be made through the Bell in Montreal. Bell bought back the New Brunswick exchanges from the Nova Scotia Telephone Company, then sold them again to the New Brunswick Telephone Company. The actual transfer of the New Brunswick exchanges at issue, took place in February, 1889.

The New Brunswick company had a hard go of it. Of the four exchanges taken over, only Saint John paid its way, and even that could hardly be called a smooth operation. The installation of a power plant by the Saint John Gas Light Co. in 1889 proved disastrous for the telephone company and a suit brought by the telephone people only proved that neither the judge, the lawyers nor the parties concerned really knew what they were talking about.

They muddled along, however, and by 1891 the first toll call from Moncton to Halifax was put through. The total New Brunswick toll business that year was worth $16.65, and this had to be split with the Nova Scotia company.

In 1907, the New Brunswick legislature passed the first Act controlling telephone companies. Among other things, Section 12 of the Act gave the Governor-in-Council the right to order a company to extend its lines, a matter of some concern to the telephone men.

113

The first telephone employees union in Canada, the Telephone Workers Association of New Brunswick, was formed early in 1918. At the association's first meeting with management, all requests made by the new union were granted. These included substantial wage increases, statutory holidays, overtime for several categories of workers, board allowances when away from home and vacation with pay.

Across Canada generally, telephones tended to be placed where the greatest demand, and, not surprisingly, the greatest potential for profit existed. This meant that city people got telephones first, country people got them later, if at all. It simply cost too much to string wire over miles of comparatively empty countryside. Especially during the first 20 years of the century, enterprising farmers and talkative people from small towns all over Canada banded together to string up their own connections. Generally, these were ramshackle affairs with wire strung along fence posts and other similar available spare parts. But they worked, more or less, and farmers were able to talk to each other on their party lines. In many cases, these co-operative ventures served as the foundations for small local companies. The large, established companies were reluctant to connect them to their lines because the standards of the local independents were usually inferior and not at all compatible with the bigger systems. However, by making some arrangements with the small independents, the larger companies were able to broaden their geographical coverage without straining their precarious finances.

Telephony developed along somewhat different lines in Newfoundland. As Newfoundland Telephone president Anthony A. Brait pointed out: "The big problem then, and it still is in some respects, was the huge uninhabited areas to be spanned; areas that couldn't possibly pay for themselves." Not only did Newfoundland have thousands of square miles of virtually empty landscape on the island, it had additional thousands of square miles of equally undeveloped landscape in Labrador. Consequently, if pulp and paper companies, utility companies or mining companies wanted telephones, they generally had to install their own systems.

Maintenance was as difficult as installation. As Brait notes: "We probably have the worst weather conditions to contend with of any place in Canada. One hundred mile an hour winds, rain, salt spray, sleet, snow and freezing conditions are the rule, not the exception, along our coastline."

Typical of Newfoundland developments was United Towns Electric Co., which was incorporated in 1902 with headquarters near Carbonear. United Towns required communications to conduct its power business and it opened

Some Modern Pirates

People who borrow telephone service—and do not pay for it.

A major turn-of-the-century marketing problem was convincing people they needed more than one telephone per village or neighbourhood. The New Brunswick Telephone Company devised this method of persuasion in 1903.

exchanges in various communities on the Avalon and Burin peninsulas. Shortly after the first World War, Anglo-American sold out to Western Union, but the telegraph company, having no interest in the telephone business, in turn offered to sell that part of its acquisition to United Towns. This led to the formation of the Avalon Telephone Company in 1919.

In 1921, Newfoundland inaugurated its first long distance line from St. John's to Carbonear, a distance of 68 miles. The same year the Telephone Association of Canada, meeting in Vancouver, raised the question of a cross-Canada toll system. Not until 1939, however, was Newfoundland, with the help of radio-relay, ready to establish its first telephone link with the mainland.

Oscar Hierlihy was among the employees of Avalon's pioneer radio station VONF. A descendant of the founder of Antigonish, Nova Scotia, Oscar stayed on Avalon's payroll when the company sold VONF to the CBC. Oscar's new assignment was to establish a radio-phone link from the island to the mainland. After several trips to Montreal and the transmitting and receiving stations in Drummondville and Yamachiche, Quebec, and with the help of a Marconi radio engineer, Oscar got the necessary equipment installed. When he was ready to test the line he was very conscious of the fact that this was an historic occasion — the first call ever from the island to the mainland. Oscar spoke into his test telephone, calling Yamachiche. There followed a breathless silence, then the slightly bored, matter-of-fact voice of the Yamachiche operator responded with, "Please cut your audio so I can measure the noise."

Oscar Hierlihy made the first radio telephone call from Newfoundland to mainland Canada from this transmitter in 1939.

What a letdown! But within a couple of weeks Oscar's spirits were justifiably raised when Sir Hymphrey Walwyn, the Governor of Newfoundland, spoke to Lord Tweedsmuir, the Governor-General of Canada to officially open the service.

Regular 'overseas' service was then installed. If a Newfoundland customer wanted to call the mainland, he phoned the long distance operator, who recorded the details. The customer would then hang up and wait. The operator contacted the radio room where the duty operator would signal Yamachiche. In Yamachiche the operator on duty in turn would signal Bell's overseas operator in Montreal and the details of the call would be passed along through the two long distance operators. When the party being called was located, the word would be signalled back through Drummondville to Newfoundland and the original caller would be summoned to the telephone — if he was still hanging around, and if atmospheric conditions permitted. The whole thing was closed down within a few weeks because of the war, and opened later only with censors standing by to cut the connection if a wrong word was said.

Just before 9 o-clock on the morning of December 6, 1917, a French munitions ship, the *Mont Blanc,* loaded with hundreds of tons of high explosives, was rammed by a Norwegian freighter in Halifax harbour. An extremely inflammable petrochemical on the ship caught fire, and the crew, knowing what was coming, fled the ship. At 9:06 the *Mont Blanc* exploded with the force of an atomic bomb, wiping out a square mile of Halifax. Piers, ships and buildings literally vanished. The harbour surged and a mushroom cloud of smoke, gases and debris reached three miles into the sky. Nearly 2,000 persons were killed and another 10,000 were injured.

All three MT&T exchanges were knocked out and service was impossible for several hours. A section of poles along the waterfront simply disappeared. The wires were left in shreds, and 852 phones were put out of service. Miraculously, no one in any of the telephone offices was killed, although many were badly cut by flying window glass. Clerical help and management executives worked side by side to clean out the shattered glass and rubble and restore the exchanges to at least partial service, and by one p.m. the first one was working. Every available operator, some in bloodsoaked bandages, stayed on duty, in some cases working 30 hours straight. That night a blizzard blew in, multiplying the difficulties and miseries. Blankets were rounded up and the weary, half-frozen and shaken staff used desks and tables for such sleep as was possible. Haligonians queued up to telephone friends and relatives and it seemed as though the entire outside world was trying to get through to Halifax.

Lloyd Mailman, (far right), and his crew in 1934 at Brooklin, King's County, Nova Scotia.

OPPOSITE
Two MT&T employees retain vivid memories of the Moose River cave-in. At the left is Dr. Allan Nickerson, and on the right, J. Allister Bowman. Both are listening through an amplifier for the voices of the men trapped below.

At a Board meeting of MT&T on December 18, the following resolution was passed:

> . . . In the face of almost unprecedented difficulties, the plant has been kept running, and a service vitally necessary to the public has been rendered. This has been chiefly due to the wholehearted co-operation of the employees, many of whom have suffered severely by the great disaster, and who remained at their posts at the cost of much personal inconvenience and not a little suffering.
>
> This Board particularly desires to direct the attention of the public to the value of the service rendered by its employees in this emergency. It is absolutely clear that the work of rescue and relief would have been hindered, and the expeditious organization of our citizens to deal with the emergent conditions delayed had not this company been able to operate its plant, which was made possible largely through the loyalty and devotion to duty of the operators and other employees of the company. They met a great emergency in a big way and worthily performed their full duty to the public.

The story of the Moose River gold mine incident in Nova Scotia was a different kind of drama. Two Toronto men, Dr. D.E. Robertson, a surgeon at Toronto's Sick Children's Hospital, and Herman Magill, a young lawyer who had just purchased the property, went down into the mine with mine timekeeper Alfred Scadding on Easter Sunday, April 12, 1936. Just as they completed their

tour of the underground workings the mine caved in, trapping them at the 141-foot level. Little hope was held out for the trio, but when diamond drillers punched a small hole through to them nearly a week later they discovered all three were still alive. Hot soup was poured through rubber tubing channelled through the tiny drill-hole (one and nine-sixteenths of an inch in diameter), and rescue digging started immediately. MT&T's line hooked up with the mining company's line, and newsmen showed up from all over the world to cover the drama which was capturing a continent's attention.

This was the golden age of radio broadcasting, and circuits were set up all over North America to 58 stations in Canada and 650 in the United States as the public listened spellbound to the rescue efforts. During the drama the first tele-photographs ever transmitted in Canada went out over the MT&T wires.

A tiny telephone transmitter was assembled in the shops in Halifax and rushed to the mine. It had to be improvised, for nothing small enough to be lowered through the rescue hole existed. The tiny microphone was lowered to the trapped men and enabled them to talk to their rescuers. For 64 hours it kept their hopes alive. Just two days before miners broke through, Magill died. When the rescued men finally reached the surface, Dr. Robertson said: "The telephone was the one thing that allowed us to consider any further stay with equanimity."

The New Brunswick Telephone Company, Limited and Maritime Telegraph and Telephone Company Limited joined the TransCanada Telephone System as origi-

This horse-drawn cook-house was used in Annapolis Valley, Nova Scotia, while building lines for the Valley Telephone Company (1891-1911)

nal members in 1931, with Prince Edward Island represented through MT&T. The long-line system had, of course, been brought up to TransCanada standards, but the Depression put a temporary halt to expansion. East coast companies lost thousands of subscribers before the tide turned, and in some cases dividends and salaries alike were cut. Not until the war-induced boom did the Maritime companies fully recover.

Newfoundland — through the Avalon company — became a full member of TCTS in 1957, thus completing the nation's long-line sytem from East to West. Newfoundland's telephone system was (and still is) split among several companies, including Canadian National Telecommunications, and was plagued by problems of great distance and sparse population. In 1962, Bell Canada bought control of Avalon and so moved in to upgrade its facilities and services.

The revitalized Avalon company promptly launched a province-wide modernization and building programme that virtually doubled its system by 1970. That year Avalon also decided to change its name to the more representative Newfoundland Telephone Company Limited, causing one local newspaper to comment, "This is nothing new, lots of people in Newfoundland have been calling the telephone company names for years."

As did other companies in the TransCanada system, Newfoundland benefited immensely from the coast-to-coast microwave network completed in 1958, although it was a year late getting to that province. In the use of microwave, however, Prince Edward Island and Nova Scotia were ahead of TransCanada — in fact, ahead of the rest of the world. The new wireless system, in the form of a 23-channel PTM* link between the two provinces, was built in 1948. The towers were erected on Fraser Mountain near New Glasgow, Nova Scotia and at Tea Hill near Charlottetown, Prince Edward Island.

Prince Edward Island had long been linked to the mainland by submarine cables, but wave action, ice conditions, errant trawlers and steamships frequently fouled the linkage in the Northumberland Strait.

MT&T's *Monthly Bulletin* noted, "This radio link is a milestone in the progress of the Maritime and Island Telephone companies, and indeed in the progress of the science of transmission, for — and the forecast was accurate — it marks the beginning of an era when pole lines and submarine cables will be challenged by a strong competitor in the provision of reliable telephone circuits."

The tropospheric scatter system, another outgrowth of the war, enabled Newfoundland in the mid-fifties to greatly improve its communication with Labrador. Unlike microwave, the tropospheric scatter system didn't depend upon line-of-sight transmission. Adverse weather and atmospheric conditions sometimes raised havoc with the 'pole vault' system, as it was called by the U.S. army, but it was nevertheless a natural for communication with isolated spots such as Goose Bay, Labrador. Eventually, it even provided Frobisher Bay on Baffin Island with a link to the rest of Canada.

All the Atlantic companies benefited from the surge of communications activity brought about by the war, and all were in on the ground floor for the tremendous expansion years immediately following the war. As members of the TransCanada Telephone System, all four provincial companies have ridden the innovative crest in digital transmission and satellite communication. In 1974, Newfoundland Telephone assumed control of Bell Canada's Labrador operations and pushed forward a $15 million improvement programme which has resulted in microwave hookups that have vastly improved communications in the area.

*PTM stands for Pulse Time Modulation, which is a method used to "stack" voices on a microwave link. It was a forerunner of Bell's TD-2 design. Inaugural ceremonies were held in the Charlottetown Hotel with A. Murray MacKay, general manager of both companies, pointing out that the people of the Island would never again have to fear being isolated from the mainland as in the past. Lieutenant-Governor Bernard of Prince Edward Island expressed gratification that the Island was again, "making history as it had done so many times in the past."

In 1976 Newfoundland Telephone offered a $1.4 million stock issue at $6.50 a share to broaden its base of ownership. The successful issue reduced Bell's percentage from 99 to 78.1. Today Newfoundland Telephone operates and maintains about 75 per cent of the telephones in the province, the remaining telephones belong to Canadian National Telecommunications and the Labrador Telephone Company.

For the Atlantic companies the seventies have been a period of continued remarkable growth. Prince Edward Island joined the TransCanada system in 1975 and Gordon Archibald, former chairman of the Board, calls that system "the slickest little company in Canada." Anthony Brait, president of Newfoundland Telephone, says with justifiable pride: "With the completion of our solid state microwave system and all electronic switching, Newfoundland has the highest quality system in Canada today."

Both NBTel and MT&T have moved into new buildings that dominate the Saint John and Halifax skylines.

The Maritimes are very much alive and well. . . .

3

The Prairies — Part One
Doing It Their Way

Great God, the Bell Telephone service in Calgary is a
disgrace!
The Eye Opener Bob Edwards (1907)

In pursuit of its dream of a national telephone network from the Atlantic to the
Rockies, the Bell Telephone Company moved west almost as quickly as it had
pushed into the Atlantic provinces.

Parliament issued a charter to the Bell Telephone Company of Canada in
April 1880, with powers of entry and right-of-way similar to those granted to the
CPR. The company set out almost immediately to build toll lines and operate
exchanges right across the country. On the Prairies, Bell's activities eventually
embroiled it in a furor over public ownership, which ended finally with the
establishment of three provincial government-owned telephone systems — the
only systems of their kind in North America. A strong populist attitude mixed
with an equally defiant Western sense of independence were a combination the
Bell had not previously encountered in Canada.

Life on the Prairies was grim and earnest. One's nearest neighbour was often
miles away and co-operation was not only a daily necessity but a way of life. There
existed a strong and growing tendency to distrust all things Eastern, monopolistic
and big — including the CPR, Standard Oil and the Bell Telephone Company.

Easteners then, as now, didn't always understand the West, and it often
seemed to Westerners that Easteners couldn't see any reason to try. Financial and
political power resided in the East. Decisions which were vitally important to life

on the Prairies were made in the East by men who had never been west and who, in the opinion of the Westerners, couldn't possibly understand the situation. Most resented were the decisions passed on with a patronizing "we-know-what-is-best for-you" air. Western anger seethed over all sorts of wrongs, both real and imagined. The Bell walked unwittingly into this hornets' nest, and it was to cost them dearly.

Winnipeg was just a random collection of shacks and saloons down river from Fort Garry at the junction of the Red and Assiniboine Rivers, when Alexander Graham Bell received his telephone patent. By 1878, however, Horace McDougall had already hooked up the first two telephones in Manitoba between his home and his office. McDougall, who was manager of the Northwest Telegraph Company, was appointed agent for the Bell and was given the great empty Canadian West as his territory — an area including most of Manitoba and all of what was later to become Saskatchewan and Alberta. McDougall didn't exactly do a land-office business. He decided to make the instruments prestige items by slapping a $60 per pair price-tag on them. People who weren't well-off couldn't afford such a toy. The Winnipeg *Free Press* decided to investigate the device as a possible aid to news-gathering, and the CPR took a set, but it was nearly two years before McDougall sold another pair. After only three years and with only 26 customers, McDougall disgustedly sold his agency back to the Bell and stomped off to work for the railway.

Unbelievably, ten of McDougall's customers were hooked into a single line, which led the Montreal *Star* to comment: "Winnipeg can brag of having ten offices on one telephone wire, which it is assured is more than has ever been attached to any single wire in any other city in this or any other hemisphere. This possibility is attained by the dryness of the Manitoba atmosphere."

Those early telephones were pretty primitive. Sometimes called "butter stamps," they were the kind that forced users to shift the instrument from mouth to ear and back again, not without the risk of cranial injury, and the only way to signal the person being called was to tap the mouthpiece with a blunt instrument.

The Bell agent who succeeded McDougall was a man named Frank Walsh. One of his first actions on becoming the agent was to send east for a switchboard which, delivered by train and Red River cart, arrived late in 1881. It was installed in a leased building on the top floor so that telephone lines, which were still strung over rooftops in those days, could be brought in through the windows.

A strong-lunged young boy was the first telephone operator in the Winnipeg exchange. He kept the window in the exchange open, presumably so that he could

124

Ida Cates

reach his customers with a good shout if any of his connections failed.

The decision to hire young boys to operate telephone exchanges in the early days of telephony stemmed from the fact that boys had worked successfully as the first telegraph clerks. It did not take telephone people long, however, to learn that girls were much better suited to working in telephone switching offices; boys were inclined to promote bedlam around an exchange, playing tricks on customers and one another, chatting up girls and generally irritating their telephone patrons.

The name of the world's first female telephone operator is not known, but the employment of women telephone operators was common practice very early on, and there were certainly female operators working in Montreal before the Bell Telephone Company of Canada was established in 1880.

In 1882 the Winnipeg office hired Ida Cates as the first female operator in Manitoba. Within 10 years the switchboards there were operated entirely by girls. Manitoba's experience was repeated right across the country.

Alberta and Saskatchewan appeared on maps for the first time in 1882 as districts within the Northwest Territories, and simultaneously the pace of the telephone business quickened. The Bell exchange at Winnipeg jumped to 110 subscribers. Meanwhile, the company moved steadily across the Prairies with the railway to Portage la Prairie and Brandon, then on to Regina.

In 1882 Regina had no electric cars, no electric light, no automobiles, no motion pictures, no typewriters, no phonographs, no radios and certainly no telephones. But by 1883 it had 20 telephones in service and 10 private lines including connections from the railway station to the Royal Hotel, and between the North-West Mounted Police barracks and the residence of the Lieutenant-Governor. Five years later Regina opened its first telephone exchange.

The first telephones had not yet arrived in Alberta in 1877, but the telegraph had as the Dominion Government continued its slow but steady process of building a telegraph line from Winnipeg to the west coast, slanting it northwest over the plains on the route first surveyed for the CPR. In those days it was generally thought that the CPR would swing through Saskatoon, Edmonton and the Yellowhead Pass. By 1877 a single strand of iron wire had been strung to Hay Lakes, 30 miles southeast of Edmonton. A year later a man named Alex Taylor arrived in Hay Lakes to work as a telegrapher. It seemed silly to him to be stuck out in the bush at Hay Lakes when, with just 30 more miles of wire, he could locate himself in Edmonton, which by then, counting St. Albert and Fort Saskatchewan, had a population of over 200.

Taylor was something of a visionary: he saw the opportunity for contact with the outside world from Edmonton if that 30-mile gap could be closed. With this in mind, he talked the community into putting up the poles and then persuaded the Government to supply an extension of that single strand of iron wire. When the spur was completed, Edmonton was indeed connected to the outside world — so long as buffalo didn't knock the poles down in the process of scratching their itchy hides on them, or Indians didn't cut the wire (as they did during the Riel Rebellion), or Prairie fires and floods didn't put the line out of service.

The next year a situation developed that was to have significant long-term effects for the Bell.

Spurred on by Alex Taylor, an Edmonton citizens' committee petitioned Frank Walsh in 1883 for an exchange to hook up Edmonton, St. Albert and Fort Saskatchewan. The agent's reply, although sensible enough, perhaps, from an Eastern point of view, was: "When Edmonton is large enough and desires an exchange I will appoint an agent for that purpose, but I think it will be a long time before that will be necessary." From the point of view of the chauvinistic pioneers, however, it was just about the worst thing he could possibly have said. It was an unforgivable insult and Alex Taylor wasted no time moving in other directions for help. He suggested to his boss in the Dominion Telegraph Service, a man named F.N. Gisborne (a one-time associate of Cyrus W. Field — who was responsible, 17 years earlier, for the laying of the first transatlantic cable), that telephone and telegraph connections should be set up for the Edmonton area.

126

Gisborne was enthusiastic about telephone prospects, which he considered to be a logical extension of the telegraph business. Telephone messages could be sent to a central telegraph office without the cost of a trained operator. According to one historian, Gisborne believed it took talent to be a telegraph man, but that any fool could answer a telephone — an argument difficult to counter even today.

It was agreed that the citizens of the area would supply the poles and the federal Government would supply the wire and put up the line. It was a form of co-operation which was both popular and common on the Prairies in those days. Business on Alberta's first commercial telephone line between Edmonton and St. Albert got under way by January 3, 1885 with Alex Taylor's first message: "We wish you a happy new year."

Shortly thereafter, the ever-restless Mr. Taylor decided to try Alberta's first long distance experiment. A telephone was connected at each end of a telegraph circuit between Battleford and Edmonton, and the operators at the intermediate offices were instructed to cut their instruments on a certain date. On the appointed day the telegraph agents in the two towns tried to signal each other, but the generators were too weak and their efforts ended in failure. Still, by shouting into the transmitters, they were able to carry on a fragmentary conversation for about 15 minutes. It was later discovered that one of the intermediate operators had gone fishing on the day of the test and had forgotten to remove his equipment from

This is how the AGT head office site looked in 1889. Matt McCauley, the gentleman on horseback was one of Alex Taylor's first customers.

A telephone booth circa 1908 located in the lobby of the Selkirk Hotel in Edmonton.

the circuit, a significant contributing factor to the poor results. Later similar experiments were more successful, boosting interest in long distance telephony.

In the 1880s and '90s the Canadian West was still very raw, sparsely settled, and decades away from tapping the rich resources that would one day give it a strong economic base. It was farm country, a rural market — difficult to reach, costly to service, and seldom able to pay its own way. Yet, somewhere along the line, the settlers became convinced that the telephone was precisely the magic wand they needed to save them from lives of toil and loneliness. Better to listen to the inane natterings of your neighbours on a party line than to sit huddled around a stove shivering to the howl of a coyote outside your window.

Under its charter, Bell has always been obliged to provide service to sparsely populated areas as well as to densely populated urban districts. Critics discovered early, however, that it was a simple matter to discredit the company merely by alleging that it naturally concentrated its efforts on the larger centres of population — where there was most opportunity to maximize return on investment — at

128

the expense of rural areas. Increasingly, farmers were persuaded that Bell's interests were not the same as their own, and that the company would never help them. As a result a strong negative feeling developed toward Bell that was countered by an equally strong positive attitude toward public or co-operative ownership. During this period Bell's every effort to maintain its corporate integrity and to improve its service, particularly in western rural areas, went for naught. It was therefore no small wonder that East versus West attitudes upset the Bell's best efforts to forge a national telephone network. Those same problems of conflicting interests and mutual misunderstanding still haunt federal-provincial relations today and separate the East from the West. In many respects, the West still resents political and economic decisions made in the East, and Easteners cannot understand why Westerners are upset by the sight of all their hard-earned wealth moving in only one direction — east.

On the other hand, Bell executives can't be blamed too much for failing to relate to a guy like Jack Innes, the Bell's first agent in Calgary. Jack was a sight for sore eyes in Calgary wearing his fringed buckskins, 'coonskin hat (in the days before the white ten-gallon Stetson) and high-heeled cowboy boots. But sombre-suited Torontonians and Montrealers took a much dimmer view, and they fired him. They thought they would do better with Major James Walker, and appointed him Innes's successor. After all, Walker had held the rank of major, and had been a responsible Mountie with a splendid service record. He looked the part. Besides, he had installed the first telephones in Calgary, connecting his wood mill and his house. Except for his easygoing attitude, he might have made a good agent. But Bell's treasurer found Walker's report on customers' outstanding bills downright maddening: "Out of 30, the first on the list has skipped out and the other 29 are away from home."

"You don't seem to understand our system. . . ." wrote the Bell treasurer plaintively.

Sise himself made the long journey to Calgary to tidy things up and, although he was appalled at the condition of the Calgary telephone system generally and the exchange specifically, he came away believing that "Calgary has a good future." And so it did, but not as a part of the Bell Telephone Company.

It didn't help matters much when Bell pulled off what appeared to be a dandy business coup — an arrangement giving Bell the exclusive right to install telephones in CPR stations. At the time, the only outfits more resented than Bell in the West were the railways.

The Mounties were among the most avid backers of the telephone in the western territories. The North West Mounted Police were few in number, the territories were vast, and they were outnumbered by outlaws. Of course, most of the whisky traders, horse thieves and the like came from south of the border. The Mounties made good use of existing telegraph lines and telephones when they arrived, but the problem was that all the lines ran east and west and most of the crooks ran north and south.

As early as 1888, the Mounties petitioned Ottawa for telephones. From Regina, Commissioner Herchmer wrote: "The introduction of telephones will . . . greatly increase our efficiency and effect an enormous saving in the wear and tear on men and horses. . . . In the few places where we have them we find them a great boon and we cannot understand how we got along without them."

The MacLeod *Gazette* editorialized: "We would suggest to the police department the advisability of constructing a telephone line between here and Pincher Creek. Such a line would save no end of horseflesh and would enable the police to act more promptly in cases of horse stealing." The needs of the Mounties, in fact, contributed substantially to telephone growth, especially in southern Alberta. Telephone facilities were established near the Montana-Alberta border, which helped the force monitor customs points and keep a sharp eye on the whisky trails to places like Fort Whoop-up. The phone lines enabled the Mounties to turn back many undesirables and to intercept some of the real "bad guys" before they could cause trouble.

The nature of the original charter granted to the Bell Telephone Company led to considerable and unnecessary friction between the company and the independent-minded Westerners. Under the terms of the charter the Bell system was declared to "be a work for the general good of Canada," similar to the Canadian Pacific Railway. This gave Bell a right-of-way through any province or municipality in Canada and led inevitably to clashes and strained relations with many communities. In Alberta, for example, Bell proceeded to set up exchanges in Medicine Hat and Wetaskiwin despite the fact that the town councils had already voted to award charters to local companies.

The autocratic use of the power of right-of-way by Sise (who seemed particularly insensitive on this point) created problems for Bell at both the municipal and provincial levels. To complicate matters, the company's apparent reluctance to extend its services into rural areas did not sit at all well. This was particularly awkward, because it was at the provincial level that pressure was applied by the rural people who wanted telephones and who were convinced that the company had no intention of providing them.

The status of the Bell charter was one of the subjects argued at great length in 1905 before a Select Committee of the House of Commons chaired by Sir William

This lady mule skinner was employed by the Manitoba Telephone System in the early 1900s.

Mulock. No conclusion was reached by the committee, and the 'clout' provision of the charter therefore remained in effect.

Although Alberta was the first province to build a government-owned line (from Calgary to Banff in 1907), Manitoba had been planning its own system for a couple of years before that. In a 1906 referendum only 54 of 123 municipalities in Manitoba backed public ownership, hardly meeting the required 60 per cent margin. Bell emissaries, who were responsible for a campaign against government ownership thought they had won the day. However, since a simple majority of the voters were in favour, the government interpreted it as a mandate. Premier Rodmond Roblin (grandfather of latter-day Premier Duff Roblin) notified the Bell Telephone Company that Manitoba intended to establish its own telephone company and system. Roblin also offered to buy out the Bell interests.

"The Company has large interests in the provinces beyond Manitoba which must be protected," Bell's Sise argued. But when Manitoba persisted, Sise agreed to deal and he eventually sold out for $3.3 million. By Janaury 15, 1908 Manitoba had its own telephone company. With the purchase of the Bell system, the new Manitoba Government Telephone Company had 17,000 subscribers, 700 employees, and assets of $3.3 million.

When Saskatchewan became a province in 1905 there were about 2,000 phones in service in the larger cities, but virtually no long distance service anywhere. In 1906 the Bell extended its long distance facilities from Manitoba to connect Winnipeg

No pole line construction job was complete without the ritual pose for pictures atop the last pole. This picture was taken in Regina, Saskatchewan in 1917.

and Regina. In 1908 Saskatchewan established a Department of Railways, Telegraphs and Telephones. From it emerged Saskatchewan Government Telephones and, eventually, today's Saskatchewan Telecommunications, or SASK TEL as it is commonly known.

In 1909, just a year after Manitoba took over Bell, the Saskatchewan government followed suit, paying Bell $358,000 for its interests in the wheat province. That, along with a few other small purchases that year and the construction of its own first two exchanges, gave the Saskatchewan system a subscriber list of 5,710, with 18 exchanges and 53 toll offices plus 492 miles of long distance lines.

By 1904, Alex Taylor had decided to divest himself of his Edmonton telephone properties. He tried to sell to Bell, but the company offered him only half of what he wanted. The problem was that Taylor's system was somewhat ramshackle and the cost of bringing it up to Bell's standards was very high. The prospect of a large expenditure is what influenced Taylor to sell; the same prospect is what influenced Bell to bid low. When the City of Edmonton made a higher offer, Taylor accepted. Edmonton, which is now one of the largest independents in the country, has operated its own telephone system ever since.

When Alberta became a province in 1905, the background of hostility to Bell, fed by such incidents as Walsh's high-handed putdown of Edmonton, erupted into virtual no-holds-barred warfare. The government promptly began planning lines into areas not served by Bell. The Calgary-Banff line was the first, but it was quickly followed by lines between Edmonton and Lloydminster, and between Lethbridge and Crowsnest.

Construction started on the Banff line in the winter of 1906-07, Alberta's worst on record. Two-thirds of the cattle on the Alberta ranges died that winter. Trains ran up to three weeks late. Telephone crews around Banff slept in tents in 50-degrees-below-zero weather. Yet by spring North America's first government-owned telephone line was in.

Sise sent a troubleshooter west offering to share the system. Alberta officials chortled in his face. Bell then threatened to build a rival exchange in Edmonton. Nothing came of it.

"War!" shrilled Alberta newspapers.

Epithets applied to the Bell at the time were equally vitriolic. W.H. Cushing, Alberta's Minister of Public Works, which had jurisdiction over telephones, called the Bell charter: "The most pernicious and iniquitous piece of legislation that has ever been perpetrated upon people claiming to be free." An Opposition member from Gleichen chimed: "A bloodsucking corporation!" Pioneer telephone man John T. Moore of Red Deer, declared: "The Bell Telephone Company should have been hewn down long ago." And he compared Sise to Belshazzar, the last king of Babylon, whose doom was forecast by handwriting on the wall.

The Alberta government offered to buy Bell out. Sise replied with a counter-offer saying he would sell to any company in which the province might be the controlling shareholder as long as the Bell could also own stock (an arrangement which had already worked for Sise in the Maritimes). Alberta sniffed. Sise, angered, retorted: "In the 27 years in which this company's stock has been offered for sale I am not aware that one citizen of Alberta has ever taken or offered to take one share of stock. . . ." But on April Fool's day, 1908 (a significant date the Bell people thought), Alberta bought the Bell interests for $675,000. When Alberta took over, the new government-owned provincial system boasted 2,270 subscribers, 150 employees, 18 toll offices, 19 exchanges and 595 miles of line.

With the Alberta sale jubilant Westerners claimed finally to have chucked the "Octopus" out. Bell spokesmen, on the other hand, claimed that the primary reason for their retreat from the Prairies had to do with the fundamental difficulty of running such a complex operation so far from home base. Either way, the loss of the Alberta system effectively ended any hopes Bell had of a national system.

The starry-eyed politicans who set up provincial companies all too soon discovered that the business of running an efficient telephone system called for considerably more know-how than the ability to yap at the heels of someone else trying to do the job.

4

The Prairies — Part Two
It Wasn't Easy

Use your telephone every day, long distance twice a week.
From a speech by the Hon. J.F. Bryant,
Minister of Telephones, Saskatchewan (January 24, 1932)

Between 1908 and 1909, the governments of Manitoba, Saskatchewan and Alberta each found themselves running telephone systems with only vague notions of how to go about it. Political interests all too often took precedence over sound business considerations, and there seemed to be few occasions when these co-incided. Fortunately, the people on the operating levels who were responsible for traffic, plant and the commercial departments, were thoroughly experienced. Most of them had previously been with the Bell and they performed with quiet efficiency.

The three provincial companies shared a number of commitments. All were committed to lowering rates and other charges; to providing service, though costly, to rural areas; and to inaugurating immense capital building programmes. Not surprisingly, therefore, all three soon found themselves being forced to adopt the very measures for which they had condemned the Bell and rousted the Eastern company from the Prairies.

The three fledgling systems faced the multiple hazards of state control, political meddling, potential corruption, and just plain bad management. And at one stage or another, each was to be tarred with the brush of political mishandling. Although in 1916 it was temporarily shaken by charges of corruption, the Saskatchewan Government Telephones seemed to come out ahead of the others in the early years. It even survived a Royal Commisison, which went the usual route of investigative buck-passing.

In Saskatchewan, the government kept the lucrative long distance lines for itself and subsidized the formation of rural co-operatives, thereby leaving local initiative to local groups. The Saskatchewan government was consequently not caught in the position of promoting telephone service where there was no strong local interest in having it. The farmers were happy with the arrangement, and the programme paid off with twice as many telephones per rural inhabitant as Manitoba or Alberta.

As in Manitoba and Alberta, Saskatchewan Government Telephones experienced an immediate construction boom. The provincial company built its first exchange in 1909, bought out several major independent companies in the province, and by 1912 had nearly 15,000 subscribers. There were, in addition, almost 9,000 subscribers who were served by rural and independent companies. Saskatoon installed one of the West's first automatic switching systems, just ahead of Edmonton. (The first was installed in Whitehorse in 1898.)

Premier Walter Scott of Saskatchewan interpreted the rapid gains in his province as proof of the wisdom of the wheat province's telephone policy, and confided to a friend that he considered the headlong course taken by his neighbours — in terms of their assuming responsibility for *all* telephones in their provinces — to be "suicidal." This view of the economics of farm telephones was espoused much earlier by Bell's Sise, and would later be shared by an Alberta Premier.

Manitoba set up a commission to operate their newly-acquired provincial system under the chairmanship of F.C. Paterson, a competent telephone man. Like its neighbours to the west, Manitoba enjoyed the benefit of retaining most of the trained personnel from the displaced Bell system. Within a year the commission proceeded with the construction of long distance lines and the number of subscribers increased by 6,000 for a total of 20,000. During the first year of operation 29 new exchanges and agencies were added along with 1,468 miles of long distance line and 408 miles of long distance pole line. Thousands of settlers poured into Canada's West during the country's great immigration wave, and by 1912, while construction crews swarmed over Manitoba, the number of subscribers jumped from 17,000 to 40,000. All of this was costly, and the drain on the treasury meant that the new Manitoba system was losing money at a phenomenal rate. In 1912 the company considered it necessary to apply for a "measured rate" — which allows a specific number of calls in a month, 40 for example, with charges for each additional call thereafter. The idea roused immediate and massive protest.

Initially, Manitoba plunged into its expansion programme without any regard to cost. Public interest was given lavish lip service but was generally disregarded by the government — which used the telephone company openly and blatantly for political ends. Telephone commissioners were forced by the government to build unnecessary and unprofitable rural lines for the sole benefit of local politicians. Cabinet Ministers recommended employees for telephone jobs, knowing that such recommendations were tantamount to assignment. Rural lines, budgeted to cost $150 a mile, cost more than $200 as hordes of hotel-keepers, suppliers and deliverymen conspired with telephone workers to cheat the government. Each year, the government happily reported profitable operations — choosing to ignore completely its depreciation and bond repayment obligations.

When the financial facts of telephone life finally caught up with the Manitoba politicians, a Royal Commission was appointed, which duly whitewashed the government of the day and sacrificed the telephone commissioners as scapegoats. The Winnipeg *Tribune* denounced Manitoba Government Telephones (now Manitoba Telephone System) as "one of the most iron-clad monoplies ever imposed on any peoples," and went on to say that "rates should be cut in half." Co-incidentally, these were the same phrases Premier Rodmond Roblin had used only a few years earlier when he was attacking Bell.

A public utilities commission was established to regulate rates and to serve as a non-political buffer between MGT and the government. Everyone's task was made more difficult inasmuch as 1912 happened to be the year Rupert's Land was added to Manitoba — increasing the size of the province from 73,732 square miles to 251,832 square miles literally overnight.

MGT was reorganized, and a principle was adopted that still serves: "All parts of the province that are accessible are to be supplied with service, regardless of the fact that supply of telephone service to rural and distant areas will, in most cases, be so supplied at a loss, but that other areas and services of the system will charge such rates as will enable Manitoba Government Telephones to avoid financial losses."

In Alberta, in 1911, construction topped the million-dollar mark for the first time. Also for the first time telephone revenue was over $500,000 and the acclaimed profit for Alberta Government Telephones was nearly $100,000. Not bad, if you don't have to worry about things like depreciation and bond repayment. Like Manitoba, the young Alberta company wasn't concerned with such mundane matters.

An editorial in the Lethbridge *Herald* acclaimed: "The government is not only providing telephones for the towns and cities and villages but every farmer in Alberta will [soon] be in a position to possess a phone in his home. Dig deep in your memory and try to find a case in Alberta where the Bell people have been interested enough to erect lines along the concession roads in order that the men who are the bone and sinew of the province could be provided with one of the great advantages of modern times."

The *Albertan* in Calgary rejoiced: "The day is near at hand when, thanks to the Alberta Government, every successful farmer in the province will be able to possess a telephone. That will help to keep the boy on the farm. He won't need to be jealous of his city friends."

Part of the campaign against the Bell hinged on what the protesters had considered to be excessive charges by the monopolistic "Octopus." Alberta experienced the same embarrassment as Manitoba when both provinces learned that rates could not be lowered simply by political whim, nor could the cost of installation and equipment be ignored indefinitely. Working on the principle that "whatever those Montreal dudes were charging was too much," Alberta's Cushing lowered the Calgary-Banff rate by 30 per cent. Within the year he had to re-adjust it to a mere 8 per cent reduction.

The key to rates in Alberta is the Edmonton-Calgary toll. From very early times this route was the heaviest in the system in terms of toll traffic. Even today it generates one-fifth of AGT's total toll revenue, and is the second heaviest toll route in Canada. The Bell charged $1.20 for a three-minute daytime call. The provincial government system cut 10 cents off that. After the second World War another dime was chopped but was later restored. Today the rate remains virtually the same as it was in 1908. What other public service can make such a claim?

Of course, in 1908 all calls were person-to-person; now the majority are station-to-station. As one early telephone ad put it: "It's cheaper to call if you don't want to talk to anybody."

The fantastic construction boom across the Prairies marked the heyday of the telephone boomers — the men who put up the poles, strung the wire and generally made the system grow. These characters were the heroes of the day for the young boys of that era. And some of them were certainly characters.

Consider Fred Daniel, a technician at the Lacombe exchange. Fred was a gun enthusiast and something of a whiz as a marksman. The Lacombe switchboard, like many manual boards at that time, had bull's-eye signals. The signal was a wooden ball painted black on one side, red on the other. When a caller lifted his

A telephone crew working in Estevan, Saskatchewan in 1909.

receiver, the ball turned, showing the red eye to attract the attention of the operator. What marksman could resist a target like that? Certainly not Fred. Discouraged by the Mounties from practising his speciality in the streets, Fred amused himself by popping off the red eyes as they appeared on the switchboard. The operators weren't exactly enamoured of this, but no one could stay mad at Fred, and he was always happy to put in a little overtime repairing the signals in his private shooting gallery.

But the real boomers were out in the field, moving from work camp to work camp as the lines lengthened. Each camp had its quota of foremen, straw bosses, cooks, linemen and grunts. The grunts were the groundsmen, the hole diggers and pole raisers. The elite of the camp were the linemen. Young boys watched in endless fascination as the linemen, wearing their spikes, walked up the poles and fastened the copper wires into place on the cross-bars. Boomers were a nomadic lot, hopping freights to wherever a passing friend suggested there might be more interesting work, warmer weather or extra pay. "It was a wonderful way to see the country," one boomer remarked. "You were always meeting someone you knew and he'd be on the move and you'd ask him where he was headed and it would be some place you'd never seen, so you'd quit and go with him." But despite what might appear to be a casual attitude toward life, the pole climbers were skilled in their trade and they were never casual about the standard of their work.

Speaking of poles, roughly a million dollars' worth of them — enough to build about five times as many miles of line as AGT had any notion of putting up — were found cluttering up Alberta's telephone equipment lots in 1913. There just happened to be an election that year, and the poles represented a step beyond the usual hanky-panky, most of them having been bought, it turned out, from people who might be useful around election time. A righteously indignant Opposition screamed corruption and mismanagement, but Liberal Premier Sifton, with a secure majority in the House, was able not only to thrust aside the allegations but to put on record that the people of Alberta were fortunate to be enjoying the country's highest quality telephone system at the lowest rates in Canada. There remained only the question of disposing of some 47,000 surplus telephone poles. Eventually, they wound up as railway ties, mining timbers and even fencing to keep buffalo herds where they belonged.

Some scholars like to argue that history repeats itself. Well, eight years later, it did. Clearly, election-time buying of telephone poles was enormously fascinating to some Alberta politicians. This time 400,000 cedars, tamaracks and jack pines cluttered up the telephone department yards. AGT was short a million dollars in much-needed cash but it had on hand a 15-year supply of poles!

It is interesting to note co-incidentally that between the first and second Alberta telephone pole episodes, some Manitoba politicians found themselves in an almost identical jackpot.

The first World War caused a general slump in the telephone business because of shortages of labour and materials. Government and military requirements, however, were responsible for an increased demand for line time. On the Prairies, the benefits that accrued from bumper wheat crops stimulated even more farmers to order, if not install, telephones. On balance, the gains in the rural areas almost offset the losses in the cities.

The roaring twenties brought major changes. After years of shortages, upset and unrest a new decade dawned — a decade of excitement, and fun, of films, phonographs, automobiles and airplanes. Telephone girls, like their sisters across the land, wanted a good time. They bobbed their hair, wore their skirts above their knees, painted their faces like Betty Boop and danced the Charleston. Curling, rugby, cricket, golf, baseball, hockey, basketball, and bowling each had devotees, and every telephone office of any size had teams in the local leagues. It was also the decade that produced the magic of the radio-telephone and thereby enabled the Prairie voice to be heard overseas.

Better and more automated equipment was also developed and in 1926 Winnipeg became one of the first Canadian cities to have a completely automatic dial service. Interprovincial hookups across the Prairies were strengthened in the twenties, but access to the East and to British Columbia still depended upon north-south connections.

Although it was true, as Premier Sifton pointed out in 1913, that AGT's rates were the lowest in the country, by 1925 it was evident that the company's financial outlook was very dim. For years Alberta Government Telephones had operated on the theory that nothing ever wore out. That was fine — as long as nothing did wear out. But, by the mid-twenties, Vernor Smith, then Minister of Telephones, had to face up to the truth. The Alberta network was beginning to fall apart. Moreover, replacement reserves were only one-and-a-half per cent of plant values. Smith advised his Premier: "We are faced with our last change to put this utility on its feet financially. Failure to raise the rates this year will mean that the Telephone Department will become insolvent." Special consultants recommended staggering rate hikes and advised that the rural network, which they warned could never pay its own way, should be directly subsidized.

The province hungrily eyed the independent Edmonton system. Calgarians, who were part of the provincial system, were well aware that Calgary had helped to pay for the widespread rural network. Officials in the provincial telephone department were equally aware that Edmonton, concerned only with its own urban area, had not. The Edmonton city system was consequently a very profitable one and its owners, the city, were not about to sell it or have it taken over without a fight. Meanwhile, the sale of the British Columbia Telephone Company to U.S. interests helped spark rumours that AGT itself might go on the block.

The national hookup of radio, telegraph and telephone for the 1927 diamond jubilee greatly increased interest in radio on the Prairies. The Manitoba system put

An Alberta Government Telephones crew raises a pole outside of Lethbridge, 1913.

its own station, CKY, on the air as early as 1923; in Calgary, Red Deer and Edmonton, CFCN, CKLC and CJCA gave Albertans a choice by 1924. At one stage CFCN leased some facilities from AGT that were designed to bring U.S. programmes into Alberta. Simply by flicking a switch, Bill Grant, a pioneer radioman in Calgary, could lift any NBC programme from KOA in Denver or KSL of Salt Lake City. Albertans were thus able to listen to "Amos 'n' Andy," Ben Bernie's orchestra, the "Lucky Strike Dance Hour" and almost anything else available in the United States. However, Ottawa ruled that Grant's operation amounted to piracy, which was a no-no. Until cable television came along nearly 40 years later AGT had to stay out of the business of leasing facilities to carry American transmission.

For a while network radio programming appeared to be the coming thing and all three Prairie telephone companies dabbled happily with it, rubbing their hands at the prospect of badly needed revenues. However, with the Dominion Government ruling that provinces could not operate radio networks and the awarding of radio network transmission to the railways — the telephone companies' arch-rivals — years were to pass before the telephone companies were able to realize

There were, at one time, thousands of independant telephone companies.
This is the switchboard of the local company in Biggar, Saskatchewan.
The operator, M. Martinson, was photographed in 1951 just before the
company became part of the SASK TEL network.

their dreams of lucrative radio accounts. In fact, radio became a serious competitor by providing services such as weather reports and grain market news, long the domain of the telephone systems.

The dirty thirties were a decade of setback for all Canadian telephone companies. All had to slash wages, let workers go, cut rates and take out thousands of phones. Unemployment, poverty, relief camps and hunger stalked the land. Farms became dust bowls and migrant workers similar to the Okies in the U.S. appeared on the scene. AGT dumped its rural network, turning such service over to scores of newly-formed mutual companies controlled by rural groups. Not until the middle thirties did things begin to look up, and then only slowly.

The only bright spots on the Canadian telephone scene during the Depression were the formation of the TransCanada Telephone System and the opening of the All-Red line from coast to coast. And even these were in jeopardy because of the individual telephone companies' hard-pressed circumstances. All of the companies had difficulty enough just coping with their ordinary day-to-day problems without the additional burden of contributing to line upgrading, rebuilding, and constructing the new facilities required for the All-Red route's high standards. In fact, had the decision to build the All-Red line come six months later, the Saskatchewan government would not have been able to go ahead with it. Once into the Depression that province simply did not have the money to pay for its stretch of the line.

Oddly enough, Saskatchewan's telephone system was in pretty good shape in 1931. The wheat province stood fourth in Canada in total phones with 94,196, and was second only to Ontario in terms of the number of rural telephones. There were 1,198 different telephone companies in the province and a total telephone investment of over $35 million. Saskatchewan had the longest pole-line mileage of any province.

In a speech marking the opening of the TransCanada Telephone System on January 24, 1932, J.F. Bryant, Saskatchewan's Minister of Telephones, made an eloquent plea for greater use of long distance:

In an emergency great or small nothing can equal the telephone. It meets everyone's need. It serves as a protector day or night. Aid from the fire station, from the police or doctor can be secured in a few seconds. Many people away from home are using the telephone these days to have regular visits with their families. Commercial travellers on the road, students attending school, college or university are calling up the folks at home regularly at least once a week. Perhaps it is your mother's birthday. No matter where she is in Saskatchewan, in Canada, in the United States or over in Europe you can pick up your telephone and get in touch with her. She would be delighted to hear your voice. If your parents or any of your relatives are sick at home, they are as near to you as the nearest telephone. Through the Saskatchewan Government Telephone System you can get the latest bedside news. You can communicate with any of the 18,500,000 telephone subscribers scattered over the North American continent within a few minutes from the time you put in your telephone call. There is no form of Christmas, New Year's, or birthday greeting to friends at a distance so cordial and friendly as a little talk by telephone. On such occasions our greetings by telephone are not only timely but very welcome, the warmth and cheer of a personal face-to-face talk will be appreciated by friends and relatives. Let them hear your voice.

There is no record of how much Bryant's impassioned plea may have added to the province's long distance revenue, but in 1977, nearly 52.2 million long distance calls were placed from within Saskatchewan. Manitobans placed nearly 35.8 million long distance calls in 1976, while Albertans recorded more than 95.5 million.

Mother Nature doesn't fool around, particularly on the Prairies. On a sultry June afternoon in 1912 she fetched Saskatchewan a mighty wallop when the worst cyclone in recorded Prairie history slammed into Regina. Black clouds over Saskatchewan's capital city swirled into a dervish funnel that developed speeds estimated as high as 500 miles per hour.

The spinning winds demolished an area three blocks by 12 blocks, blowing to smithereens everything in its path. In just three terrifying minutes, 28 people were killed, hundreds were injured and 2,500 were made homeless. The telephone exchange at Lorne Street and 11th Avenue crumpled quickly. Before they knew what had hit them, three telephone operators on the second floor had tumbled into the basement along with their 15-ton switchboard. Miraculously, none of the people in the exchange at the time was killed. Scrambling out of the wreckage they made their way to the Regina *Leader* office. The editors there were not even aware of the storm and thought the distraught telephone operators were pulling some kind of publicity stunt.

Canadian Pacific Telegraph repairmen patched together a wire and within an hour a message was sent to the outside world: "Cyclone hit Regina . . . City in Ruins." Telephone repairmen were soon on the job and opened a line to Moose

144

On June 30, 1912 the Regina cyclone swept through the city. Among the buildings destroyed was Regina's telephone exchange office. The extent of the damage can be seen here.

Jaw. Next day, long distance service was restored and a new switchboard started on its way from Montreal.

Stories reaching the rest of the country were more horrifying than the actual event. There were rumours that Moose Jaw had been wiped out, that 40 telephone girls had been killed, and that a passenger train had been swept off its track. Over 8,000 messages poured into Regina in a single day.

It was a month before telephone service was fully restored. Canny Regina took advantage of the necessary reconstruction to install modern automatic telephones and switching equipment.

Spring flooding on Manitoba's Red River is a regular event. In April 1950, however, the Red outdid itself. Heavy rains the fall before were followed by a record winter snowfall. Then in April an unusually warm thaw unlocked the flood and the waters came pouring across southern Manitoba. As the waters rose, telephone girls in Emerson donned hip waders and splashed to work, crawling over sandbag barricades to clamber into the exchange through a window. By April 30, downtown Emerson was part of a gigantic new lake extending from south of the U.S. border to Winnipeg! That same day the foundations under the exchange finally crumbled and the girls were hauled away in a Red Cross rescue boat.

Five hundred and fifty square miles of Manitoba were inundated. At Morris, girls ran the exchange until May 11 when they had to be evacuated across 50 miles of white-capped flood waters. (Nearly 1,200 people were evacuated by boat from Morris where the flood waters were 10 feet deep on the main street.) During the final days in the Morris exchange, the girls entered the building by way of a floating wooden ramp. When one of the operators slipped she found herself up to her chin in muddy water, but she managed to keep the bag of goodies she was carrying perfectly dry!

In Winnipeg, one-tenth of the city was under water and 8,500 telephones were knocked out of service before the rampaging waters finally subsided. The high-water mark of the flood was matched only by the high sense of duty displayed by the telephone people.

Saskatchewan still gets some dandy winter blizzards, but for real ice doozies nothing can beat a good spring sleet storm in Alberta. Typical of the better ones was a spring ice blizzard in 1932, which blew in just in time to test the spanking new pride of the province — the TransCanada Telephone System line. In the early morning darkness of April 20, 1932, snow, sleet and freezing rain began to fall over a large part of southern Alberta. The midnight shift reporting to work in Calgary through heavy wet snow found conditions going rapidly from bad to worse. In the toll office operators began to hear a peculiar crackling and gabbling in the circuits to the east and northeast; then, one by one, the lines went dead. The older hands had a pretty good idea of what was happening out there and the signs didn't augur well.

Incredible weights of ice — up to seven tons per span — were forming on telephone wires from Sylvan Lake to Lethbridge and from Calgary to Gleichen, an area 200 miles long and 60 miles wide. Rain, freezing as it fell, loaded and stretched the copper wires to hair-thin strands, which then snapped, one by one. Yanked and whipsawed by the pressure of the wires, poles almost leaped from the ground and hurled themselves to one side or the other. In Calgary there was no information — just certain knowledge. Circuits, including the new trans-Canada line, were going dead. Tests located the break areas and crews started out in the teeth of the storm to do what they could to restore service. But the highways were in no better shape than the telephone lines. Truckloads of repairmen were unable even to get out of Calgary. By nightfall the next day, 2,000 poles were down and access to them was still blocked by hard-packed drifts.

Temporary routes detouring the trans-Canada line from Calgary through Lethbridge and on to Medicine Hat reopened the critical national span the next night, but it took emergency crews two months and it cost AGT a quarter of a million dollars to repair the damage done by a typical bit of Prairie spring nuisance weather.

By 1938 the Depression eased slightly and the number of installations passed the number of telephones removed. By 1939, however, and the beginning of the second World War, the telephone companies were again plagued by shortages of both men and materials, as many of the trained telephone workers joined the armed forces just as they had 25 years earlier.

Acting as operator for TCTS, Alberta Government Telephones co-operated with the U.S. army to build a 2,000-mile open-wire carrier to Fairbanks, Alaska, the longest such circuit in the world. Alberta crews were assisted by Bell Canada work gangs, and equipment was rushed from both Northern Electric and Western Electric. Spurred by fear of Japanese action against Alaska, the immense job was completed in 18 months. Although no Japanese campaign was ever launched, Albertans in the Peace River country were linked, for the first time, to their neighbours in the southern half of the province.

After the war the telephone business took off like a rocket. Telephone companies across Canada could not get equipment fast enough to keep up with current orders, let alone catch up on the thousands of accumulated back orders. When Gordon Taylor became Alberta Minister of Telephones and Railways in 1950, it took him three years to get a telephone. Of course, he could have gone to the head of the list, but no politician in his right mind would have put himself in that position. When complaining customers whined that they had been waiting over a year for a telephone, the Minister sympathized: "I know, I'm the Minister and I've been waiting for three years."

In the explosive decade from 1945 to 1955 telephone use mushroomed. During that 10-year period more telephones were added to the Manitoba network than had been installed in all previous years, right back to Horace McDougall.

In the past two decades, the Prairie systems have kept pace with the rest of Canada and the world in step-by-step technological advances which have produced the microwave highway in the sky, television from virtually any spot on the globe, satellite links to every telephone in the world and computerized digital services. Through the TransCanada Telephone System, Canada's Prairie provinces are linked to the rest of the world. With the rest of Canada, they stand firmly at the forefront of world communications.

5

British Columbia
The Other Side of the Mountain

What a wonderful invention is the telephone. . . . Social greetings between friends may be interchanged. The butcher, the baker or the grocer may be reminded of forgotten orders or furnished with new ones. The gudwife and man may exchange signals when far apart.

The Victoria *Colonist* (1878)

There is a long toll line running from Williams Lake in British Columbia's Cariboo country all the way up to Bella Coola, a little fishing port on the northwest coast of the province. It's pretty much a rural line. If, for instance, someone wanted to speak to Bert Jones at Tatla Landing, he merely called Tatla two, the number.

A cheery voice would come on the line identifying herself as the operator at Anahim.

"What number was it you wanted?" she would ask.

"Tatla two," would be the reply.

"Tatla two, oh yes, that's Bert Jones. Well, let's see now. Oh Bert's not in Tatla today. He's gone down to the coast for a couple of days. Can I get you anyone else?"

Hazel Mars, the cheery voice on the line at Anahim, is the last of the old-time operator-agents in British Columbia. For years she ran an ancient magneto switchboard out of her store but at the end of 1978 her voice was stilled. B.C. Tel, in its continuing drive to improve service, installed an unattended automatic exchange on that line. Presumably service is better. As it was, Hazel had to impose

148

some restrictions on the use of the line — for instance, no calls except emergencies after certain hours during the week and only emergencies on Sundays. After all, she had to get her sleep sometime. The new service is right up-to-date — but it certainly isn't personal, and it isn't nearly as much fun. Everybody on the line misses Hazel Mars' cheery voice, unfailing good humour and her sure knowledge of where her customers could be found.

Gordon MacFarlane, chairman of the Board and chief executive officer of British Columbia Telephone Company, addressed himself to that sort of thing in the company's 1977 annual report:

> One new electronic installation and a small, unattended automatic office placed in a remote section of the northeastern part of British Columbia during the year serve as examples of the nature of the company's business as a public utility serving the entire community.
>
> In the populous Lower Mainland region of the province, a $12.5 million computer-controlled electronic switching centre was completed at Whalley. It is the largest switching facility of its kind in the system to date, serving 35,000 customers. At Presptatou, some 1,100 kilometres north of Fort St. John, $1.2 million was invested to install a portable exchange which by year-end had about 150 customers connected. The settlement previously had only a single coin phone in a general store.
>
> The Presptatou installation is a prime example of the companys' acceptance of its obligation to provide service not only in the populous areas but also in high-cost, low-return rural regions whose people make important contributions to the total provincial economy.

Even in their wildest moments of dreaming of a "national" telephone system, the Bell people never seriously considered the idea of hurdling the mountain barrier that separated the East from British Columbia. Sometimes it seemed to people on the west coast who wanted to do business with the East that Easterners were downright discouraging. Orders were misinterpreted, unfilled, ignored or shipped so late as to drive the Westerners up the tall trees that surrounded them.

However, nothing seemed to discourage Robert Burns McMicking, a trim and tidy inhabitant of Vancouver Island who was already superintendent of the government's telegraph company, but who wanted more than anything else to get a telephone system started. McMicking popped off a letter (there being no way to telephone) to Alexander Graham Bell himself, offering his services as the Bell agent for British Columbia. Eventually, back came a letter from Thomas Henderson, Bell's associate, advising: ". . . I have pleasure in learning that you . . . accept the agency of our company for British Columbia. . . . I will immediately send per mail a pair of hand telephones. . . ." And so he did, but it seemed to McMicking that it took forever for the telephones to reach him.

McMicking was born on a farm near Queenston Heights on the Niagara Peninsula and had taken up telegraphy at the age of 13. He was also one of a hardy band of Overlanders, an idealist bunch of adventurers who travelled across Canada by wagontrain in the summer of 1862 to seek their fortunes in the Cariboo gold fields. McMicking found no gold but he tried his hand at storekeeping for a while — raking in the gold of those who had found it. He was an accomplished electrician and had no difficulty signing on with the ill-fated Collins Overland Telegraph Company. McMicking was probably the first man in the far western province to get excited about telephones.

The two hand-sets promised by Henderson eventually arrived in March 1878, and McMicking tested them between his home and his office. They worked fine so he switched one to the office of the Victoria *Colonist* where it created a sensation. As the *Colonist* put it: "Scores visited the office and went away amused and instructed . . . whistling and singing could be heard, the notes being distinct and clear. Other tests of an interesting character were afforded. Those wishing to inspect this curious little transmitter of the human voice may find it in the editor's office."

A couple of coal miners, using the *Scientific American* article (September 1876) on how to build a telephone constructed a pair of telephone sets, installing one in the mine and one at the pit-head. William Wall, a young mechanic with the Dunsmuir and Diggle coal mine at Nanaimo, connected them using such handy items as a borrowed magnet, copper bands from old powder kegs and — for diaphragms — a couple of tintypes of his wife. The result was so good that mine officials suggested using them on the telegraph line which ran from the colliery to the dock on Departure Bay, four miles away. However, on the chance that they might be violating one of Mr. Bell's patents, the mine owner, Mr. Dunsmuir, bought a couple of Edison phones in San Francisco. They worked fine, too. In fact they worked so well that the editor of the Nanaimo *Free Press* was moved to applaud them under a heading, "The Wonder of the Age."

All this enthusiasm, however, didn't help to sell any telephones. More than a year after he had received his first two sets, McMicking was unable to rent even a single pair.

He correctly diagnosed the problem. Set up on direct lines, the telephones being displayed were really no more than an intercom system. What was needed,

McMicking concluded, was some sort of exchange system which would permit owners of sets to converse with any other owners in the vicinity. He promptly wrote to the Bell people requesting the necessary equipment plus some additional phones. Meanwhile, he and his friends went ahead with plans for the Victoria and Esquimalt Telephone Company, to be capitalized at $10,000.

The Bell people couldn't seem to deliver what the new company needed. In order to sustain interest in the area, the Victoria and Esquimalt company set up a couple of phones in the shop of clothing merchant W.J. Jeffree, and in the soapworks of Jeffree's cousin, W.J. Pendray. The installation wasn't an exchange or a switching centre but at least it placed the telephones in central locations and people were invited to transact business on the instruments. Some 11 subscribers had signed up by March 11, 1879, but it was July before the equipment finally arrived and the exchange was working. It was one of the first exchanges in Canada and the third on the west coast — after San Francisco and Portland. (The city of Vancouver did not yet exist.)

By 1880 the Victoria exchange had 35 customers hooked up. One of the biggest problems was a line crossing the mud flats of James Bay, in the vicinity of the Empress Hotel today. The flats were crossed by a wooden bridge and the telephone wires extended in one 600-foot span across the flats, using only the bridge for support. "The first thing we did each morning," noted George B. Kelly, the company's outside construction man, "was to climb the poles at either end and shake the lines clear." Gulls flying in during the night would invariably run afoul of the lines.

What is considered to be the first long distance telephone line in the province operated between Victoria and a mill in North Saanich, a distance of approximatly 22 miles.

When electric lighting and electric railways came to Victoria, the induction from their power lines gave the phone people trouble. Finally they solved the problem in part by putting the lines on enormous poles, 80 feet in the air. The poles, painted white and bearing bright red cross-arms, were a feature of Victoria streets until about 1912, when wires and cables were put underground. The poles greatly offended the tender sensibilities of British Columbia's second Premier, a curious and eccentric gentleman named Amor de Cosmos, who, if he had had his way, would have burned the lot.

The first telephones on the mainland were installed in Metlakatla, a Tsimshian Indian fishing village near Prince Rupert. An unordained and very unorthodox Anglican missionary there named William Duncan ran a line between his store and his sawmill. The Indian fishermen hooked into the line from their huts.

In turn-of-the-century Victoria, the telephone line was one of the tallest structures in the city. The high poles on the right were being replaced by the shorter poles on the left when this picture of Johnson Street was taken.

In the Fraser Canyon, a contractor named Andrew Onderdonk, building the first leg of the Canadian Pacific Railway, put up 16 miles of line to keep in touch with his foremen.

Gradually, service spread through the province. New Westminster and Port Moody had telephones by 1884, and by 1885 there was a line into Tilley's bookstore in Granville village. Small systems were also opened in the Okanagan Valley and at Nanaimo, Mission City and Chilliwack, and shortly afterward in the Kootenays.

In 1886 Tilley's bookstore burned down along with the rest of Granville village, which had only just become Vancouver. However, the bookstore owner's son, Charlie, was able to rescue the exchange switchboard from the fire. The newly-named settlement was rebuilt as was the bookstore which, of course, contained the exchange switchboard. The telephone business flourished. The hundred subscribers didn't get a directory until 1890, but they could find one another's names and numbers on the back page of the local paper, the *News Advertiser*.

Young Charlie Tilley managed the bookstore office by day and worked as a "telephone boy" operator by night at the bookstore exchange. He was also a pretty fair singer and guitarist. Occasionally some of his equally musical chums would visit the exchange on an evening to play their instruments and belt out tunes. One night Charlie opened the lines and invited subscribers to enjoy a "broadcast." For years thereafter Charlie and the boys were the top entertainment of the area.

In 1904, with the amalgamation of several small companies, the Vernon and Nelson Telephone Company changed its name to the British Columbia Telephone Company. A cable was laid via the Gulf Islands, connecting the mainland and Vancouver Island.

When the Telephone Association of Canada began talking about an all-Canada transcontinental line in 1921, B.C. Tel's president George Halse was one of the strongest backers of the idea. Later, in 1928, it was B.C. Tel's Jim Hamilton who testily admonished the Telephone Association members to get off their duffs and get the All-Red line built.

A year earlier (1927) the British Columbia Telephone Company acquired the East Kootenay system adjacent to the Alberta border. This enabled the company to establish a link between Calgary and Vancouver on November 6, 1927. Shortly thereafter, B.C. Tel also picked up several thousand miles of pole line enclosing a rough circle beginning at Kamloops and continuing down through Merritt, Princeton, Keremeos, Penticton and Oliver and back up again through Kelowna and Vernon to Kamloops. The original line to Kamloops followed the CPR tracks along the Fraser and Thompson Rivers. Engineers using motor truck, horse and handcar, laid out a new route from Hope to Merritt through the Nicola Valley to Kamloops. At the same time they strung wire on CPR poles from Kamloops to the Alberta border. In the rugged country between Kingsvale and Kamloops the wires were strung from reels mounted on pack saddles on horses.

Cyrus H. McLean of the British Columbia company recalls: "The Connaught Tunnel in the Rogers Pass was eight miles long. We tried running our wire through the Pioneer Bore which runs parallel to it. The open wire didn't work very well because the heavy soot and smoke from the steam engines coated the insulators and wire with coal dust. The insulation dropped and the circuit suffered too much loss to operate.

"We had to go into the tunnel on speeders with the CPR men. The tunnel was lined with a thick coating of soot and it filled with smoke every time a train came through. You couldn't hear a train coming; you had to feel it and get off and stand in a niche. Once the railroad men decided to give me — a city-slicker — a fast ride. The speeder derailed with a train coming in on us. There was nowhere to run and we were very lucky to find a niche. We had to move like Hell. When the train went by, it scared the liver out of all of us!

"After a great deal of difficulty we managed to put cable through the main tunnel, but this upset the balance of the repeaters, ... We talked about putting carrier on the line to generate more circuits, but we never got to it, because the TransCanada came along."

Another notable event in 1927 had to do with the sale of the British Columbia Telephone Company to the Theodore Gary interests in Kansas City, Missouri. (In present-day TransCanada Telephone System circles, B.C. Tel still enjoys the unique position of being the only member company that is not Canadian-owned.) The Gary people were in an empire-building race with Chicago's Samuel Insull, buying up whatever utility companies they could get their hands on. Although the Canadians realized it meant relinquishing control of the company to Americans, the B.C. company was hard-pressed at the time. It needed an infusion of both capital and know-how.

One of the company's greatest problems was providing service to settlements along the rocky coastline north to Prince Rupert. There was no way to get land-lines into the hundreds of fjords, so Cyrus McLean, a transmission engineer who was to become president of the company, turned to radio.

The Gary people put up the $100,000 that they estimated it would cost to set up a coastal radio-phone system, but they also had to contend with another problem. The RCA and Marconi people in the U.S. were also interested in the business of installing a radio-telephone system along the fjord-dotted coast of Alaska. They had a patent-pool agreement on the equipment needed to do the job and they didn't want the Gary people (through B.C. Tel) getting in on the act.

The British Columbians were caught in a bind — they wanted their own system, but they couldn't get the help they needed from Gary. So they went to the Bell. Through Northern Electric, Bell supplied the required gear. Bell's President, C.F. Sise, Jr. (the son of Bell's founder), agreed to back B.C. Tel if RCA and Marconi raised a fuss or sued for patent infringement, and McLean was on his way.

As McLean remembers it:

The first job was between Campbell River and Powell River on Vancouver

The motor yacht "Belmont" was chartered by B.C. Tel for experiments in radio-telephone communications along the coast of B.C.

finally got a system to work. It was pretty chintzy homemade stuff for the most part, without much power, but it was better than anything they had before — which was nothing!

Western Electric made some equipment for airlines and we glommed on to some of that. I got a boat and we went testing all the way to Alaska. It was a 72-footer with room for 13 but there were just four of us.

AT&T heard what we were doing and sent a man up to see Halse. The man said we were embarrassing AT&T but Halse told him we were just extending wire lines.

We made one demonstration at Ocean Falls that I particularly remember. The government of British Columbia had been trying to get a radio-telephone system in there for years but they couldn't get it to work because it's located on a closed inlet. Some government official told me I was wasting my time and I'd better call my boss or I'd get fired for fooling around there. I had a transmitter out in a boat and a receiver in a cemetery where it was quiet and I made my call. When they found out where I was calling from they were so pleased they wanted to send radios up for every tree there.

We put into Ketchikan, where the U.S. Signal Corps had 65 men on communication. The editor of the paper came down to the boat and asked what we were up to. So I told him about the 'skip' effect* but he wanted proof. So I 'bootlegged' a call through to Seattle for him where he talked to the Associated Press.

He was all excited. 'This is just what we need.' So I bootlegged another call through to New York.

Associated Press came out with a story about the start of telephone service to Alaska. Someone in Washington said, 'If the Canadians can do that, why can't we?'

Someone else said, 'It sounds like McLean.' I got a lot of Hell for doing that.

McLean also laid the groundwork for the formation of the North-West Telephone Company, which for years operated as a subsidiary, pioneering radio telephone long-haul operations in British Columbia from McLean's ship-to-shore radio experiments. North-West reported to the Gary interests until October 1955, when General Telephone and Electronics of New York obtained control of B.C. Tel and North-West. Under the new arrangement B.C. became officially responsible for the operational and administrative problems of North-West.

North-West had its exchanges in long-haul areas up and down the coast — Alert Bay, Ocean Falls, Powell River — but went as far inland as Dawson Creek on the Alberta border. Because of its experience with radio, North-West was the logical choice in British Columbia to head up the technical side of the microwave system and do all the experimental work for B.C. Tel on that system. North-West was amalgamated with B.C. Tel on January 1, 1961.

But in the meantime a lot more people had a lot more fun with the ship-to-shore radio principle that McLean had put to work. Larry Williams, a veteran radioman with North-West, recalls:

There was no confidentiality with North-West Tel. It was all radio and anyone could listen in. I went to Kelsey Bay in 1954 and my wife called and said, 'You forgot your underwear.' All summer long people were asking me if I'd remembered my underwear.

Then there was a fisherman who phoned home to his wife, and everyone heard him say, 'If I don't get home soon I'm going to have to buy it.' She

---

*The 'skip' effect is achieved by bouncing signals off the ionosphere instead of the troposphere. Since the ionosphere is the layer above the troposphere, a more acute angle of reflection can be achieved. This enables radiowaves to come almost straight down over the mountains surrounding valleys or fjords. "Bootlegging" a call simply means using an unassigned frequency.

answered, 'If you don't get home soon with some money I'm going to have to sell it.'

There were no private conversations on North-West Tel.

With 1.6 million telephones in service, the British Columbia Telephone Company is ranked second in Canada only to Bell Canada. Earnings for 1977, despite a year-long labour dispute which saw chief executive officer Gordon MacFarlane out repairing telephones, exceeded those of 1976. MacFarlane reported: "We are confident that the future will see a significant improvement in the economy of this province. We continue to make plans and initiate projects which will contribute to that growth and enable us to meet the telecommunications needs of our customers."

During the summer of 1977, while the company was wrestling with some difficult labour troubles, Vancouver *Province* columnist Chuck Davis teased:

"I see in the paper that B.C. Tel's doing really well. They netted $10.6 million in their third quarter this year, a jump of over $3 million from last year. I called them up to congratulate them, but the phone kept going ka-chunk, ka-chunk, ka-chunk, and on my second call the dial tone came back after I'd dialed a couple of numbers, and on my third call there was no ring, and on my fourth call another phone started to ring before I'd finished dialing, and on the fifth call I got someone in Ethiopia, and on my sixth call I couldn't make myself heard over the static, so I'll have to resort to print to get my message across.

"Congratulations, fellas!"

The company has been at home in its striking new 22-story, $32.6 million headquarters building since 1977. Employees affectionally call it "the boot" because of its silhouette from certain angles, but tourists no longer stop to see if any rooms are available.

Howls of consumer rage continue to be heard every time a request for a rate increase is made and local media comment is not always devoid of a certain malicious tinge. On the whole, however, the public credits the company with doing a pretty good job.

6

Telesat Canada
Anik *and the Space Age*

*I would like to mention a possibility of the more remote
future—perhaps a half a century ahead. An artificial satellite
at the correct distance from the Earth would make one
revolution every 24 hours; i.e., it would remain stationary
above the same spot and would be within optical range of
nearly half the Earth's surface. Three repeater stations, 120
degrees apart in the correct orbit, could give television and
microwave coverage to the entire planet.*

Wireless World
from an article by Arthur C. Clarke (February 1948)

A. Gordon Archibald, chairman and president of the Maritime Telegraph and
Telephone Company Limited, was upset one morning in May 1969. In fact, he
was angry — because the federal Government had just rejected a proposal put
forward by the TransCanada Telephone System (in conjunction with CNCP
Telecommunications) to build an $80 million domestic satellite communications
system. And when A. Gordon Archibald was angry, people knew about it.

He dictated a letter to the editor of the Toronto *Telegram*. It began:

There is a story about a mother whale who once gave a warning to her son,
saying, 'Remember, it's when you're on top and spouting that you'll get
harpooned.'

Well, last Tuesday, the TransCanada Telephone System, through its
chairman, Z.H. Krupski, was up spouting before the Broadcasting Commit-

tee re participation with the Government in the satellite project, and boy, did we get harpooned!

Archibald went on to say that the TransCanada Telephone System (which is *not* the voice of Bell), had offered to pay the Canadian Government approximately three-and-one-half times as much to rent TV channels from Telesat as it would cost its members to use its own channels in its existing ground microwave network:

> That is the only way Telesat can be viable, and TransCanada is willing to do this in order to maintain its place in telecommunications and grow with one of the new technologies.
>
> If you were to pay $4 million for a facility from a company when you could provide it for yourself for $1 million how would you justify that to your customers, to your Board of Directors, and to your regulatory body? Particularly if the company to which you were paying the money to make it viable — yes, even possible — would in turn compete with you for the 'cream' of your business?
>
> And bear in mind that you will pay more for your telephone service if regulated common carriers can't be the 'prime contractors.' What TransCanada Telephone is asking for is not to exclude CTV or IBM or anyone else from using Telesat, but rather to integrate Telesat facilities into the present microwave network.
>
> And while the word 'monopoly' is a dirty word to some, it happens to be the best method by which to operate telecommunications. It saves you having three or four telephones on your desk from three or four different companies.

In their brief to the Commons Committee on Broadcasting concerning the Government bill to establish a communications satellite corporation, TCTS pointed out, quite convincingly they thought, that,

> "The System companies have consistently pioneered and applied every new mode of transmission technology to expand and modernize their services to meet the ever-increasing telecommunications needs of the Canadian public. From the early days of open wire to the modern coaxial cable and microwave radio systems, there has been a steady evolution in the development and modernization of the telecommunications network. The introduction of communications by satellite will mark just another step in this process. . . . It is only natural, therefore, that having carried the responsibility for advancing the national telecommunications network to its present stage of develop-

159

ment, the System companies expect to play an equally responsible role in the introduction and use of the new satellite communications technology. The TransCanada Telephone System is in a position to make a unique and valuable contribution to the success of the satellite enterprise through the use of its trained manpower, its experience and technical knowledge and its material resources. It is ready to co-operate with the Government in developing the satellite system, and so ensure the maintenance of Canada's place in the forefront of world communication. . . .

Obviously, Archibald was upset, as were many others at TCTS because the Government had rejected the suggestion that the carriers build, own and control the satellite system. They could not help but conclude that the rejection was based on political reasons and on a lack of understanding of the entire proposition.

Z. H. Krupski, the chairman of TCTS at the time, wasn't happy either. Referring to the carriers' failure to put across their satellite proposal, he commented:

Looking back, the saddest aspect of this whole business was our inability to persuade Government that the telephone companies should be free to build a Canadian satellite system. There are reasons, both practical and political, to justify controls because satellites have far-reaching international implications. We never expected to have full freedom in this matter, but on the other hand to be completely excluded from satellite technology must be considered a major setback. It significantly affects our ability to attract young people into our companies who want to go into this field.

We had hoped to make the satellite corporation a carriers' carrier. We had also hoped to have the right to build Earth stations. We did not succeed. This was one of our first experiences with the Canadian political and parliamentary system. We worked hard but we were inexperienced and, in retrospect, we were run over as if by a steamroller. We managed to get a few very limited concessions but we were unable to change legislation significantly.

It really started back in 1957 with Russia's *Sputnik*, the world's first satellite. Just five years later Canada became the third nation in the world to own and operate an unmanned scientific spacecraft when *Alouette I* was rocketed into orbit. Experiments with *Alouette I* and *Alouette II* (which was launched in 1965) and with two *Isis* satellites (launched in 1969 and 1971) established Canada firmly in the new technology. It also became clear that satellites could play very important roles in resolving many of the communications problems peculiar to

160

A helicopter was used to install the equipment shed of the remote TV Earth station at Haines Junction, Yukon.

Canada — its enormous land mass, varied terrain, the remoteness of its northern communities and the accelerating demand for telecommunications services.

Comprehensive studies focusing on the best ways to utilize the new technology were undertaken by both the federal Government and the companies already providing telecommunications service. As a matter of long-range policy, the federal Government had to decide whether telecommunications by satellite should come under the direct jurisdiction of a Government agency or be the responsibility of private telecommunications companies.

The TCTS-CNCP Telecommunications proposal was submitted in May 1967. In July the same year the Government set up a task force to advise on the question of domestic communications by satellite for Canada. In March 1968 that task force issued a Government white paper stating essentially that it considered such a domestic satellite system to be vital to the growth, prosperity and unity of Canada and that one should be established as soon as possible. Everyone favoured the concept — the CBC, CTV, the Board of Broadcast Governors, the carriers and, of course, the TransCanada Telephone System. At that stage it was virtually a motherhood issue, and most of those supporting it, including TCTS, had obvious hopes of playing an important or dominant role.

Following consultation with interested parties, which included the common carriers, the provinces, related industries and Government departments, Bill C-184 was produced setting up the Telesat Canada Corporation. The new corporation was to establish, own and operate the space and Earth segments of a single domestic satellite system on a commercial basis. This meant that the sole ownership and operation of the domestic satellite system would *not* be placed under the jurisdiction of the common carriers.

The carriers, through briefs and other representations to the satellite project office, argued that *they* ought to finance, operate and own the system as an integrated part of a multi-purpose domestic communications system. To support their case they pointed out that the carriers were in the sole business of providing communications systems and services under federal charter and that they alone had built up the required expert knowledge of communications and satellite Earth station technology. They were confident they could finance the entire system — absorbing whatever losses, if any, might be incurred — and spread the costs of uneconomical services to the North over a large number of users of their other facilities. They were in a position to assure orderly integration of satellites with terrestrial facilities, and help with the problems of technical co-ordination with the microwave network. In addition, they felt certain they could avoid waste and duplication of effort and resolve any conflicts of interest between the ground networks and the satellite systems. The carriers felt that the Government would still be in a position to handle any international aspects of the programme.

From the federal point of view, that apparently wasn't enough. Ottawa was afraid that the carriers would not have the same objectives as the Government, or at least not have the priorities the Government felt should be observed, and that such differences might delay both Northern and space communications development. Consequently the white paper came out in favour of a separate organization in corporate form apparently designed to promote *competition* among the technologies, companies, and potential suppliers of parts of the system.

The carriers objected on grounds that they considered to be obvious, but to no avail. They next sought to secure ownership of the ground segment (Earth stations) of the system. Again they pointed to their particular experience acquired through the development of a prototype Earth station at Bouchette, Ontario. But this, too, was rejected by the federal Government on the grounds that it would "unnecessarily complicate operations."

As the thrust of federal thinking on the satellite system became clearer, the carriers realized that unless there was a dramatic development to change the minds of the Government people, the likely course of events would disallow them from having any involvement in or influence over the new satellite system. At that point, TCTS chairman Krupski informed the Government that his organization was no longer prepared to support the objectives of the bill. In addition, he insisted that the use of the new system be restricted to the common carriers. He also reserved the right to opt out of any arrangement altogether if this condition was not met.

Krupski argued that the TCTS east-west microwave network was already meeting current needs and that it could easily be expanded to meet all future requirements. He effectively relegated the satellite system to a position of mere utility — a system that "might be useful" for bringing television to very remote areas — but not the only system available for future development. Krupski pointed out forcefully that the early years of Telesat would not be profitable because there was at best only a marginal need for such a system, in terms of both North-South and East-West communications. He also warned that without heavy traffic, the revenues from the services provided by the satellite system would not be enough to offset the costs and that the resulting losses would necessarily mean higher rates for regular services already being provided.

The carriers argued that if the satellite system was set up to compete with existing services, their response might be to expand their microwave ground sytems and accelerate the development of laser beam technology. A.G. Lester, of Bell Canada, had to be taken very seriously when he suggested that: ". . . the long-term future of telephone facilities does not lie only with satellite; it may lie more in the directions of wave guides and lasers."

When A.E. Gotlieb, then Deputy Minister of the Department of Communications, was confronted with the argument that very little satellite business (apart from the delivery of television programming) would be generated in the North under the conditions which then appeared to be developing, he responded: "I hate to use clichés but I think there is an analogy with the railways here. When the railroad was opened up I imagine very few people lived at the end of the line where the last spike was driven, but the very fact that this facility went in, I think, transformed the character of the country. When it is national policy to open up the North, to make these vast regions more attractive and to develop the resources of the North, the philosophy of the bill and of the Government is that this system can create the capability of transforming the character of the North over the longer period."

The carriers' argument was really not at odds with the philosophy of the bill. Their quarrel was an economic one, and they proved that, under prevailing conditions, basing a viable case for Telesat on purely economic considerations

Anik performance is monitored from this satellite control centre located at
Telesat headquarters in Ottawa.

Satellites have revolutionized life in the North. Here an Inuit girl is shown
taking notes during a video lecture being transmitted to her via satellite.

was not possible; there were too many variables. At that point, the Government turned to socio-political arguments — including national unity and pride, the challenge to keep pace with space-age technology and the "right" of Canadians everywhere to high quality communications services.

"It will introduce a new dimension into life in the North and thereby make it much more possible for that part of Canada to be a single national cohesive whole by integrating the more remote areas into the Commonwealth," Gotlieb exhorted.

Finally, a solution in terms of a compromise was reached and on September 1969, Telesat Canada was incorporated by an Act of Parliament, the first time in Canadian history that a private corporation has been so established. Initially, the Government and the carriers own equal shares, but a provision was included in the Act that allows for public investment at some time in the future.

David Golden, the first president of Telesat Canada, describes Telesat as ". . . an investment in the future of Canada, in our aerospace industries and in our people."

On November 9, 1972, *Anik I* (*Anik* is Inuit for "brother") was launched atop a Delta rocket from Cape Kennedy by the U.S. Aeronatics and Space Administration. Just 26 minutes after lift-off, the 1,265-pound satellite was taken over, tracked and controlled by the Telesat satellite control centre at Ottawa headquarters and the Allan Park satellite Earth station near Toronto. (The satellite control centre in Ottawa still continually monitors and adjusts satellite positions.) Telesat's commercial service via satellite began two months later on January 11, 1973.

Basically, a satellite such as *Anik I* is a microwave tower high in the sky. The space segment of the Telesat system consists of three geostationary satellites in equatorial orbit. What this means simply is that *Anik I* is stationed, in orbit, directly over the equator at 114 degrees W. longitude (in line with Calgary) 22,300 miles above the surface of the Earth; backup "birds" *Anik II* and *Anik III* were later "parked" in similar space slots. The satellites are similar to one another; each is about six feet in diameter and 11 feet high. Like microwave stations on the ground, each satellite has a dish-shaped antenna and electronic gear which amplifies and redirects signals.

The communications system incorporated in the *Anik*-type satellite includes an antenna that "sees" all of Canada. It also includes a sensitive receiver that detects and amplifies up to 12 microwave channels, and 12 powerful transmitters, each capable of transmitting one studio-quality television programme or up to 960 voice channels. Each satellite picks up signals from an Earth station, amplifies them and then retransmits the boosted signals to other Earth stations. Every type of telecommunication is handled: telephone conversations, radio and television programmes, teletype messages and electronic conversations between computers.

Earth stations in the system have two basic components, an antenna aimed at the satellite and a packet of electronic equipment designed to receive and transmit signals. Such installations range in size from the two original major stations — at Allan Park, Ontario, and Lake Cowichan, B.C. — each of which has a 98-foot antenna for network television and northern communications, to smaller stations such as the *Anikom,* which is portable and has only a 12-foot antenna. (A similar device was used to cover the hearings on the Mackenzie Valley gas pipeline when Mr. Justice Thomas Berger visited the small settlements in the Mackenzie Valley itself.)

Because the life expectancy of satellites is relatively short, ranging from only five to seven years, a second series of *Aniks,* the *Anik B* series, was launched in 1978. In the early 1980s a third series will be lofted into position.

The present *Anik* series transmits on a 6/4 gigahertz (GHz) waveband (the figures indicate billions of cycles per second), and this poses a problem. That same frequency is used by the microwave system on the ground, and so Earth stations cannot be located near major centres, or they might interfere with ground signals. The first Earth stations, therefore, had to be located outside cities and well-removed from existing microwave facilites. Expensive cable hookups had to be installed to carry the signal its last few miles. With the new series the new 14/12 gigahertz (GHz) system will make it possible to build Earth stations anywhere — even atop a building in the centre of a city — thus eliminating the costly back-haul systems.

The Government gave Telesat a good shove to get it off and running, with Eric Kierans, the Communications Minister at the time, applying pressure to Telesat's potential customers. The CBC took three channels of the 10 full-time, fully redundant satellite responders. TCTS shared two channels with CNCP Telecommunications. Then Bell Canada took two and finally Teleglobe Canada, one. However, despite vigorous attempts to sell more channels, Telesat has been unable to pick up any additional permanent business.

From its very beginnings Telesat operated under handicaps and restrictions that prevented it from realizing anything near its full potential. It had to begin immediately as a commercial enterprise, which meant that it operated under the constraint of profit (and loss); from the outset it had to maintain and operate (a *complete* system, which meant owning all its Earth stations (a contentious point with its customers); it could *sell* full channels only; it was not allowed to sell

Three generations of Anik satellites orbit 22,230 miles above the earth. At the left is Anik I which was launched in 1972. Anik B, in the centre, was launched in 1978. Anik C, on the right, is scheduled to be launched by 1981.

part-time on any channel; it had to deal with customers who felt they were being pressured by the Government to buy services; and finally it was required to exploit a technology that was not (yet) competitive with other facilities. As a result Telesat was hard-pressed to sell enough of its services to cover the cost of operating the system. Only eight of the 10 prime channels available for lease were occupied on a full-time basis. (If it had buyers, Telesat could have provided as many as 11 further channels on a non-protected basis.) Furthermore, Telesat had no guarantees that any of its customers would renew their contracts.

Then TCTS stepped forward with what amounted to an offer Telesat couldn't refuse. "Join our system," said TCTS. "Become a member and we will commit ourselves to maximum utilization of the satellite facilities." The Canadian Radio-television and Telecommunications Commission, however, heard more than 24 complaints from other carriers throughout the industry. Mainly as a result of this opposition, the CRTC ruled in November 1977, that *any* agreement between Telesat and the nine members of the TransCanada Telephone System was not in the public interest.

Shortly thereafter, in an almost unprecedented action, the Cabinet overruled its own regulatory agency and sanctioned Telesat's membership in the Trans-Canada Telephone System. The Toronto *Star* screamed that the decision would cost Canadians millions of dollars. G.E. Inns, Bell Canada spokesman, rebutted the story, asserting that the action would in fact save, not cost, millions. Inns wrote that the decision would permit Telesat to maintain its position as a world leader in satellite technology without further Government funding. He stated: "Full integration of the satellite system with the ground network will provide cheaper service to telecommunications users because it will bring about maximum utilization of the service. Without such utilization," he warned (and as Telesat had pointed out during the hearings) "Telesat would have no choice but to ask for increases in rates charged to common carriers."

Minister of Communications, Jeanne Sauvé said it all, however: "We now think competition in this whole area would be bad for the consumer. We think the telephone companies are right and that their land-based system should be integrated with the satellite system so that the industry as a whole can enjoy the economies of scale. We believe the amalgamation of Telesat and TCTS is of direct benefit to all Canadians."

Under an agreement signed in January 1978, Telesat became a full member of TCTS, and, like the other members, now draws revenue based on usage.

And so there were ten . . .

PART FOUR

The Middle Years

1

The Radio Battle
Plenty of Static

*We were very disappointed when we didn't get the contract.
We used to look in at the CPR office and laugh at the stuff
they were using. They had tomato cans over tubes, that kind
of thing.*

Ron Peddle, Saskatchewan Telecommunications (1976)

The great stock-market crash of 1929 came only a month before the seven members of the Telephone Association of Canada agreed to build the Trans-Canada Telephone System. By 1930 the three government-owned Prairie telephone companies, in particular, were counting heavily on revenues from radio network transmission to make up for the costly drain on their treasuries. This was in part caused by their participation in the newly-formed System and the building of new lines. But by then the telephone companies and the railways were engaged in a fierce battle for the prize represented by radio business.

The telephone companies have been active in Canadian radio broadcasting since its inception. In the early years, telephone engineers undertook vigorous research directed toward improving transmission facilities for broadcasting purposes.

In the early 1920s the expanding use of carrier systems enabled both the telephone and telegraph companies to obtain additional circuits for every set of wires installed. At night, however, many of these circuits were clear and were available for radio transmission or, as it was then called, chain broadcasting.

The Canadian National Railway was among the first carriers to become involved in radio. On December 20, 1923, CNR sponsored the first network broadcast in Canada, leasing time from Station CHYC in Montreal (owned by the

170

Northern Electric Company Limited) and Station OA in Ottawa (owned by the Ottawa Radio Association), and using wires leased from the Bell Telephone Company of Canada to link them together.

By the end of 1923 there were 34 radio stations in Canada, and Sir Henry Thornton, the new president of CNR, began putting radios on CN trains. It wasn't long before people were booking train rides just to listen to music on radio. The CNR subsequently established its own radio stations in Ottawa, Vancouver and Moncton, leased a dozen other stations, and proceeded to sponsor a variety of programmes.

The Canadian Pacific Railway never owned a radio station and did not become involved in broadcast transmission until 1930. By 1932, however, when the Duff Commission* was studying railway problems, a witness could fairly claim: "The railways are the principal programme-builders in the Dominion and their programmes represent one-half of all the coast-to-coast broadcasts." So, by the time the TransCanada Telephone System was being formed and its members were looking for new sources of revenue, the railway companies had already secured a large part of the radio business for their own telegraph lines.

On May 26, 1932, the federal Government set up the Canadian Radio Broadcasting Commission to control all broadcasting in Canada. One of its first items of business was to award a contract for wire lines to link the stations in its network, thereby providing for its sustaining programmes (programmes without advertising) across the country.

During 1925 and 1926, chain broadcasting was developed using telephone facilities almost entirely. It was not until 1926 that the railway telegraph lines were actually adapted for such purposes, and then only for limited mileage, as they had no repeater equipment. In 1927, telephone and railway facilities were combined for the diamond jubilee broadcast, the nation's first sea-to-sea broadcast.

Until the establishment of the Canadian Radio Broadcasting Commission in 1932, the telephone systems competed successfully for and secured over 60 per cent of the available commercial radio business. When the Commission started operations in 1933 it dutifully consulted both railway and telephone interests. Both groups submitted rate bids that remained approximately the same until February 17, 1933, when the three Prairie telephone systems, which had for several years been transmitting programmes over a network of their own, submit-

*The Duff Commission was established in 1931 by Prime Minister R.B. Bennett and was chaired by Sir Lymon Duff of the Supreme Court of Canada. The Commission was to investigate the Canadian railway situation thoroughly. One of its investigative areas was the allegation that CNR was exploiting radio.

ted a rate bid 25 per cent lower than any so far quoted — on the condition that they should be given the business on the Prairies exclusively. They were given the business, all right, but not in the sense requested.

On April 1, 1933, the Commission signed an exclusive agreement with the joint services of Canadian Pacific and Canadian National Telegraphs. The telephone companies were not even advised of the decision. The uproar and the static were horrendous. The Prairie telephone companies simply couldn't believe it. Considering the circumstances, they had every reason to be shocked. But they should not have been surprised.

Nearly a year earlier, on April 15, 1932, James F. Bryant, the Minister of Telephones in Saskatchewan, had written to Paul McFarlane, a Bell vice-president and the chairman of the TransCanada Telephone System:

> . . . About ten days ago, acting on behalf of the provincial system I wrote to the chairman of the Committee on Radio Broadcasting principally relating to the fact that I understood that there was a strong move on in certain quarters to have the radio broadcasting left in the hands of the railway telegraph companies. I stated that we in Saskatchewan were entirely opposed to this on the grounds that voice production and transmission were properly the sphere of the telephone companies which were created for that purpose and was not the sphere of the telegraph companies. I stated also that our equipment was more modern and up-to-date and better suited for the purpose and that so far as the Saskatchewan Government Telephone System was concerned we could not back any broadcasting brought over the railway telegraph lines.
>
> I have been in communication with Mr. Lowry, Mr. Smith of Alberta and Mr. Hamilton of British Columbia and we intend presenting a letter from each of the systems outlining a proposition to the effect that we believe in the creation of a high-power station in each province by either the government itself or by some company authorized by the government to be operated under provincial control but subject to federal regulations.

Five days later, Mr. McFarlane replied:

> . . . I hope you appreciate the delicate position that the TransCanada Telephone System had to take in not putting forward any suggestion in reference to the control of radio broadcasting, or interfere in any way with the programme or station management. We were merely advancing an argument for the use of proper communication facilities in any scheme, plan or organization that the committee may suggest to Parliament.

On November 22 and 23, 1932, the four Western telephone companies held a conference in Calgary. A resolution was drafted to be sent to the Radio Commission. It read, in part, as follows:

> Whereas the major telephone systems of Canada have recently spent very large sums of money in the provision of telephone circuits across the Dominion for the transmission of sound; and whereas these circuits are built for this express purpose and no other, therefore, the telephone systems of the Prairie provinces do urge upon the Radio Commission of Canada the justice and right of the TransCanada Telephone System to transmit and carry the proposed national radio broadcast programmes across the Dominion of Canada. It is further urged that the highest grade results can only be expected from circuits designed and built for the purpose of sound transmission and that the only circuits in Canada designed and built for this express purpose are those owned and operated by the TransCanada Telephone System across the Dominion and in the inter-provincial networks provided by the telephone systems and the respective provinces. . . .

After "considerable conversation" with Mr. McFarlane it was agreed that the resolution would be presented by him as representing all the companies in TCTS.

On December 1, 1932, McFarlane wrote to J.E. Lowry, Commissioner, Manitoba Telephone System:

> On Tuesday I had a meeting with Mr. Charlesworth*, chairman of the Radio Broadcasting Commission and Mr. Maher, Commissioner, and submitted on behalf of the TransCanada Telephone System a memorandum outlining the essential feature of programme supply service in Canada and using as the principal facilities the telephone circuits, but suggested for the broadcast programmes of the Radio Broadcasting Commission, that the Canadian National Railway, the Canadian Pacific Railway and the TCTS facilities be brought together, using the shortest, most economical and best facilities of each system in a general wire arrangement. I believe it would be unreasonable and would not be accepted by the Commission, if it were suggested and forced the recommendation of the exclusive use of telephone circuits in the Commission's programmes.

McFarlane went on:

> . . . I am in disagreement with your contention that only telephone lines should be used, particularly in Manitoba. I am quite conscious of the better facilities of the telephone lines for broadcasting purposes, as well as the

*Sir Hector Charlesworth.

fundamental nature of the telephone business lending itself more closely for broadcasting service than an improved telegraph system. But at the same time we must accept that the telegraph facilities are in service, and so far as the public are aware, rendering satisfactory broadcasting and to deny them a portion of this business would be putting ourselves entirely out of court with the Commisison. If we are successful in interesting the Commission in our recommendation then we should be satisfied.

On December 5, 1932, W.H. Warren, Deputy Minister of Telephones in Saskatchewan, advised his Minister of the Calgary resolution, stating that he understood Mr. McFarlane had presented it to the Radio Commission, and adding:

> . . . but the stand which he is now taking with respect to the use of telegraph and telephone lines for the transmission of radio programmes is one which does not, in my opinion, meet the approval of our system. . . . I do not agree with Mr. McFarlane that the telegraph companies should have any part of the transmission of sound across the province of Saskatchewan. . . .

On that same day, Mr. Warren took some satisfaction in disputing another McFarlane contention ("we must accept that the telegraph facilities are in service, and so far as the public are aware rendering satisfactory broadcasting"), passing the following memo on to his superior:

> . . . I would point out that if you had not listened to the transmission of the rugby match from Hamilton on Saturday, December 3, or the symphony orchestra from Vancouver on Sunday afternoon that these programmes came through in very poor shape due to the fact that they were transmitted over telegraph lines. In fact the latter programme was so poor that the station at Regina finally apologized for the quality of the programme and stated that it was so poor they declined to broadcast further. . . .

Mr. Warren noted:

> While I am not particularly anxious to stress the inferior quality of our competitors' lines I believe that when the proper occasion arrives this information should not be lost sight of.

The next day, Minister of Telephones Bryant wired Sir Hector Charlesworth, chairman of the Broadcasting Commission:

> . . . understand that McFarlane of the Bell has suggested division of radio broadcasting between Canadian National Telegraph systems and Western

provinces. Desire to protest on behalf of Saskatchewan. We do not care what division the Bell makes in the East but our system is equipped solely for this purpose. Can give better service than any telegraph lines and desire to insist on what we believe to be our rights in the matter. . . .

On January 28, 1933, Saskatchewan's Mr. Bryant enlisted the aid of Manitoba's Minister of Telephones in drafting a letter to be sent to the Commission. Points Mr. Bryant wished to make included:

1) That when the *Free Press* and *Tribune* were running radio stations at a loss, the government of Manitoba took over the stations on the definite understanding in writing that they should have the exclusive broadcasting privileges for the Province of Manitoba, and also that they should have one-half of the radio license fees collected in Manitoba.
2) That at a later date the three Prairie provinces, having in view the future of the broadcasting business, especially equipped their telephone lines with the very latest and best equipment in the world for voice frequency transmission.
3) That for some considerable time the government systems of Manitoba, Saskatchewan and Alberta have been producing radio broadcasts which for quality of reception have not been surpassed in Canada, and which the press stated . . . is very superior in quality and tone to the broadcasts over the telegraph lines of the railway companies.
4) That nowhere except in Canada are telegraph lines used for the purpose of transmission of radio programmes.
5) That the railways had no right to infringe on the field of telephone or radio communication.
6) That if it is desirable to divide the radio broadcasting work among the two railway companies and the Bell Telephone Company of Canada this should be done only as far as the boundary of Manitoba. . . .

On February 2, 1933, the telephone Ministers of the three Prairie provinces presented a joint submission to the Radio Commission, calling a number of points to its attention:

. . . when the trans-Canada telephone circuits were first contemplated over eight years ago, one of the byproducts considered to make these lines more productive was that of possible revenue from radio broadcasting.

Since nowhere in the world, as far as we are aware, have circuits over telegraph routes been used for chain broadcasts — outside Canada — it was felt that this being properly telephone business, the western systems should equip special circuits for this purpose. This was done and is now known, and has been known as 'the Prairie Loop.'

The western systems have had a commercial hookup for over six years on which very low rates are quoted for the benefit of sponsors which in turn reacts to the advantage of radio users.

The prairie telephone systems are publicly owned with an investment in telephone plant over $60,000,000.

The submission also pointed out that while the telephone companies had to provide service for 60,000 farmers at a loss, the telegraph companies were, in effect, subsidized by the railways and had no such obligation; that Manitoba had been in the broadcasting business before either of the railway companies; that the railways had no right to infringe on the field of telephone and radio broadcasting; that use of railway circuits would be more expensive; and that all the Prairie systems wanted was "our proportion of the revenue from the Dominion chains."

Chairman Charlesworth acknowledged receipt of the submission and assured the Western Ministers:

The whole question of our land-wire arrangements will be taken up between now and March 31st, when we hope to strike an arrangement equitable to all interests concerned. While it is, of course, impossible for the Commission at the present time to give exclusive business in coverage to the Prairie telephone systems, it is the opinion of myself and also of the prime minister that your organizations should share in any agreement that we may in future arrive at.

The letter was dated February 17, 1933.

J.E. Lowry, Manitoba's Commissioneriof Telephones, along with Mr. Mitchell, Comptroller of the Alberta system, and Mr. Delaney of the Saskatchewan system, met with the Radio Commission in Ottawa on February 21, 22 and 23. On the 22nd the three Prairie representatives met with McFarlane, who advised them that they "had little chance of success since unofficially at least the business seemed to be already the property of the telegraph companies."

The Westerners, having spent three hours the day before with E.A. Weir, programme director for the Commission, did not, in Lowry's words, feel that "this was a fair interpretation of the views of the Commission." The Commission agreed again to advise the Westerners when any decision was made — a promise never kept.

After the award of the contracts to the railways, the Telephone Association

176

sent a resolution of protest to the Prime Minister, the Minister of Marine (responsible for allocation of frequencies) and the chairman of the Radio Commission.

The resolution said in essence:

The Telephone Association of Canada wish to draw to the Minister's attention that Canadian interests are not best served by turning over revenue secured for broadcasting purposes and expended on behalf of broadcasting exclusively to the railway transportation system of Canada, but that a co-ordinated use of all available broadcasting facilities of both the telegraph and telephone systems could be secured at no increased cost, and will be in the interest and improvement of radio broadcasting giving complete coverage throughout Canada. The flexibility of such co-ordination of all wire facilities at the command of the Radio Commission is obvious in the interest of broadcasting service. We, the major telephone systems of Canada, submit and offer our wire facilities to co-ordinate upon an equitable basis with those of the telegraph systems.

The Commission also agreed not to employ the lines it leased from the telegraph companies to carry commercially sponsored programmes and not to compete with the railways in the commercial broadcasting field.

On September 1, 1934, a pooling arrangement for sponsored programmes was entered into by which both the telephone and telegraph companies agreed to pool their broadcasting revenues, the telephone interests getting 40 per cent, the telegraph companies 30 per cent each.

Beat out of the first contract, the telephone companies sought to tender on the next contract but they couldn't even find out when the first contract expired.

Again the Commission handed the contract to the railway companies, this time without even a boo for the telephone companies. The contract, dated July 19, 1935, provided that the Commission could use the circuits for commercial as well as sustaining programmes. When the three Prairie provinces learned this they seriously threatened to enter the telegraph business themselves, but were disuaded by the combined efforts of the other TCTS members.

Although the telephone companies were assured that the new contract did not mean that the Commission intended to go into the commercial field, the Commission's earnings from such programmes nearly doubled in the following year. As a result, the earnings of the telegraph-telephone pool fell off seriously.

In the spring of 1936, a special committee was set up "to inquire into the operations of the Canadian Radio Commission and its administration of the Candian Radio Broadcasting Act of 1932."

Testimony by commissioners before that committee failed to offer any satisfactory rationale for the Commission's actions.

TCTS's submission to the Parliamentary committee on May 12, 1936, suggested that the "whole matter of the leasing of land lines by the Canadian Broadcasting Commission be revised with a view to affording to the telephone systems of Canada an equitable share of the business." The telephone submission pointed out that the telephone systems were built to a considerably higher standard than the telegraph systems, that the telephone systems had more routes available, that the total mileage of the telephone systems was nearly 12 times that of the telegraph companies' wire mileage, and that the telephone systems had been intensively active in the early development of broadcasting.

Testifying in May 1936, Manitoba's Attorney-General, W.J. Major, pointed out that Manitoba had been broadcasting since 1922 by special arrangement with the federal Government and that: "We had an arrangement which was made by the Government in 1922 whereby our own broadcasting station in Manitoba would be the exclusive station; that no licences would be granted until an opinion had been sought from the Minister of Telephones. At the same time we were collecting the licence fees and 50 per cent of those fees were paid to the radio station CKY which was used in the development of radio."

For the *third* time, the Commission refused to bother with TCTS's tender and signed a new contract with the railways under which the telephone systems were excluded until August 1, 1940.

At a meeting of TCTS in Winnipeg, February 10 and 11, 1936, the Prairie members again wanted to protest. But as the minutes show: "After some discussion, however, the question was dropped." The attitude of TCTS was summed up by McFarlane, who said he had felt from the beginning that the Commission was going to give the business to the telegraph companies and he was therefore willing to settle for a 40-60 split, because the telegraph companies had the inside track.

The three Prairie provinces never accepted that line. When they found out the Commission was appropriating to itself the revenues from the commercial programmes, they threatened to withdraw from the pooling arrangement and again were induced to stay on only at the last minute by other members of TCTS — and then just on a month-to-month basis.

Although the Prairie companies felt they had not been given the full support of the other TCTS members in the bitter radio battle, when they considered their situation pragmatically they decided that the advantages of their membership and TCTS outweighed the disadvantages. It was not, however, to be the last time a member company would have to swallow hard and accept, for the sake of the common good, a situation or solution that was not to its own advantage.

The radio fracas clearly illustrated that a key problem faced by the Trans-Canada Telephone System stemmed from the dual business-political character of the Prairie telephone systems. Although they were of different political persuasions, each of the three Prairie governments stood quite ready to make common political cause when the business aspect of their telephone systems was threatened.

It was a point which those guiding the destiny of TCTS had to keep carefully in mind. The Prairie companies clearly felt they had received the short-end of the stick in the radio imbroglio. If they had decided that that was to be the pattern of their future TCTS relations, they could easily have withdrawn as members. If that had happened, TCTS would unquestionably have foundered in its early years.

2

The War Effort
All the Screech You Want for a Dollar

*The year 1939 will appear on the pages of history as the year
in which the world was plunged into the second Great War.
From the telephone point of view, however, it will appear as
the year during which, co-incident with the outbreak of war,
an unprecedented demand for telephone service commenced.*

Minutes of Board meeting,
Maritime Telegraph and Telephone Company Limited (December 1939)

Member companies of the TransCanada Telephone System were heavily involved
in defence projects during the second World War. In subsequent years the System
as a whole was also called upon to carry out several major national defence
projects for the federal Government.

The Bell Telephone Company, which was by far the largest of the Trans-
Canada group, handled the bulk of the war effort projects mainly because it
possessed the greatest resources in terms of both trained personnel and materials.
However, all the member companies suffered similar shortages of men and
equipment at a time when demand was exploding. All across the country, able and
talented communications workers left telephone offices to go to war. Some of the
best wireless operators who joined the signal corps had gained their vital experience in the Northwest Territories and the Yukon, and they pulled together to form
the nucleus of the finest Allied military wireless group in the world.

Vital communications materials such as copper, nickel, zinc and tin were in
short supply as war production gobbled them up. By 1942, with demand increasing faster than ever before, B.C. Tel had to stop providing phones to ordinary

civilian subscribers. The same year, in order to meet national defense commitments and provide other essential services, Bell had to turn back 30,000 applications for telephones. Shortages of men and equipment also affected service. One of
the wartime stories tells of an Alberta businessman who got so tired waiting for a
connection to Calgary that he chartered a plane and flew there before the connection was made.

By the end of 1941 Bell crews alone had installed 114 military switchboards
in Ontario and Quebec, in addition to priority installations in munitions factories,
shipyards and aircraft plants. Two major military projects in the East — one in
Nova Scotia, the other in Newfoundland — involved large Bell Telephone crews.

The Newfoundland project was undoubtedly one of the Bell Telephone
Company's major contributions to the war effort. It provided reliable and secure
communications, in one of the country's most vital and strategic areas, for the
Battle of the Atlantic. The project was a triumph over time constraints, rugged
terrain, impossible weather, transportation hazards and wartime shortages. Because the work was shrouded in wartime secrecy it has never received any
publicity or been given any of the credit it deserves. Even its location was kept
secret by the military censors who referred to it as "somewhere in Canada,"
although at the time Newfoundland had not entered Confederation.

The Newfoundland project got under way early in the war when Britain
granted the United States permission to build several military bases in Newfoundland in (partial) exchange for 50 elderly destroyers that Britian urgently needed
for convoy work. It was to serve these bases — Fort Pepperrell in St. John's,
Harmon Field near Corner Brook, and Argentia at Placentia Bay — that the
United States Signals Corps asked the Bell Telephone Company for assistance.
The Americans recognized that the strategic importance of their bases depended
very much on a first-class integrated communications setup and they asked Bell to
put up the aerial cable to link the installations.

The first of 330 Bell employees arrived in Newfoundland in April 1942; they
completed their assigned jobs in less than a year. To work on the project Bell
workers left the comforts of their homes and lived in 18 Spartan-like work camps,
which were built along the 500-mile route of the main cable. Their difficulties
were carefully chronicled in a history written by J.B. McGeachie, one of the Bell
work gang. Accounts of snow drifting over the top and burying 30-foot telephone
poles, gales that blew trains off their tracks, trains that appeared unexpectedly
dead-ahead of the railway speeder used by the work crews, muskeg that swallowed up poles overnight, and bare rocks on which poles had to be erected, are
only a few of the many stories McGeachie relates.

Tom Eadie was at that time Bell's general plant manager, western division, Toronto. He was assigned the task of putting together the nucleus of the organization to do the job.

Eadie wrote:

The Newfoundland project dawned as one of considerable glamour but it soon became evident that [although] it would be a challenging task . . . the project had a number of special problems, both for the men who carried out the work and those who had the responsibility of ensuring that it was completed on schedule. . . . There were no ships to transport poles, so we had to find our own on the island. . . . The narrow-gauge railway which runs from Port aux Basques in the west to St. John's on the east coast was to be our supply line — and the route for most of the cable. . . . Equipment on the railway was in short supply, as were most things at that time and there was no good highway across the island. . . .

To those of us used to the mainland system, the Newfoundland railway seemed to be a thing of wonder. While close contact was kept with the dispatcher to guarantee the safety of crews using railway speeders as transport, yesterday's train or even the one from the day before was likely to confront them as they rounded one of the many bends in the track.

The train was always overcrowded. . . . In many places the train was buffeted by high winds, and at strategic spots anchors were buried in the right-of-way so that chains could be attached to the tops of coaches to keep the train upright until the winds abated. When heavy snow accompanied the wind the train was sometimes buried solidly.

The railway connected with the ferry service which operated between Port aux Basques and North Sydney, Nova Scotia. There was never even deck space to sit down and the trip was not without hazard. The 'Caribou,' the main ship, was torpedoed with heavy loss of life on October 14, 1942.

Frequently, Newfoundland could be reached only by military aircraft, and this brought home the meaning of 'isolation pay,' to which the men on the project were entitled. A trip by air to Newfoundland often meant sitting — waiting — for hours on a folded parachute in a cold hangar at [Montreal's] Dorval only to find at the end of the day that the pilot of the aircraft on which you were hoping to hitchhike a ride had decided to ferry the aircraft to Britain in a single hop. Since the ferry pilots were paid on the number of machines they delivered safely, the wishes of an itinerant telephone man to get to Gander were not considered.

There was little in the way of entertainment to distract the men in their off-duty hours. I know nothing of screech (a well-known Newfoundland rum derivative) but I understand it is the favourite drink of the Newfoundlanders. Some of the boys told me that in certain establishments you could enter a room, lay down a dollar bill, and were then entitled to drink as much as you wished. The catch was that you were flat on your back — and ejected — long before you had consumed anything like a dollar's worth of the potent liquor.

Many of the men who went to Newfoundland for the Bell encountered difficulties undreamed of on the mainland. Skilled labour on the island was in short supply, and the skills of the labourers who were available were legendary as well as limited. Somewhat unexpectedly many of the project people at all levels found themselves involved in providing special training and instruction for the work crews. The process was costly, time-consuming and often frustrating. However, the combination of circumstances under war-time conditions left no alternatives. The training had to be provided in order to get the job done — so it was.

In an account of the project in the March 1945 issue of the *Blue Bell,* H.G. Owen told of newly planted telephone poles sinking from eight to nine feet into the muskeg overnight and of a winter storm that swept down 60 miles of pole line as cleanly as if cut by a scythe. Work trains on the little narrow-gauge railway were used to lay the cable beside the pole line while the train was in motion. It is believed to be the first time such a trick was accomplished.

Seven hundred Newfoundlanders worked alongside the 330 Bell men. When the job was finished, the importance of the work done by the Bell crews was formally recognized by the U.S. army, which presented the company with a special citation paying tribute to all the men who had worked on the job.

The experience gained on the big Newfoundland project proved to be of great value when the urgent need arose to expand communications along the east coast of Nova Scotia to beat back the German submarine menace. Air fields, army camps, command centres and dockyards, all of which had proliferated with the war, needed better and more secure communications links. Military and naval communications badly needed better co-ordination.

Defence Communications Limited, a Crown corporation, was formed in 1942 to implement the installation of new telephone facilities and the upgrading of existing ones — from Yarmouth to Cape North. DCL was also to establish a radio link with Newfoundland, requiring new open-wire circuits, cable extensions and pole lines. Some of the organizations assigned to these vital defence projects included the Royal Canadian Navy; the Royal Canadian Corps of Signals, Atlantic Command; the Royal Canadian Air Force, Signals; Maritime Telegraph and Telephone Company Limited; The New Brunswick Telephone Company, Limited; and The Bell Telephone Company of Canada. Once again Eadie drew the tough assignment of organizing the projects.

On a projected Dartmouth to Truro connection in 1943, one eight-mile stretch was so rocky and uneven that it took five hours just to walk the distance. Of the three contractors invited to bid on the road job, the first flatly refused, the second furnished an estimate but withdrew it the next day, and the third agreed to try it but only on a cost-plus basis. It was promptly dubbed the "Burma Road" by the work gangs. A mile-and-a-half stretch of terrain in the middle was so rugged that it made little sense at the time to persist with the road. The crews finally settled on pulling cable in from either end to close the gap. Meanwhile, other emergency tasks kept the work crews racing against time.

In November 1943, H.G. Black, general manager of NBTel, put out a desperate call for help. A heavy sleet storm had levelled the TransCanada circuits north of Saint John. Crews ready to go home were shifted to the storm zone.

Japan's entry into the war, in December 1941, suddenly shifted attention to the west coast and the Alberta-Yukon-Alaska corridor.

All of the companies west of Ontario were hard pressed for manpower long before 1941. The long years of attrition during the Depression had taken their toll. Hiring had been necessarily minimal and had left the three Prairie companies, especially, with few employees of military age and generally low on staff. During 1940-41 the British Commonwealth Air Training Plan peppered the flatlands of Manitoba, Saskatchewan and Alberta with new air bases for the training of air crew. The Prairie companies stretched their resources to meet mushrooming demands for telephone services for these training bases.

Such multiplying defence requirements, the general upsurge in business activity and an increase in civilian travel during the war, placed enormous additional strains on the TransCanada's regular system.

In the AGT annual report for 1943-44, the general manager noted: "Our commercial staffs are exerting their best efforts to see that no person whose services are vital to the war effort is without telephone service. The situation in Alberta is not unique. The various telephone companies in Canada have on hand approximately 100,000 orders for telephone service which they are not able to fill."

Telephone operators found their switchboards swamped with calls, presumably all of which were important. The operators were often called upon to exercise great tact and tenacity in getting calls put through and they developed considerable skill in judging which ones should get priority.

Wartime business helped the companies to accumulate revenues as toll equipment was used to the maximum, but the companies were unable to plough their surpluses back into new equipment because of war shortages. There was simply no replacement equipment available.

At AGT no sooner had they gotten used to the British airmen who had made clipped demands for all sorts of improved communications facilities, than they had to adjust to a rowdy bunch of Americans who in 1942 swarmed north to build a highway, a pipeline and a signal system from Alberta to Alaska. Communications were deemed to be a Canadian responsibility.

AGT, as hard hit by the war as any other company, simply didn't have the manpower to do the job — so it borrowed a crew from Bell. It didn't help AGT's morale much to learn that the foreman of the borrowed Bell construction team made nearly as much money as the general manager of the Alberta company. Working day and night on the rush job, J.D. Baker, the Alberta general manager, died of a heart attack in 1943. The strain of the war effort also shortened the life of his successor, Alex Mitchell.

American colonels were very good at pounding on desks and bellowing, "Dammit, man, give us the phones!" But they couldn't seem to understand that AGT management had neither the staff nor the equipment to grant even their most reasonable requests. The American attitude seemed to be, "We're building your damned road for free; the least you can do is supply the phones we need to do the job."

The soldiers of the U.S. signal corps, under the direction of AGT technical staff, were given 18 months to build a 2,000-mile pole line from Edmonton to Fairbanks, the longest open-wire carrier circuit in the world at the time. Most of this distance was over mountains, through forest and across muskeg and untouched wilderness. Moreover, the line had to be pushed through irrespective of the condition of the road. Eight hundred and thirty miles of additional line also had to be put up as offshoots from the main line to connect the 13 airfields built along what became known as the Alaska, or Alcan, Highway, to handle lend-lease aircraft bound for Russia.

In Washington, an American general named Stoners served notice unilaterally that December 1, 1942, was to be the date for the ceremonies at Dawson Creek inaugurating the military highway: "At 7:45 p.m. on that day I'm going to call from Washington, D.C., and talk to the colonel at Dawson and God help everyone if I can't."

AGT made it . . . but barely. Literally at the last minute, Tommy Goodsir had to get on a railway speeder and head west from Grand Prairie at 42-below-zero to find a broken circuit. Tommy froze his cheeks and toes but he found the break — a bad splice — made the repair and the call went through.

The spread of the war to the Pacific resulted in the largest single construction job in the history of communications in British Columbia. Begun early in 1942, a vast network of telephone land lines and radio-telephone circuits for the exclusive use of the armed forces, was rushed to completion in the coastal region of the province. The job of engineering the system — a vital part of the Pacific coast defences — was given to the British Columbia Telephone Company.

Hundreds of miles of pole line were built, much of it through forbidding forest and mountain country. Almost 5,500 poles were erected; nearly 17,000 miles of telephone wire were strung — enough to span Canada from coast to coast four times; radio-telephone stations were erected; and buildings were constructed at intervals along the new lines to house the equipment needed to amplify the voice currents.

The task of engineering the lines was so extensive that even the blueprints prepared for the job, if laid end to end, would have covered five-and-a-half miles!

Moving men and materials in the rough country was a major problem. Shipments to one crew working just over 100 miles from Vancouver had to travel by ferry, train, barge, truck and finally by pack horse. The engineering crews themselves used nearly every conceivable mode of transport: airplane, crash boat, army boat, army truck, jeep, rowboat, horse and gas speeder. Still, things moved so quickly with construction crews following so closely on the heels of the engineers that the lines were completed one month after the survey was finished.

An interesting aspect of the war effort in Vancouver was the construction of a bombproof addition to the B.C. Tel Building (now known as the William Farrell Building) to serve as headquarters for the Pacific Communications System. The ground floor of the massively-built addition was to be used as the emergency headquarters for Pacific Command if the Jericho Beach station were bombed out. The walls are three-and-a-half feet thick, and the roof had five feet of reinforced steel and concrete. After the war, when additions were built to expand the building, half of the roof thickness was eliminated. But the massive building remains as a monument, in a sense, to the fear of Japanese attack.

In 1943 the late Paul A. McFarlane, then a vice-president of the Canadian Bell Telephone Company, was called to New York and sworn to secrecy. He was then informed that President Roosevelt, Prime Minister Churchill and Prime Minsiter Mackenzie King were going to hold a very important conference at the Château

Quebec City, November, 1944. Seated are Prime Minister Mackenzie King, President Franklin Roosevelt, and Prime Minister Winston Churchill. The military officers behind the three leaders are, from left to right, General H.H. Arnold, Sir Charles Portal, Sir Allan Brooke, Admiral E. J. King, Field Marshall Sir John Dill, General George C. Marshall, Admiral Sir Dudley Pound and Admiral W. D. Leahy.

Frontenac in Quebec City and that a completely new, "200 per cent secure" communications setup would be required. McFarlane looked at the specifications and estimated it to be an 18-month job. He was told he had nine days.

Within 24 hours Bell Telephone crews were swarming over the old fortress-like hotel, ripping our every inch of existing wiring and installing a completely new complex. The new installation was not only "200 per cent secure," but could also be used by any of the three leaders or their glittering retinues of Ministers, field-marshals, admirals and generals in attendance to call London, Washington, Ottawa or, indeed, any battlefront in the world in absolute security at any time of the day or night.

At one point a Northern Electric crew worked 72 consecutive hours to assemble a switchboard which they then accompanied in a moving van from Montreal to Quebec. A second switchboard was also shipped in from Philadelphia. When Roosevelt's train arrived on the ninth day, all was ready. He and the other leaders had only to be plugged in.

Twenty-five American army telephone operators were brought in to run the switchboards. They were trained for their Quebec conference duties by Bell Canada personnel. For security reasons each of the operators — all of them women — came from different states. During the conference the telephone directory, which listed the names and numbers of over 400 various officials, was updated and reprinted several times.

Immediately following the conference, over a million words of press news reports were filed in a single day from Quebec. (For security reasons no news reports could be filed *during* the conference. R.H. Spencer, who was then a Bell public relations representative (and subsequently Bell historian, now retired) was called in and given two days to write the only story of how the incredible job was accomplished. Later, he had to watch helplessly as all copies of his report were shredded when authorities changed their minds about publicizing that part of the event.

C'est la guerre!

3

The DEW Line
There's No Adventure in Telephony?

*"Finally the dogs just sat down and said the Hell with it. It
was 55 below zero and their eyes had frozen shut"*
Interview with Don Archibald, manager, general services,
Maritime Telegraph and Telephone Co. Ltd. (1977)

In 1953 the Americans began building an air defence radar system across Alaska designed to warn of the approach of "enemy" bombers. The cold war was heating up and the following year it was decided to extend the defence line across the top of the continent. Western Electric and Bell Laboratories in association with the Lincoln Laboratories of the Massachusetts Institute of Technology were in charge of the project.

Although the DEW Line eventually stretched across thousands of miles of Canadian territory, Canada's involvement was actually miniscule. But because of geographical considerations and the requirements of the United States air force, the U.S. Government decided that it was not only important to secure Canadian help, it was downright foolish not to have some Canadians on the job. The air force went to Western Electric with that thought, and Western in turn came to the TransCanada Telephone System. They asked for eight Canadians to join the project and TCTS advertised the jobs.

Don Archibald, then a husky, adventurous 29-year-old plant man in a Maritime Telegraph and Telephone toll central office, was intrigued. He was told he would be sent to the Arctic for a year at $202 a week and that he would have to make a quick decision. "How quick?" he asked. "Within an hour," was the reply.

He signed on as a candidate for the assignment then and there and was later chosen as one of the eight-man Canadian contingent, drawn mostly from Bell Canada and Northern Electric (as Northern Telecom was then known).

The Canadians were flown to a point near the Alaska border which was a radar site technically designated NAE (North Auxiliary East). The precise location was about 90 miles east of Barter Island just inside the Canadian border. They landed on an air strip built on Bagnall Beach, but an old Inuit told them the proper name for the place was *Kamakuk,* an Inuit word meaning "hill." There was a 3,000-foot-high mountain in the background, which, according to Archibald, was presumably the reason for the name.

A convoy of supply ships, escorted by ice breakers, had arrived with the station — packed in 5,000 crates — just ahead of the men. The first job was to sort out the crates, which were waiting on the beach.

"The radar device we were to install was called an MTI. The letters stood for moving target indicator," Archibald recalls. "It was designed to spot anything moving in the sky and it did — *everything,* including clouds, geese and even airplanes. We had to work out an adjustment so we wouldn't be triggering false alarms back at headquarters every time a Canada goose flew by."

Two hundred workers from the United States were brought in for the construction job along with a support staff of five to assist the eight Canadian technical men who were to man the station. DC-3s, flown by U.S. Air Transport Command pilots, were supposed to take over the supply chore for the station once it was in, but according to Archibald they failed miserably:

They simply didn't know how to fly in that part of the world under the prevailing conditions. We eventually had to arrange for an Alaska bush outfit named Wien to take on the job. From then on we had no trouble; the Wien pilots were a real bunch of cowboys — but great flyers!

My first job was to get the teletype working, both at our station and at the main American camp where they had no one experienced in teletype. We had the latest in radar, radio and wire equipment. We also had a radio-teletype circuit back to headquarters capable of handling 75 words a minute using precut tapes. Our station served as a sort of model for the other stations being built to the East.

Three Eskimo families had moved into the area, and I used to go hunting with some of the men. One time, another member and I and one of the Eskimos took a dog team and went hunting. We ran into a bad storm and were out for three days. We didn't know if we were going to get back or not.

190

At least *I* didn't know. We nearly froze. Finally the dogs just sat down and said the Hell with it and wouldn't go any farther. It was 55 below zero and their eyes had frozen shut. We had to take our mitts off and hold our bare hands over their eyes until they could see again. Then we would go a little farther, but after a time we'd have to do the same thing again.

Another of Archibald's recollections has to do with operating the station:

Once we were operational, the U.S. air force was anxious to run a test on us. They decided to fly a bunch of SAC bombers into our sector from Thule in Greenland to see if we could spot them. They called it 'Exercise Snowbird.' A guy named Ray Petley and I were to take the watch at the time the attack was expected. We were to report every target to headquarters as it came into range.

Ray and I agreed he would take the radar and I would handle the teletype. Just in case it got really busy, I cut some tapes in advance so that when the targets showed up and Ray called them out, I just had to fill in the blanks in the tapes and shove them through.

It worked just fine. We had those targets reported so fast we saturated the system. After about an hour, they sent us a message, 'Okay, okay, you can stop now.' They never did figure out how we were able to spot those targets and report them so fast.

Archibald served 363 days, then hitchhiked a ride out on a Wien Airline C-46. "It was a great experience," he says. "I wouldn't have missed it for anything."

4

The Mid-Canada Line
Not Even a Goose Shall Pass

Service is a telephone company's only stock-in-trade. . . . For a fee it gives someone the opportunity to communicate. In order to provide this service it secures land, erects buildings, constructs lines, cables and microwave systems, installs central office and long distance terminal equipment. These things together form the speedy, dependable but highly complex modern communications of Canada. The telephone company's skill lies in being able to put those things together. That is the service the TransCanada Telephone System was able to offer the Canadian government to build . . . the Mid-Canada Line.

The Blue Bell (June, 1956)

Four years after the end of the second World War, the Soviet Union exploded its first atomic bomb, signalling the end of United States, monopoly on atomic weaponry. Not long thereafter Winston Churchill dropped something of a bomb himself with his famed "Iron Curtain" speech at Fulton, Missouri, which more or less formally marked the beginning of the cold war. For the Canadian telecommunications industry these developments were to mean hundreds of millions of dollars in defence-related projects.

Literally overnight, Russian bombers (and later, missiles) became as much a menace to the free world as Stalin's rampaging troops had once been to Hitler's defence bunker in the heart of Berlin. The Russian menace was particularly

192

significant for Canada because the shortest route for Soviet bombers and missiles to targets in the United States, was over the polar wastes on top of the world . . . across Canada.

Obviously, effective defence lines were required across Canada's northland — and their construction was quickly started. A vast complex of aircraft and missile early warning lines was established, mostly on Canadian soil. Eventually, these included:

The Ballistic Missile Early Warning System (BMEWS), established at three points across the top of the Western world — in Alaska, Greenland and England — massive stations with radar antennae the size of football fields. These could detect approaching missiles almost from the moment of launching.

The Distant Early Warning (DEW) Line, backstopping BMEWS, a string of radar stations stretching across the northern rim of the continent to warn against possible manned bomber attack.

The Mid-Canada Line, a second string of radar stations, along Canada's 55th parallel. The Mid-Canada Line's purpose was to serve as a sort of electronic picket fence, and was designed to track invaders, plot their courses and provide data for their interception and destruction in the air north of settled areas.

The Pine Tree Line, a back-up radar screen running the length of the Canadian-U.S. border and up the Labrador coast to Baffin Island.

All such detection points were connected to North American Air Defense Command (NORAD) headquarters in Colorado Springs in the United States. There, acting on the vital information gained through the detection apparatus in northern Canada, appropriate defensive measures could be initiated by a joint Canadian-American military command.

Canadians played minor roles in the establishment of BMEWS and the DEW line, a considerably greater one in Pine Tree, and carried the entire responsibility for Mid-Canada, which was to become one of the historic projects of the Trans-Canada Telephone System.

TCTS's involvement in postwar defence projects really started in 1953, when the Bell Telephone Company was awarded a contract to connect a number of Pine Tree radar stations along the Labrador coast (as far as Frobisher on Baffin Island) to the overall defence system. For this purpose, Bell's president, Thomas Eadie, formed the Special Contract department within Bell. Boasting only six people as its nucleus, this department was to become a major work-force, at one stage totalling 5,500 workmen (including contractors), 1,286 of them Bell people.

More than anyone else, Alex G. Lester, with the strong support of Eadie who appointed him to the post, was responsible for Canada's success in the building of part of Pine Tree and all of Mid-Canada. A man of bulldog determination, Lester came to the Mid-Canada project well-qualified for the job. He had been in the Royal Canadian Corps of Signals during the war, had attended the National Defence College, and had been chairman of TCTS's Engineering committee. One of Lester's first jobs was to supervise the installation of the world's first tropospheric scatter systems along Canada's eastern coastline (code named "Pole Vault").

The principle of the tropospheric system is based on sending high-powered signals into the troposphere and catching the reflected signals on huge dish-antennae; the signals are reamplified and shot to the next dish. A variation of microwave, its big advantage over conventional radio-wave relay lay in its ability to span 150-220 miles at a jump, thus overcoming the 30-mile line of sight limitation. Anyone familiar with the Labrador coast can appreciate the difficulty and high cost of establishing a conventional microwave system there (a task accomplished only recently by the Newfoundland Telephone Company).

As work was winding down on the tropospheric scatter system in 1955, C.D. Howe, then Minister of Defence Production, called Bell president Eadie to his office in Ottawa and informed him that Canada was going to build a middle-distance electronic warning line. Code named "Mongoose," this was the Mid-Canada Line, which was to extend 2,800 miles along the 55th parallel. It would supplement both Pine Tree to the south and the DEW Line being built by the Americans north of the Arctic Circle.

The Mid-Canada Line was to be based on a system of aircraft detection developed by scientists at McGill University and the Canadian Defence Research Board. The equipment could spot and track any flying object — from a lurking enemy bomber to a flight of Canada geese. In addition to detection gear, the line included radio-relay communications systems for both telephone and telegraph, air-to-ground radio, and an automatic alarm and control system which allowed intermediate stations to operate on an unattended basis.

The TransCanada Telephone System was to act as management contractor on the line for the Canadian Department of Defence Production, with the Special Contract department of Bell Canada serving as project agent.

At the peak of construction 5,500 people worked on the line, recruited from the telephone, electronics and construction industries in Canada, as well as from associated British and American firms. Over 200,000 tons of material were transported to the subarctic. In addition to the line's primary purpose of defence, the Canadian Government saw the project as an important step in developing the vast northern regions of the country.

As with the building of the DEW Line, transportation proved to be the dominant problem. Construction materials, trucks, tractors, electronic instruments, food, fuel and people had to be delivered to their isolated destinations in good time, and in good shape. The means utilized to get the men and materials where they were needed varied greatly with differences in terrain and the season of the year.

Marshalling areas were established at the end of the few roads and railroads that ran to the north. From depots such as Moosonee, Churchill and Great Whale, aircraft, tractor trains and even ships pushed into the uninhabited or sparsely settled areas where the installations were to be built.

The western part of the line proved to be the easiest because the proposed western sites were in rolling, heavily-wooded country which, for the most part, could be reached by extending existing roads and trails. In Manitoba and Ontario, however, the line crossed the muskeg of the southwest shores of Hudson Bay. In these regions barges, tank-landing craft, tractors and float planes were used in summer; tractor-trains, snowmobiles and ski planes took over in winter. Throughout the year, helicopters made the final lifts to the more inaccessible sites. Hudson Bay provided a helpful waterway but its western edges are so shallow that even a relatively small 2,000-ton freighter had to stand eight to 10 miles offshore while its cargo was unloaded and brought in on lighters.

Further east in northern Quebec, the terrain was dotted with thousands of lakes and high rocky ridges running north and south. Materials were moved first by ship and train to Knob Lake, the centre of the Quebec iron ore industry; then by amphibians or ski planes to lakes which served as trans-shipment points; and finally by helicopter to hilltop sites.

The basic construction material used for most Mid-Canada Line buildings was prefabricated steel panels. Foundations were a real headache. Soil conditions ranged from 100-foot clay beds to muskeg, permafrost, sand, shale and granite. The permafrost and bitter weather also combined to create some tricky insulating problems, for water and sewer pipes as well as buildings.

The electronic detection and communications equipment required extensive detailed testing under quite new operating conditions. Some sites actually had to be shifted from their intended locations because they were too close to the summer nesting grounds of Canada geese and local ducks.

Nor was the job made any easier by its very complicated management setup.

Firmly supported by guy wires, the antenna towers of the Mid-Canada Line went up over 300 feet. This tower is located in northern Manitoba.

One of the major stumbling blocks was that lines of authority were never clearly established. Everyone seemed to have a finger in the pie. Bell Canada had understood that it would be the prime construction authority, but the company was named management contractor with considerably more responsibility than matching authority. As the ultimate end-user, the Department of National Defence was the obvious customer; but Defence Minister Ralph Campney had no say in the choice of Bell to do the job. Howe's Department of Defence Production was the procurement agency, which hired TCTS and also awarded major contracts for equipment. But Defence Construction Limited, a Crown corporation, awarded construction contracts and was responsible for construction with Bell serving as its agent. The Department of Transport controlled the drastically vital transportation facilities and the Royal Canadian Air Force was the design authority. Each agency was loaded with people who thought that they alone knew the job.

"The Government process is inherently a slow one," Alex Lester was to say in a bit of understatement. "I've met some solid people in Government agencies, but the system of checks and balances makes it very difficult to get approvals." Lester was very much the man on the spot. Later he was to observe: "Thirty-five per cent of my time was spent keeping lines of communication open with Government people, and that left only 65 per cent to get the job done."

Costs were underestimated and soared from an early figure of $100 million to Bell's original estimate of $161 million, then were quickly revised upward to $169 million. The eventual total was $215 million, *plus* $15 million for RCAF helicopters. The building phase alone was underestimated by 25 per cent.

The difficulties relating to supply were also constantly underrated and, therefore, underestimated. Fire at one camp wiped out quarters for 200 men. One ship was caught in ice and sank in James Bay. Others were stuck in the ice of Hudson Strait. During the winter supplies had to be flown in to frozen lakes and unloaded in howling gales and below-zero weather. Some equipment had to be hauled 300 miles by tractor train over winter roads. Many camps housed idle men waiting for supplies. Transportation alone cost $42 million. Still, despite these difficulties and delays, the western half of the line was finished on schedule in January 1957, and the entire line was operational before the end of the year.

During the five years or so of its existence, the Special Contract department generated total revenues of over $30 million. Among its achievements, the Special Contract group built the tropospheric scatter system along 1,400 miles of the Labrador coast (over a time period of 13 months — a pace never equalled before or since), built the entire Mid-Canada Line, and undertook myriad small outside plant jobs right across the country. "At one time," noted Lester, "we had people working from London, England, to San Francisco."

An interesting sidelight to the work in Canada's frontier regions had to do with the difficulty in getting Canadian engineers to go out into the field. The tropo job was under way for over a year before the crews in Labrador were able to celebrate the arrival of the first Canadian engineer. Most of the field engineers on both the Labrador and the Mid-Canada jobs were not from Canada; they were Irish, English, Scottish, Dutch and German. "The Canadians gradually took hold," Lester says, "but I came to the conclusion as a result of this experience that the spirit of adventure is not a particularly striking characteristic of the modern generation of Canadians. However, I think the experience was great for the Bell people, and for many others as well. It made everyone appreciate the scope of this country and the work and the achievements of the Canadian pioneers. We did a lot of pioneering ourselves."

Bell historian R.H. Spencer visited three of the stations during the construction and operation periods. Although he found a few workers who were counting the minutes until they could fly back to civilization, for the most part he saw people who were enjoying their experience and making the most of it. At one camp he found 15 different nationalities represented. "The Section Plant Superintendent is French-Canadian," he wrote, "and the male nurse is a young Australian; the Chief Clerk hails from the Portuguese Island of Goa (India); the buildings foreman is of Italian descent; the Security Safety and Recreation Foreman is a Scotsman; the Supplies Foreman is English; and the Vehicles Foreman, born in Luxembourg, is from France. . . ."

Workers who freely admitted to missing their families in the south nonetheless said they would do it again. Supervising central office foreman James E. Morana of Montreal told Spencer: "I'd certainly do it again. When a fellow leaves here, besides the money, he takes a lot of experience with him."

J. Vernon Leworthy, a retired Bell engineer and vice-president, remembers with considerable and obvious pleasure some of his adventures on the line, even though at the time they were a bit frightening. Once, while flying from Lac La Ronge in Saskatchewan to Lac la Biche in Alberta in a small plane, Leworthy and his pilot ran into a storm. Within minutes their radio went out and they were thoroughly lost. The pilot's maps didn't seem to relate to any of the winter terrain. Finally, they spotted a trapper's cabin beside a small lake. They landed on the lake and taxied across the ice to the cabin.

The Indian trapper greeted them warmly and gave them hot coffee. With the flick of a couple of dials on his shortwave set he re-established radio contact for them, and from a desk he produced more detailed maps than the pilot carried in his case. "We felt a little silly," Leworthy recalls, "but we were enormously grateful."

Some months after the completion of the project, an RCAF memorandum, strongly critical of Bell's role in the building of Mid-Canada, was leaked to Arnold Edinborough, then editor of *Saturday Night* Magazine. Edinborough wrote a couple of articles based on the document, in essence charging that haste and divided authority on the project had cost the Canadian taxpayer $30 million in waste. Lester was quick to respond, alleging the air force document to be "impertinent" and "harmful interference," but adding that he wouldn't argue the point that the job could have been done for $30 million less. However, irrespective of the costs, no one can deny that the construction of Mid-Canada was, as one observer put it, "one Hell of a job."

The Mid-Canada Line served as a sort of life-insurance policy for North

America during the dangerous period it was intended to serve — the late fifties and early sixties. There is no sure way to measure its true worth or the importance of its role in terms of the defence of North America. One point to ponder is that the Mid-Canada Line was functioning on full alert during the tense days of the Cuban missile crisis. Suppose it hadn't been there? It is capricious to suggest that its presence as part of a North American deterrent to possible aggressors was not important — and indeed worth every cent spent on it.

Perhaps in the long-run, the spinoff benefits of Mid-Canada will prove to be of greatest value to Canada. As the Government had hoped, the project did open up immense areas of the nation's northland to settlement and economic development. One hopes that it has also helped stir up a little of the spirit of adventure in Canadians.

5

Special Projects
Royal Visits

*Near Soda Creek, Princess Margaret dropped her gold and
diamond cigarette lighter off the back of the observation car.
She demanded that the train be stopped and a search be
made. Nearly 50 men with strong flashlights, lanterns and
torches, walked the track a mile in the dark before the bauble
was found. Meanwhile the train's microwave telephone
system was put to a good test as other traffic was warned of
the delay and the track to Vancouver was kept clear.*

From a file to *Time* Magazine by a reporter (E. Ogle)
on the royal train (1958)

On several occasions, special efforts have been made by members of the Trans-
Canada Telephone System to provide telephone service when royal persons have
visited Canada.

In 1939, members of TCTS collaborated to provide telephone service for the
visit of King George VI and Queen Elizabeth to Canada and the United States.
Local telephone directories for use on the royal train were bound with covers
bearing the title, "Trans-Canada Telephone System,"* and featuring the royal
coat of arms.

A switchboard and 16 telephones (number 13 was skipped) were installed in
the 12-car royal blue and silver train which carried their Majesties on their
8,000-mile trip between May 17 and June 22. The King's personal telephone was
a gold-finished handset "of the latest bell-in-base design."

*This was the correct spelling at the time.

200

At 31 stopping points across Canada and three in the United States, the switchboard was connected to the nearest telephone exchange by means of special cables that terminated near the track on which the train stood during its stopovers. Local operators came on board to run the switchboard at these stops.

Nearly every day the Queen talked by trans-Atlantic radio-telephone with the royal children in London, Princesses Elizabeth and Margaret Rose directly from the train. Altogether, 5,500 calls were made: 3,500 between the telephones on the cars and 2,000 to or from the train and various points around the world. At least 1,500 times during the trip, the King's special telephone rang to signal him that a crowd was gathering along the railway tracks. A special observer riding at the head of the train would signal each time he spotted a crowd, and when the special ring sounded in their Majesties' private car, they would hurry to a window so the crowd could see them.

Princess Elizabeth using the telephone installed on the royal train during her tour of Canada in 1951.

The late J.M. Hay, assistant vice-president of Bell Canada at the time, was in charge of the telephone system on the royal train. He recalled one especially interesting detail:

"At some point in the tour practically every member of the royal party made a transatlantic call. In accepting the first of these calls, we were somewhat taken aback when we were asked [by members of the royal staff], 'Will you send the cable or shall I?' By careful questioning we learned that our distinguished British passengers thought that a cable in advance was necessary to advise the party being called of the intended conversation."

On the pilot train that travelled ahead of the royal train, carrying officials and members of the press, six telephones were similarly installed and plugged into the nearest exchange at all overnight stops. There was no intercommunicating system between the cars. The telephones could be used at both dial and magneto exchanges.

The federal Government picked up the tab for the installation of the telephone equipment on the royal train. On the pilot train, the costs of the equipment and the connecting cables at the many stopover points were borne by members of the TransCanada Telephone System.

Again, during the visit of Princess Elizabeth and the Duke of Edinburgh in 1951, the royal train was linked with land lines at all major stopover points. The telephones on that royal train were three ivory-coloured sets, one in the lounge of their Highnesses' private car and two in the car of the Secretary of State.

Similar services were provided for Queen Elizabeth II during her six-week tour of Canada in 1959. There were no interconnections betwen the five green telephone sets installed on that royal train, but connections were made with the local system at 16 stops, mainly in western Canada.

Whenever the royal yacht, *Britannia,* is moored at a Canadian dock, its telephones are connected to local exchanges by means of special cable installations.

PART FIVE
Highway in the Sky

1

Missionary for Microwave
A War Baby to the Rescue

---

*This great advance in Canadian communications history
which we are celebrating today is made possible by a
comparatively new invention — microwave radio relay — an
invention by means of which all sorts of human intelligence
— telephone calls, printed messages, statistics for electronic
calculators, television pictures in black and white or in colour
— can be beamed across the nation at the speed of light —
186,000 miles per second. Over the network in use today, a
television picture travels from Sydney on the Atlantic to
Victoria on the Pacific faster than you can wink an eye — in
one-fiftieth of a second. . . .*

Thomas W. Eadie, president of The Bell Telephone Company of Canada
and chairman of the TransCanada Telephone System (1958)

By the end of the second World War it seemed that everyone in Canada wanted to
talk to everyone else. The demand for telephones was staggering. The difficulty
was that virtually none of the TransCanada members had the facilities or equipment to provide the much-needed services. At the beginning of 1946 Bell Canada
held 77,000 applications for telephones. Installers worked frantically all year, but
by the end of December 84,000 people were still waiting. By the end of 1955 Bell's
million telephones had more than doubled to 2.3 million. It was the same all
across the country.

In its brief to the Royal Commission on Canada's Economic Prospects in

The tallest microwave tower in Canada at Olive, Ontario, is 350 feet high and equipped with its antennae weighs over 120 tons.

1956, TCTS said: "Telephone service has more than kept pace with the spectacular growth of the national economy of recent years. While, since the end of the second World War, the population has increased 29 per cent and the volume of gross national product has risen 38 per cent, the number of telephones (4.1 million) and the volume of long-distance calls (475,000 daily), have more than doubled. In [the last] 10 years more telephones have been added to the Canadian telephone system than were accumulated in the preceding 70 years following the invention of the telephone."

Every trick of the trade was utilized to expand service capacity. Phantom circuits, carrier circuits and emergency facilities increased substantially the number of voice paths available on the existing open-wire lines without adding hard to get copper and other materials that were still in short supply.

Arnold Groleau, formerly chairman of the TCTS Engineering committee and an executive vice-president of Bell when he retired in 1973, recalls: "Because growth so continually exceeded estimates it was necessary to supplement the open-wire and carrier circuits by leasing circuits from the telegraph companies. It was also necessary to lease circuits through the United States and use substantial numbers of emergency circuits at the expense of degrading transmission quality."

Jack Noyes, a retired Bell engineer, said: "At the rate of growth we were experiencing, it was obvious that our open-wire line could not last more than three or four more years before it was completely exhausted. We had to go with something new."

By 1947 the vital Sudbury-Winnipeg line, which had been leased from the railways, reached the limit of the service it could handle. And so, in the late forties, TCTS members began the costly process of installing the "J" carrier system. It was the most expensive undertaking yet attempted by TCTS in its efforts to keep abreast of steadily accelerating public demand for long-distance lines. The "J" carrier system added 12 channels to the existing network, and it certainly seemed like a big jump at the time.

In 1953, before the system was completed, British Columbia dropped a large spanner in the works. At a meeting of the TCTS Engineering committee, the British Columbia representatives proposed that a carrier system manufactured by their affiliate, the Lenkurt Electric Company, be put into service instead of the final "J" carrier system, which was manufactured by Northern Electric, to complete the capacity of the existing lines between Manitoba and British Columbia. Unquestionably, the Lenkurt system was cheaper, a vital consideration as far as B.C. Tel was concerned, but no one was certain that it would work over the 1,720-mile span from Winnipeg to Vancouver. The Lenkurt system had not been tested for distances over 300 miles and, furthermore, required back-to-back terminals at Calgary — which AGT was not prepared to pay for. As usual, a compromise solution was hammered out, which led retired Bell engineer Jack Noyes to remark: "I remember one of our top vice-presidents, coming back after one of the more difficult TransCanada meetings with B.C. Tel and saying that they were milking all four teats at once — and they had one for cream!"

The TCTS Engineering committee finally recommended that the "J" system be carried through for 1955 but that a Lenkurt system be installed between Calgary and Vancouver for trial purposes. However good the Lenkurt system proved to be, the British Columbia attempt to force an issue at a time when equipment had not been fully tested illustrates the strains to which TCTS has sometimes been put. Only the arrival of microwave at this time prevented a "shoot-out" across the mountains.

Microwave was new. It was so new, in fact, that according to R.H. Spencer many telephone people referred to it as "jump jump."

Indeed, voices did seem to "jump" between the strange new towers that had gone up near Charlottetown, Prince Edward Island and New Glasgow, Nova Scotia. Prince Edward Island and Nova Scotia were the first provinces to install a commercially successful "jump jump," or microwave radio relay. Built in 1948, the 23-channel PTM system bridged the Northumberland Strait where tides and currents inflicted constant damage to the submarine cables. (PTM stands for Pulse Time Modulation, which is a method used to stack voices on a microwave link. It was a forerunner of the Bell system's TD-2 design.)

The world's first microwave radio communications system Nova Scotia — Prince Edward Island 1948. The Tea Hill, P.E.I. station.

Microwave radio relay was a war-baby, a sort of "son of radar." Not one in a thousand Canadians had any idea what microwave was. To understand how it works one must know a little about radio waves and how they behave.

Radio waves are measured both in terms of length and frequency. The *length* of these invisible waves (wavelength) varies immensely, from millimetres to miles. *Frequency* is measured in cycles per second, called "hertz" after the scientist who discovered their properties.

The longer the wave the lower the frequency; conversely, the shorter the wave the higher the frequency. A 10 kilohertz (KHz) wave (a wave having a frequency of 10,000 cycles per second) has a wavelength of 18.6 miles and doesn't concern us much here. A megahertz (MHz) is a wave with a frequency of a million cycles per second and a gigahertz (GHz) has a billion cycles per second. Micro means small, and ultra means extreme. So, ultra-short waves or microwaves are about the length of a regular size cigarette, and fit nicely into the range of one GHz and up.

Waves in the very high frequency (vhf) range — around 300 MHz — carry today's television programmes and FM broadcasts.

Certain special properties displayed by these very short radio waves led to the development of radar, that magic electronic system with its invisible eye in the sky which played such a vital part in the smashing of Hermann Goering's bomber fleets by the outnumbered RAF fighters during the Battle of Britain. Unlike longer waves, microwaves bounce off most solid objects in their path. These "reflected" waves can be seen on a radar screen as the image of any object that is within range of the waves. Like light waves, microwaves travel in straight lines. They can no more be bent than a flashlight beam can be directed around a corner. The curvature of the Earth therefore ensures that, left to their own devices, microwaves simply continue into space. Because of this they must constantly be redirected to a target device that will channel them. This is the function of the huge, queer-looking towers topped by antennae that look like great horns. These horns are designed to catch the light-fast shortwaves and redirect them to the next target tower.

A microwave circuit operates broadly in this way. Words spoken into the telephone (or images picked up by the television camera) are converted into electrical impulses. These impulses are fed into carrier equipment, then the frequency of the original transmission is boosted to that of the microwave system. The signal is channelled up the inside of a long, hollow rectangular pipe measuring approximately three inches by four inches (known technically as "wave-guide") to a huge metal antenna weighing approximately 1,700 pounds and measuring about 20 feet high by 11 feet wide. The antenna focuses the microwaves into a

An outpost of humanity in a barren land, the repeater station at Sand Hill, Labrador.

narrow beam (two degrees wide), which is aimed directly at the antenna on the next tower in the chain. The antenna is so efficient that less than one watt of power — about the amount needed to operate a flashlight bulb — is required to span the distance of 30 or so miles between the two stations. Gathered in by the wide-mouthed antenna at the next station, the signals shoot down another length of wave-guide to the microwave relay equipment in the equipment building at the base of the tower. Here the signals receive another boost in power and are then sent up through another antenna from which they are beamed to the next tower. This procedure is followed all along the route.

At the reception end of the network, equipment more or less reverses the original microwave transmission process and restores the telephone conversations and the television programmes back to their original frequencies. After further processing these signals are fed to their proper outlets — the telephone receiver or the television broadcasting station. The time it takes for a signal to travel from coast to coast is one-fiftieth of a second, far less time than it takes to read this description.

After the second World War, people interested in telecommunications began to consider seriously the possibilities of using microwave radio relay to carry hundreds of telephone channels as well as FM radio and television channels. Tom Eadie became convinced that microwave was the answer to the looming logjam in Canadian telecommunications. According to him:

> It soon became obvious that we could not possibly keep pace with future demand and continue to provide a high level of service using the type of equipment we'd been using up to that time. We knew about microwave and we decided to dig into it very thoroughly. On the basis of our research we built microwave systems in the early fifties between Montreal and Ottawa, Montreal and Toronto, and Toronto and Buffalo. Our experience gave us the real foundation of understanding of microwave we needed and our technical people became well-informed on the design and operation of a microwave system.
>
> When we turned our attention to TransCanada, we were talking about a multi-unit line that is *thousands* of miles rather than hundreds of miles long. We were talking about spanning a continent! And there was nothing available, no experience anywhere we could draw upon that proved our idea would work. Even the people from the Bell laboratory would not give us absolute assurance that the system would do what we wanted it to do — provide the CBC and TCTS with a system that could transmit a photograph from the Atlantic to the Pacific without visible distortion!
>
> So there *was* uncertainty, but we couldn't be blinded by uncertainty. As far as I was concerned, I had great faith in the technical people around me and after consultation with them I was confident the system would work.

Eadie also had long discussions with Alphonse Ouimet, head of the CBC at the time, on the development of communications in Canada. Between them, there emerged a striking "uniformity of thinking in terms of what should be provided for Canadians."

In 1952, Eadie started beating the drum for a TCTS transcontinental microwave system. But there were problems. Microwave was expensive; the huge, costly towers, 139 of them, had to be built right across the country. The first conservative cost estimate was $50 million. Considering the depleted financial reserves of each TCTS member at the time — including even Bell — it was no wonder that the prospect was genuinely frightening.

Many agreed with Jim Mills, general manager of the Manitoba Telephone System, who observed: "In the early fifites we thought Canada's long-haul telephone problems were licked with the "J" carrier system, then Mr. Eadie made a trip across Canada and told us that what we really needed was the TD-2

210

[microwave system]. He certainly was a missionary for microwave."

Indeed, Eadie did become a sort of flying missionary for microwave. As fast as trouble or disagreements bubbled up, he was there to dispose of them. He flew to the U.S. to confer with the owners of B.C. Tel; on the Prairies he conferred with Ministers of the provincially-owned companies; and he met with executives of other member companies whenever and wherever necessary.

Some of the companies were far from convinced that microwave was the answer. One by one, however, Eadie persuaded them.

It was obvious that building microwave towers on the peaks of British Columbia's mountains would be more difficult, as well as more expensive, than stringing towers across Saskatchewan. It was equally obvious that Bell would benefit more than any other member company from the establishment of the microwave network. (It had the largest and most heavily populated territory as well as an interest in Northern Electric — the major manufacturer of Canadian telecommunications equipment.)

British Columbia, pushed by its American owners, wanted to use cheaper, U.S.-made equipment. Eadie emphasized the importance of uniformity of equipment and discreetly offered help in obtaining the more expensive Canadian hardware.

As a director of the British Columbia Telephone Company, Cyrus McLean was responsible for financial arrangments for microwave in British Columbia. McLean recalls:

> We were having a tough time financially. We didn't have any reserves for a $5 or $6 million investment in microwave. Some of the Bell fellows were talking about going through the State of Washington to reach Vancouver, but we were certain the federal Government would never agree to that. Ottawa wouldn't go for a trans-Canada system if it didn't go all the way through Canada.
>
> We met with Tom Eadie in Montreal and said, 'Okay, we'll go along with it, but there'll have to be a compromise. We need a preferred tariff. . . a mountain differential, if you want to call it that. Also, we don't want to pay any more for our equipment than you fellows do.' That meant that Northern Electric was to supply us at the same price as they supplied Bell. And we wanted credit, too. We also said, 'If you want to stop in Alberta, fine.'
>
> Some of the Bell fellows were sticky, but Tom Eadie said 'Fair enough. I'll go along with that.'
>
> We drove a hard bargain but we knew the Government wouldn't ap-

prove the project without us. Besides, when you are at the end of the line you have an advantage.

Later Eadie acknowledged:

For a great many years, we of TransCanada adhered to the concept of an All-Red route and we did everything we could to keep it in Canada. There have been several occasions over the years when it would probably have been cheaper to route certain projects through the United States rather than through Canada, but we didn't think it would be wise. The TransCanada Telephone System didn't think so."

The railway companies were as keenly aware of the potential of microwave as anyone else, and both the CPR and the CNR lobbied strongly against Eadie — particularly in the Western provinces — doing their best to talk Alberta out of going along. There was no question that Bell Canada, being centrally located, had to go with microwave. But there was uncertainty, particularly in the West, as to going with Bell and whether companies should even stick with TCTS or go into the microwave venture with the railway telegraph systems.

Coming right on the heels of the expensive installation of the "J" carrier system, which the Alberta government had been led to believe would solve all long distance problems for a while at least, AGT was reluctant to pour more money into anything new.

Gordon Taylor, then Alberta's Minister of Highways and Telephones, remembers: "The railroads were keen to build and control the microwave system. There were arguments in the Social Credit caucus as well as in the legislature and many people were of the mind that we should let private industry handle this one. So I talked to the railway people in Montreal who suggested that Alberta Government Telephones should simply step aside. Their plan was interesting and would have saved us a lot of money, but one thing bothered me — who then would control our long distance facilities? When I finally outlined the plan — and my concerns — to the legislature there were still a few members who were sceptical about microwave but they still went along with the TCTS proposal. I wish we'd had a *Hansard* then so you could read the type of questions that were asked."

Stuart Muirhead, who was running SASK TEL, recalls that the government of Saskatchewan was reluctant to commit SASK TEL to the microwave project because it meant "trafficking with the enemy" — meaning the Bell. Saskatchewan was so obdurate that at one stage Eadie considered going around — or over — the wheat province if he could find a way to do it.

The Saskatchewan Government Telephones people were sulky over the cost.

W.S. Pipes, then vice-president and general manager of B.C. Tel, recalls: "The Saskatchewan government was squeezing every nickel it had. The Saskatchewan government sent out their comptroller or treasurer to deal for them. He was holding out for costs that were unreal. Muirhead was terribly embarrassed."

In the end it was T.C. Douglas, the socialist Premier, who made the hard and statesmanlike decision for Saskatchewan to go along with microwave.

In 1953, the CBC called for tenders on its television network. The effect was to put enormous pressure on the microwave decision. Eadie was ready:

> Our study showed that if we got the CBC contract, the ensuing television, radio and audio revenues would be more remunerative to some sections of the line than to others. With the support of the board of directors of Bell Canada, I was given approval to allocate some of the excess earnings from our Bell affiliates to assist other companies that might have difficulties. Such payments were made over a period of years to assist those companies which would have found themselves in a position of having earnings that made investment unattractive. Such transfers of funds were made only from Bell to other companies because the Bell had the best-paying section in the country to support microwave.

In terms of the size of the construction phase alone, the Prairie members of TCTS were faced with a task which was much larger, relatively speaking, than the transcontinental network undertaken in the United States by AT&T. Having the benefit of hindsight, however, microwave was the best possible solution to the country's telecommunications problems. But it wasn't apparent, and it certainly wasn't simple at the time. Most telephone people today credit Tom Eadie for pushing the microwave decision through, and they emphasize the courage it took to do so.

In British Columbia, Gil Kennedy remembers: "Those were interesting days. There was so much going on. I was involved in accounts and finance and I had to have answers for our directors and government people concerning our need for money. Many of our directors were uneasy about spending so much on something they weren't familiar with. After one particularly hard session I recall sitting with an associate and saying, 'Wouldn't it be nice now to be sitting on a ranch-house patio watching white-faced cattle.' He answered, 'Yes, I'd much prefer that to talking to white-faced directors.' "

Canada's first television network went "on the air" on May 14, 1953, between Montreal and Toronto. Ottawa had TV telecasting a few weeks later, just in time for the coronation of Queen Elizabeth II. A microwave relay system between Buffalo and Toronto, which had been put in service earlier in the year, connected the Canadian network with United States television links.

On January 7, 1954, the CBC called for tenders on a coast-to-coast microwave system. The contract was awarded to TCTS on March 8, 1955. Shortly thereafter, the imposing microwave towers with their giant antenna "eyes" began marching across the Canadian landscape.

In the summer of 1954 Bell's 180-mile link between Montreal and Quebec City was opened; construction of the 1,200 mile TCTS connection from Toronto to Winnipeg was already under way. Two years later, on September 30, 1956, that section was inaugurated both for telephone purposes and television programming. The Saint John-Moncton-Halifax-Sydney section went into service in December 1956, the Winnipeg-Regina section in April 1957, the Regina-Calgary and the Edmonton-Calgary-Lethbridge section in November 1957. The Maritimes were linked with the main network on February 2, 1958, when the Quebec City-Saint John and Charlottetown-Hardwood Hill, Nova Scotia, sections were cut in. The Calgary-Vancouver-Victoria section went into service on July 1, 1958, marking the completion of the backbone of the network across the continent. (Many spur links to Canadian cities that were not part of the backbone route had already been built or were being planned.)

Tom Eadie describes one of his most vivid recollections. He was sitting beside Alphonse Ouimet in the Toronto studios of the CBC at the ceremony introducing the television network on July 1, 1957:

We were chatting and Alphonse said, 'Tom, when we talked about television in Montreal back in 1951, I didn't really believe that within six years we [the CBC] would be able to introduce a [coast-to-coast] television network — I still find it hard to believe that it's happening!' That pleased me very much. I know he meant it.

During our initial discussions it didn't seem realistic, even to me, to think in terms of a continental microwave system for communications in six years. That accomplishment stands out for me over everything else. But I don't think it's a good idea to give one particular achievement too much emphasis because everything that has been done by TCTS had been really outstanding — the switching system, the wire lines, the cable lines, the operating practice — every one of these achievements was significant in its day.

The completion of the project was marked by a 90-minute CBC special from Toronto on June 18, 1958, which was carried by 40 stations. At the inaugural ceremony, Eadie lauded the people who built the electronic highway in the sky:

"The completion of this coast-to-coast job, exactly according to the schedule drawn up three years ago, is a great triumph for Canadian engineering, manufacturing and construction. It leads me to a strengthened conviction of the unexcelled capacity of Canadians to meet new challenges. The ideas, efforts and ingenuity of men have created this new medium for our home and business life. We pay tribute to these people rather than to the machine they created."

The final connection, to Canada's tenth province, Newfoundland, was completed a year later. Although Newfoundland's Avalon Telephone Company, which subsequently became the Newfoundland Telephone Company Limited, had become a full member of TCTS in 1957, it was Canadian National Telegraphs who built the microwave link that was completed in 1959.

The TransCanada microwave network was the longest single system in the world, stretching 3,900 miles from Halifax to Vancouver. Its 139 tower installations housed 20,000 vacuum tubes. It had cost $50 million. (The United States' transcontinental system, finished in August 1951, was 2,992 miles long and had cost $40 million.)

Completion of the microwave network enabled TCTS to land contracts for television services from the CBC and, later, television and radio services from CTV. The first agreement with CTV was announced in 1961. Initially, CTV service was provided to Toronto, Ottawa and Monteral on existing facilities. Service to the rest of the network was provided over CBC channels outside contract hours with programmes taped for later broadcasts by the stations involved. By September 1962, a CTV channel was established between Montreal and Vancouver, and service to Halifax was provided a year later. On October 1, 1962, when the CBC's trans-Canada and Dominion radio networks were combined, TCTS started carrying the Corporation's radio programmes. On November 3, 1975, TCTS began transmitting radio programmes over the world's longest stereo network — extending from St. John's to Victoria.

Initially, the microwave system was designed to accommodate only black and white television transmission. It was subsequently upgraded, however, and by October 1, 1966 both the CBC TV and CTV were broadcasting almost entirely in colour. Other improvements were also required as the system expanded. New equipment eventually tripled the total capacity of the network. Ultimately, a single microwave channel *simultaneously* carried more than 1,200 telephone channels (conversations) or their equivalent in telegraph, data, network radio and television, and TWX (customer-dialled teleprinters) and computer communications.

In March 1962 CNCP Telecommunications announced their intention to build their own microwave system from Montreal to Vancouver. The Trans-

Canada Telephone System in a brief to the Department of Transport (at that time, the pertinent Government agency), argued that the building of the CNCP network was "unnecessary, economically unsound, and not in the public interest." The brief pointed out that TCTS had offered all the communication facilities CNCP required at rental rates which were far below the costs the railways would incur if they built the facilities themselves. CNCP, however, received a go-ahead from the Department of Transport. It completed its rival system, on May 11, 1964.

Since the sixties, new microwave routes have been built to bypass centres of population and spur lines have been added to connect outlying and distant centres. In effect, the result of this construction has been to add a parallel microwave system across the continent, which virtually guarantees uninterrupted service. Concurrently, technological advances have been made which have improved transmission performance, increased circuit capacity and reduced overall costs per message channel.

A.G. Lester succinctly sums up the developments of the past 30 years:

"In the old days we used to worry about whether or not we could add just one "J" system circuit of 12 channels across the mountains. In the fifties we wrestled with the problems of building the microwave. In the sixties telecommunications technology really took off and we had to run like the devil just to keep pace. In the seventies, of course, the system has really come of age; nowadays TCTS approves a hundred circuits at a time. However, microwave has been the real keystone in all this development."

Microwave, the true workhorse of the Canadian telecommunications system, has in every way justified the zeal of missionary Tom Eadie.

2

Up Dog Mountain
How to Skin a TCTS Cat

Bringing together the peoples of the vast, sprawling land that is Canada — giving them a sense of common goals and the means of carrying them out as one nation — has been a challenge that has taxed the best brains of the country since Confederation. The nub of the solution has been — and remains — speedy, effective and economical communications.

The Blue Bell (June, 1958)

The construction of the TransCanada Telephone System's microwave network remains one of the great construction sagas in a land where Bunyanesque projects are commonplace.

In the main, the larger-than-life heroics occurred among the lofty peaks of British Columbia. Ten of the 13 microwave tower sites in that province are on mountain ridges, the highest of which is 7,000 feet above sea level. And in winter some of these sites are all but buried in snow and ice.

Still, other areas of Canada also offered unique and tough building problems. Gumbo soil and high winds in some parts of the Prairies forced engineers to design unusually large tower footings and to improvise extraordinary guy-wire arrangements to ensure the stability of towers on the plains. Much of the route through northern Ontario ran through virtually uninhabited areas along the old No. 2 Highway, and forest, muskeg, swamp and rocky hills were obstacles, particularly in providing access roads. In eastern Quebec and in much of the Maritimes, the microwave route passed through similar rough and undeveloped countryside.

In Toronto, where the tower perched high atop the downtown Bell Canada building, problems with jumbled signals persisted until engineers discovered that incoming radio waves were bouncing off the surrounding high buildings. More precise beaming of the microwaves had to be arranged.

Across the Prairies, where the flatness of the land was expected to assist the builders, unexpected difficulties arose. The countless Prairie sloughs, while great for duck hunters, acted as reflectors, deflecting microwave signals in unexpected and unwanted directions. Even the staggering of the towers, which is intended to prevent overlapping of signals, caused problems. As everyone knows, Prairie roads run in long, beautifully engineered, straight lines. The need to stagger the towers put some of them miles away from the nearest highway.

According to Doug Mallet-Paret, Alberta Government Telephone's first radio systems engineer and microwave project engineer, Alberta was sort of dragged into microwave because TCTS had opted for it. "Microwave was not immediately accepted," he says. "There was resistance, particularly among the old plant men. They thought it was a gimmick, a second-best ploy. The old-timers thought you could only get good transmission with open wires on poles. When I spoke to the Calgary Electric Club [on March 28, 1957] I had to be very diplomatic about the importance of pole lines and say I did not predict that microwave would replace them."

Mallet-Paret's experience was not an isolated one. There was a great deal of resistance to microwave among old open-wire men in all TransCanada companies. These men, after all, had spent most of their working lives dedicated to solid construction — such as the TransCanada pole line. They considered microwave to be a threat to the system they had built and knew.

Once the decision to go with microwave was confirmed, the first step was to plot the route. Engineers pored over the best maps obtainable, paying special attention to elevation contours. They indicated the most likely spots for the huge towers with their loads of electronic gear. The terrain had always to be considered, but for the most part relays were spotted approximately 25 to 30 miles apart. Having laid out a tentative route, the next step was to dispatch pathfinder crews to test and verify the suitability of the sites spotted. The pathfinders quickly realized they had problems.

B.C. Tel veteran Frank Wolokoff put it bluntly: "The first problem was that all the site locations had been picked for us in Montreal. Mount Cheam, for example, was a logical choice if you only looked at a map. But there was no way we could get up there. It was too high. There was simply no access to many of the locations. Another guy and I hiked all over those mountain sites. Dog Mountain? I

218

hiked up that one three times. Last time I went up in a helicopter. That, at least, was an improvement."

In Alberta, Mallet-Paret and an engineer loaned to Alberta by the Bell for the job, set out on the Saskatchewan border to do the pathfinding for Alberta's sites. The job took them 46 days, and during that time they travelled 11,000 miles. Mallet-Paret says: "The pioneering was the most fun, of course. We had a wild time getting through the Crowsnest Pass. Our last tower was on Crowsnest ridge. We tried our best to fudge it a few feet over on the British Columbia side so *they* would have to build it, but the ridge dropped off too sharply for that.

"The terrain was so rugged we had a cable-car lift strung up the side of the mountain. In some places you would be a good 200 feet above the ground. One day another fellow and I got stuck halfway up when the cable jumped the track and tipped us half-over. We took off our scarves and waved to the people below for help. They happily waved back.

"That was when we realized we had made a mistake when we rigged the emergency telephone on the lift. We used one of the cables as a transmission line. But when it twisted, of course, the line shorted out.

"We also tried light-testing rather than radio. At one site we climbed a hill and set up floodlights. They were clearly visible from the proposed site for the next tower, so we counted that experiment a success. Quite incidentally we found that light would bend slightly with the curvature of the Earth. Experts from the United States heard about that and came up to see what we were doing."

Before any site was accepted another crew of technical pathfinders had to okay it. These crews mounted small antennae on temporary aluminum test towers, which could be erected in a matter of hours, like giant "Meccano" sets, to a height of over 200 feet. Their tests determined whether a site was suitable and whether there were any obstacles blocking the route. They also determined how high the tower should be for each site. Most ranged between 50 and 200 feet, but many are higher. There is a 350-foot tower at a site near Olive in Northern Ontario.

Once the locations were approved, sites had to be prepared for the towers. Power had to be brought in, access roads built — one in British Columbia was 12 miles long — and enough clearing had to be done to provide adequate fire-breaks.

The massive towers themselves are sturdy galvanized steel structures, built for extreme rigidity. Each tower is anchored to four massive concrete footings, which contain an average of 170 cubic yards of concrete. The 350-footer at Olive weighs 120 tons and is so strong that not even a hundred-mile-an-hour hurricane-force wind can deflect the structure more than half a degree.

Mounted on each tower are large antennae which receive and transmit the microwave signals. Each antenna weighs approximately 1,700 pounds and looks like a giant sugar scoop or horn. At ground level a compact equipment building completes the complex. The setup cost of each such station or relay point was in the neighbourhood of $300,000.

Ron Peddle, microwave project co-ordinator for Saskatchewan, says: "When the microwave system was installed you couldn't do anything that didn't affect everyone else in the system. Everybody had to work out schedules for when they were going to do anything and everything. There were very fine tolerances to be met and all within equally tight time frames. *Everything* had to be standardized. The construction phase, too, required tight co-ordination among contractors. The site preparation, the footings, the tower, and the building had each to be ready at its proper moment. Equipment had to be on site when the structures were ready and the structures had to be ready for the equipment. You couldn't leave valuable stuff lying around and if a job was done out of sequence you could run into trouble. At Gladwith, Saskatchewan, a horn was moved on site on schedule but the erection of the tower was a bit behind schedule. In the resulting overlap, someone dropped an angle-iron through the horn and *that* caused even more trouble.

"A microwave system requires a lot more co-ordination than a pole line."

Larry Williams, a jovial radio specialist with North-West Telephone Company, a subsidiary of B.C. Tel, went out with some colleagues to look over the sites selected for British Columbia:

We chartered a Beaver and took a flying trip from Vancouver to the Alberta border to see what we were up against. We looked at Abbotsford first; we never built there. Then on to Ryder Lake, Dog Mountain, Granite Mountain and Lost Horse. We didn't even slow down at Anarchist Mountain because it looked like a cinch; it turned out to be something else. We went to Phoenix, then at Santa Rosa Mountain — 14 miles from Christina Lake, the nearest flat place — our engine quit.

The pilot wasn't concerned. He said he had used two tanks and it was a simple matter of switching to the third. He switched. Nothing happened. Gosh, it was quiet. Then the pilot realized he'd used that tank already, so he hit another lever and the engine came on again. Did that sound beautiful!

We gassed up again at Nelson and took a look at Salmo, then Thompson Mountain near Creston. Moyie was the damndest sight you ever saw with snow on the trees built out in cones, driven into that shape by the constant wind. The Lizards near Cranbrook was literally a sheer wall. We eventually abandoned the Lizards and used Morrissey ridge instead.

After we had seen the Lizards we were ready to head home. So the pilot cranked the plane around in a very steep bank and pointed it at Vancouver — we thought. We planned to get another view of the sites from the opposite side as we returned. But when we got to the Kootenay River we realized we were crossing it at about 45 degrees off the angle we should have shown. The pilot had thrown his compass out of whack when he made his steep turn and we were down by the American border. The pilot headed for Nelson. When we got there he said 'To heck with you guys, I'm going home on the beam.'

That was all the 'site-seeing' we did on that trip.

Jack Noyes recalls: "The microwave project was really quite something. It was a massive job and I remember getting a picture of one of the sites up in the mountains where they had to erect an aerial tramway to service the site. The chap who sent me the picture had written on the back, 'It takes a weak mind and a strong stomach to travel on this thing.'"

The reference was to the 11,800-foot aerial tramway — one of the longest in the world — erected to lift men and materials 4,400 feet to the site on Dog Mountain near Hope in B.C. The cable-car was equipped with a two-way radio for instant communication with the operator, plus a winch and cable emergency device and it could carry four passengers comfortably. There was no way an access road could be built up that mass of rock.

Another B.C. Tel veteran, Alec Gordon, had a scary experience on the Dog Mountain tramway. He was taking some 20-foot reinforcing steel rods to the top. He laid them across the gondola so they stuck out about six feet on either side. He passed six support towers on the tramway safely, but at the seventh the rods caught in the tower. The gondola kept moving forward and Alec found himself being tipped over. He hung on for dear life, but just before he would have gone over the rods bent and the gondola slipped away from the tower.

Dog Mountain sits right at the point where the wet Pacific air and the dry air of the interior come together. The extreme snow and icing conditions, normal in this zone, give the maintenance boys enormous headaches. It is not unusual to have the site covered by 30 to 40 feet of snow and have the tramway cables caked with six to eight inches of ice.

Working on the access road at a site in the B.C. interior, one of the catskinners (bulldozer operators) stopped for a drink. He lay on his stomach with his face in the creek, to drink and cool off. When he leisurely started to get to his feet he realized he was lying on a rattlesnake. There was nothing leisurely about his next movements.

Bob Rotter, a contractor on the Salmo site, ran into trouble with porcupines. In fact, they nearly drove him up the mountain. They ate the seats out of his tractors, they ate his tires, and they chewed up his crew's axehandles. It seems they were attracted by the salt from sweaty hands. One morning Bob had difficulty starting a gasoline engine for a compressor. When he finally got it going it was terribly rough. When he lifted the cover to investigate he found a porcupine sitting on the engine chewing on the spark plug leads.

Rotter was hired by North-West Telephone's Larry Williams one winter to clear the road to the site. Near the top of the 7,000-foot ridge the stakes marking the edge of the road were completely buried in the deep snow. Williams relates:

"Bob had to more or less guess where the road was. I looked up where he was working and I almost died. He'd gotten off the track in his big D-8 cat and was way out on a snow precipice. That cat weighed over 30 tons. I ran up that road as hard as I could go, yelling my head off, but he couldn't hear me. Fortunately, the snow held and he worked his way back onto solid ground. Brother, I was scared. The mountain drops off about 3,000 feet there!"

Williams decided to contract the provincial government to build the access road to Blackwell peak. "That was a funny experience," he says. "We figured it would cost $150,000 to put a road through to the tower at the top of the peak. We gave the money to the government and they did a beautiful job with a lookout point and turnouts and all that. The only trouble was they used up the $150,000 and only built two miles of road. It was seven miles to the site at the top of the mountain, so that didn't do us much good."

After looking at some of the construction problems in British Columbia, G. Gordon Milne, a SASK TEL engineer, chuckled about the project in his province: "I remember one of Bell's hotshot engineers taking a look here and saying, 'Why the Hell don't you people just plough a cable between here and Moose Jaw?' He thought Saskatchewan was very convenient country in which to plant a coaxial cable."

In contrast to the 350-foot tower at Olive, Ontario, the shortest tower is located at Cross, Saskatchewan, just west of Regina. Ross Bearman, a SASK TEL veteran, says: "I believe the Cross tower is the shortest one in the system — about 30 feet high, just big enough to hold its antenna off the ground. It looks kind of cute, that little stub of a tower and the huge horn. People pull off the road to take pictures of it all the time. Some American tourists think it's part of the DEW Line."

As usual in the telecommunications business in Canada, no sooner is one service supplied than up comes the need for another. Jack Noyes says that was the way it was with the microwave network:

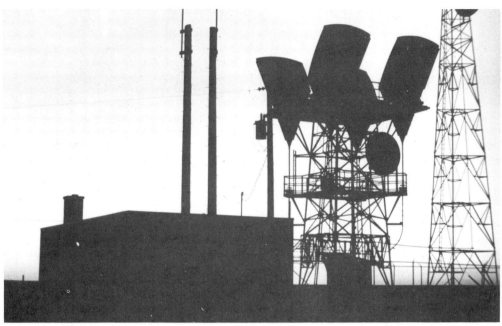
The microwave tower at Cross, Saskatchewan, silhouetted against the prairie sky.

At my level, the working level you might say, we had the feeling in the early days that we were putting all our eggs into one basket with the first microwave system we built across Canada.

Microwave got heavy development very fast and we began to get really worried. We did a study in conjunction with the other systems, with a second (back-up) route in mind. We had a little trouble selling the then vice-president of the toll area on the second route but we finally convinced him it was needed. He talked to Mr. Eadie and at one point he remarked that we were planning a second system between the Bell and Manitoba as far as Winnipeg and that we would be needing $27 million. Apparently there was a long silence, then Mr. Eadie asked with heavy sarcasm, 'What $27 million?'

That put the lid on the matter as far as official support in the company was concerned, but there is more than one way to skin a cat. Our Engineering committee, which consisted of the chief engineers of Bell and the other TransCanada companies, also recognized the need for a second microwave route across the country. By nibbling away across the country, a hundred-mile segment here, a three- or four- hundred mile bit there, each designed to fit into a second TransCanada route at some future date, we finally got so many sections built across the country that eventually the problem of selling the idea to top management was no problem at all. In the end we just had to interconnect sections we already had.

That really is the true story of how we got our second microwave system across Canada. I feel safe in admitting now that we skinned the cat in a different way. I suppose you could say we were working against the wishes of top management, but over the long view, I think everyone agrees we were right.

In 1958, the Grey Cup game was played in Vancouver. In 1956 it had been televised live from Toronto as far west as Winnipeg, and in 1957 as far as Calgary. But in 1958 the CBC wasn't yet ready with the new microwave network to broadcast the game east live from Vancouver, so the local telephone whizzes took over.

Harold Bourne, a B.C. Tel football enthusiast, tells how they worked it:

We haywired a setup across Burrard Inlet to Vancouver's north shore and bootlegged a signal into Seattle and across American lines through Buffalo and back up to Toronto.

I was in Ottawa the morning of the game. I'd taken the odd bet here and there on the game but also on whether we'd be able to get it on the air. I don't remember how the game came out but I do remember winning my other bets. The game came through clear and sharp. It certainly was a poor man's hookup and I'm not altogether sure it was legal. We should have applied to the Department of Transport (DOT) and the U.S. Federal Communications Commission (FCC) for permission, but we figured it was a TransCanada exercise in the public interest.

PART SIX

Ushering in the Future

1

The Regulators
Telephones and the Public Interest

When an industry tends to develop monopolistic characteristics, it is a concern of governments to consider whether this tendency is in the public interest and, if it is, to determine the limits within which the entrepreneur should be protected from competition.

From *Instant World:* A report on telecommunications in Canada,
prepared under the direction of A.E. Gotlieb,
Deputy Minister of Communications (1971).

Everyone has his own idea of what constitutes the public interest. Theorists argue that it is the realization of the greatest good for the most people over the long term. But that is far too simple and vague a definition for practical purposes.

In the grey paper on Communications issued by the federal Minister of Communications in 1975, it was stated that: "The people of Canada are entitled to the best possible telecommunications services, and their proper interests will be best served by a mutual understanding among governments as to the common objectives to be pursued."

It also went on to say: " . . . there is an urgent need for agreement on cooperative arrangements that will enable better account to be taken of provincial concerns while avoiding the fragmentation of Canadian telecommunications systems and protecting the interests of Canada as a whole."

Focusing attention squarely on Canadian circumstances and conditions, the Public Service Committee of the Faculty of Law at Dalhousie University in Halifax, organized a conference in February 1976, to consider the specific topic of

Canadian telecommunications "Regulation at the Crossroads". In commenting at the end of the conference, Eldon Thompson, president of TCTS at the time, stated the TCTS position very clearly:

> Speaking for my own carriers, I don't think that we care which level of government regulates us. We do care *how* we are regulated. We are proud of the level of service which has resulted through the mixture we have of regulation by the . . . regulating bodies, by a mix of . . . provincial government-owned corporations and . . . privately-owned corporations, by a mix of companies which ranges from the largest [telephone] company in Canada to one of the smallest, and of our system which guarantees equal concern for national and regional telecommunications needs. I feel this level of service reflects to the credit, not only of the people who have worked in the operating agencies, but to the people in the regulatory agencies as well. If results are a basis for judgement, then we have been responsible operators and the regulators have been responsible regulators. But regardless of who regulates the industry, *we* know who is responsible for delivery of service and cost to the public. We are; the telephone companies are. And because we have this responsibility we have over the years set objectives and, by and large, we have achieved these objectives and . . . they have either direct or tacit approval by our several regulatory authorities. . . . We've been able to achieve consensus."

Controls are by no means new to the telephone business. Not far behind the first salesman of the strange little box arrangments called telephones were men anxious to see that their use, one way or another, was "properly" regulated. In 1892, Parliament ruled that telephone rates could not be raised without government permission. Ten years later Ottawa went on to declare that the telephone companies had an *obligation* to provide service anywhere in Canada — where it was technically possible to provide such service — without any regard whatever to the economics involved.

At the turn of the century, when nearly every town or city had its own telephone company, city fathers obviously had to have some control over the wires that festooned rooftops and the poles that sprouted like denuded forests along downtown streets. The Union of Canadian Municipalities argued for federal operation of long distance telephone lines. The Bell Telephone Company of Canada faced growing competition in the East, and virtual rebellion in the West. Regulation was the mood of the day.

In such an atmosphere, the Select Committee of the House of Commons on Telephone Service in Canada was convened in 1905 to untangle the wires. There could be no question about the committee's bias. Its chairman, Postmaster-General Sir William Mulock, a bearded elder statesman, made it short and sweet: "I cannot see why it is not as much the duty of the state to take charge of the telephone as it is to conduct the postal service", he told the Commons. Small wonder that the Bell directors cabled their president, Charles Fleetford Sise, on holiday in Italy, that it might be best if he returned home.

The charges against Bell were straightforward enough: that its service was inadequate; that its American parentage was to Canada's disadvantage; that it used its entrenched position to defeat efforts of rival interest groups to establish effective competition; that it evaded legal restrictions on matters of rates and practised arbitrary discrimination; that the interests of its officers, bondholders and shareholders were given more consideration than those of the public, whose interest the company should primarily serve; that manufacturing privileges were used to the public's disadvantage; and that the company was controlled by Wall Street and St. James Street — and it should therefore suffer for the sins of its financial backers.

Herbert Laws Webb, a British lawyer and expert witness called to testify for Bell, electrified the Committee when he stated: "Government monopoly is a blight on the telephone business in Europe. Government monopoly in England is the fundamental reason for telephone service being behind that of the United States. The universal result of government . . . control with regard to telephones is that . . . it represses initiative and the improvement of plant and systems, in accordance with invention and . . . [advances in] the state of art."

When Sise took the stand the questioning was, as he noted in his famous Log Book, "venomous." His hearing was failing and his hair had long since turned grey, but his steel-blue eyes retained their piercing quality and at 71 his stance was as sturdy as the masts on the ships he once captained. Records of the hearings show that Sise's incisive answers cut the legs out from under his accusers. Quite simply, the Committee was no match for the old man.

On July 15, 1905, after hearing 50 witnesses in 43 sittings, the Committee issued a surprising statement: "Owing to the voluminous nature of the evidence submitted and to the late period of the session, your Committee feels that it is impossible for them, during the present session, to come to any conclusions, or to make any recommendations to the House upon the subject referred to them."

And that, for the time being at least, was that.

In the United States, Theodore Vail, president of American Telegraph and Telephone, very early in the twentieth century, adopted a statesmanlike attitude and a philosophy of what he saw as proper relations between the telephone industry and the government; an attitude which was, for many years, the accepted view of both government and industry. Simply stated it was:

> Telephony, by its technical nature, is a form of service that is most efficiently provided without local competition as a *natural monopoly*. Therefore, in the public interest the telephone business should be operated as a monopoly insofar as possible. As such, it incurs an obligation to submit to and co-operate with regulation by state and federal authorities to serve as a check — in the absence of the traditional check of competition — on the abuse of powers by the monopoly holder.
>
> The character of regulation should be such as to encourage the highest possible standards in plant, the utmost extension of facilities, the highest efficiency in service and, for these purposes, the regulation should allow rates that will warrant highest wages for best service, some reward for high efficiency in administration, and such certainty of return as will induce investors . . . to supply all the capital needed to meet the demand of the public.

The natural monopoly Vail referred to is based on a principle called the economy of scale. Basically, this means that in an industry which requires immense capital investment to provide its service or produce its product, entry into the market will naturally be restricted to producers who can afford to conduct that business on a large scale. Sometimes practicality and economics dictate that only one producer should operate in a market.

Imagine what would happen if everyone had a choice of, say, six electrical power suppliers. Where we now have one power line running down our city streets, we would have six — which would amount to a full traffic lane just to serve the electricity companies. If we had more than one water supplier, the underside of our cities would be a hopeless tangle of criss-crossing pipes. Since they would all be underground we probably could live with it — but imagine the chaos involved in tracing and shutting off a burst water main!

Life would be just as complicated with three competing telephone companies; in order for all users to have universal service all would need three telephones in their offices and homes, three sets of telephone books, three directory assistance operators — and there wouldn't necessarily be a cost reduction for all the trouble.

Through the years, as the Canadian telecommunications industry has developed, various levels of regulation have been imposed. Today, all of the members of the TransCanada Telephone System are regulated in one way or another. Bell Canada, British Columbia Telephone Company and Telesat Canada are regulated federally by the Canadian Radio-television and Telecommunications Commission (CRTC); the other seven member companies are provincially regulated. The provincial regulatory bodies, such as the Public Utilities Board of Manitoba and the Board of Commissioners of Public Utilities of Nova Scotia, regulate the carriers in their provinces under provincial legislation.

The province of Saskatchewan does not have a regulatory tribunal as such. Saskatchewan Telecommunications is directly responsible to Cabinet, however, and therefore comes under direct government scrutiny. In addition, a select standing committee of the provincial legislature regularly reviews the operations of the Crown corporation.

The divided system that regulates the telephone industry across Canada reflects the uncertain constitutional divisions of powers between the federal and provincial governments.

The Railway Act of 1903 created a Board of Railway Commissioners for Canada to regulate rail transportation and, almost as an afterthought, gave that Board powers and responsibilities in non-railway fields, including jurisdiction over the telephone rates of the Bell Telephone Company (and later B.C. Tel and several other private communications companies). In addition to being made responsible for approving telephone rates, the Board was also empowered to approve the amount, terms and conditions of capital stock issues and the placement of lines along public highways. The Railway Act provides for "just and reasonable rates" and prohibits "unjust discrimination" and "undue preference" with regard to telegraph and telephone use. Under the Act, telegraph and telephone companies, as well as railway companies, file returns to the Board relating to their revenues, expenses, assets, traffic and other items of business.

In September 1967, the Canadian Transport Commission was created by passage of the National Transportation Act. The CTC was primarily concerned with the regulation of transportation, but telephone and telegraph companies, which were federally incorporated, were subject to the jurisdiction of the CTC on matters of rates and practices under the Railway Act. Because of mounting regulatory activity relating to telephone and telegraph rates, a separate telecommunications committee was formed in 1972. In the spring of 1976, all sections of the Railway Act and the National Transportation Act that were applicable to communications under the telecommunications committee were transferred from the jurisdiction of the CTC (which answered to the Minister of Transport), to the CRTC (which reports to the Minister of Communications).

A new draft federal Act on telecommunications in Canada died with the defeat of the Liberal government in 1979, and so, oddly enough, Canadian telecommunications is today still regulated federally by the Railway Act of 1903.

Orland Tropea, executive vice-president of Bell Canada and until recently the person in charge of the company's division concerned with regulatory matters, observes bemusedly: "I find it a little archaic that the largest telecommunications company in Canada [Bell] is still regulated by a 1903 Railway Act."

As early as 1971, R.C. Scrivener, then president of Bell Canada, anticipated future developments when he remarked that: " . . . Any business today that isn't contemplating that a great many of its decisions will be made jointly with government or subsequent to government statements of policy is just not being realistic." A fair indication of the accuracy of this observation is attested to by the growth in the number of "departments of government relations" in recent years — not only in relation to Canadian public utilities, but in terms of Canadian industry, generally. At TCTS, the culmination of this trend resulted in the establishment, in 1975, of a separate department of Government Relations at a senior management level.

One of the recent decisions handed down by the CRTC requires the telecommunications companies under its jurisdiction, in some circumstances, to pay the costs of public interest groups and interveners participating in hearings — particularly hearings relating to rate increase applications. The reasoning is that such hearings are usually lengthy, complicated and costly; telecommunications companies can afford to pay for their officials to sit through such hearings whereas special interest groups representing opposing views cannot; the telecommunications companies should therefore bear a large part, if not all, of the financial burden of having both sides of any policy issue fairly presented to the regulator to ensure informed decision-making.

In 1978, the CRTC also announced its decision to retain a consulting firm to carry out a comprehensive study of TCTS revenue-settlement procedures and other matters. This was a significant decision for TCTS inasmuch it was the first decision made by the commission which focussed specifically on a TCTS function.

Many telephone people were not entirely saddened by the death of the draft telecommunications Act as a result of the 1979 change in government. Some saw in the proposed legislation signs of a growing trend to move regulatory authorities away from their primary position — ensuring that government policies are implemented in accordance with established legislation — and into areas which relate directly to the management of the utility concerned.

During the first half of this century, regulatory practices developed pretty much independently of each other in the various parts of Canada. During those years the Canadian telecommunications companies provided reliable service to Canadians with virtually no intervention by anyone. After 1930, however, Canada became involved in the building of a completely new integrated telephone system — which has become one of the most sophisticated and efficient in the world, and certainly one of the most economical in terms of its cost of service to users.

It is noteworthy that for decades the regulations governing Canadian telephone companies were mainly concerned with arbitrating rates to the consumer. "Public" hearings for over half a century were carried on in grey anonymity to almost total public indifference. Attendance was usually limited to representatives from the regulatory body, a handful of telephone people (most of whom gave testimony in support of the requested rate hike) and a few observers.

B.C. Tel's first rate hearing was held in 1921. There wasn't another until 1949 and after that there were none until the mid-sixties. In Edmonton, Jim Dodds, now a retired general manager of Alberta Government Telephones, recalls: "Early hearings were concerned mainly with traffic operations. Until 1958 we had virtually no regulation in Alberta and our first rate hearing was not held until 1966."

There is an apocryphal story that the regulatory body in Manitoba went on for so long without anything to do that, when a rate hearing was finally called in the sixties, the regulators had to be coached in their duties. "Not so!" reply the Manitobans. "We kept our skills honed on other utilities!"

Dodds recalls getting complaints from ranchers and chicken farmers when the first microwave towers were erected: "Regulatory bodies were asked to investigate the harmful effects on milk and eggs from the 'radiation' from such towers."

But all that changed abruptly in the 1960s. With the advent of McLuhanism, *communications* suddenly became a centre-stage media proposition, attracting ambitious politicians, bureaucrats and intellectuals seeking the limelight. Public hearings assumed the atmosphere of the arena, attracting noisy but articulate interveners skilled in getting the attention of, and exploiting, the media. During the prosperous fifties and sixties, rapidly advancing technology enabled communications companies to increase their profits by lowering unit costs; rates rose relatively slowly, however. According to a report published in the *Financial Times* early in 1975, the cost of local and long distance telephone service to the Canadian consumer between 1958 and 1974 went up less than 20 per cent, although the consumer price index (representing *all* goods and services) for the same period rose nearly 70 per cent. Recently, however, spiralling costs of plant maintenance, conversion to new equipment and labour have increased overall operating costs. Rate increases have consequently become a necessity for the telecommunications industry — and in some instances, bear-baiting events for the media.

Tony Brait, president and chief executive officer of Newfoundland Telephone Company Ltd., in discussing the regulatory process, recalls part of the address given by W.D. Outhit, then chairman of the Board of Commissioners of Public Utilities of Nova Scotia, to the 1976 Dalhousie University conference "Regulation at the Crossroads".

"He echoed the thoughts and beliefs of many telecommunications carriers, and certainly my own," said Brait, "when he struck the analogy between a well-built, much-travelled road and the enlightened regulatory process in Atlantic Canada. Outhit's analogy was:

> When you come to a crossroad and there are no signposts, I suggest that you pause and give the best consideration and weight you can to the signs that are visible though not posted. I suggest that you take note that the regulatory road you have been travelling is straight and wide, that it was solidly built, many years ago . . . . has been well-maintained and improved to carry the continuing increases in traffic, and that it extends far beyond the crossroads that intersect it toward the distant horizon. And if you are concerned enough to take a core sample or two of this road to determine its composition, you will discover the many ingredients that have combined to produce a road that has weathered the storms of depression and the floods of prosperity and is continuing to provide acceptable regulated services to those who travel it. . . . In the construction of the road, portions have been blasted out of solid rock, bridges and causeways have been constructed, sluiceways and culverts have been installed and hills have been levelled to provide a usable service.

Later, Outhit added:

I think, too, that you should take some pains to discover who . . . conceived the idea of constructing the crossroad and . . . uncover, if you can, the real purpose of such work. It seems plausible that some of the crossroads we see will prove to be merely byroads that terminate in the backyard of an aggressive entrepreneur, or chartered accountant or consulting engineer.

"He went on," Brait recalls, "to strike a much-needed note of caution to those who would follow the U.S. example and bow to pressures from self-interest and political groups to travel an uncharted road. I am sure," adds Brait, "that history will record the appropriateness of Mr. Outhit's remarks. His sage advice is even more applicable today than in 1976."

At the time of writing, hearings were under way concerning vertical integration of the telecommunications industry, the CNCP interconnection application and the role of cable TV operators. Decisions in these cases — as well as the regulations contained in any new telecommunications Act — will be determining factors in the shaping of telecommunications in Canada over the next decade.

The question of the vertical integration of the Canadian telecommunications industry came to a head late in 1976 after a 10-year study. The director of Investigation and Research, under the authority of the Combines Investigation Act, recommended that Bell Canada divest itself of Northern Telecom, its manufacturing subsidiary, which had earned a strong international reputation as a manufacturer and supplier of telecommunications equipment. With Bell Canada as an affiliate, Northern Telecom had 70 per cent of the telecommunications equipment market in Canada. The federal report objected to such concentration, charging that lack of competition had stifled innovation in the field, reduced the choice of equipment and raised its cost. The report contended that the association between Northern Telecom and Bell damaged the vitality and profitability of Northern Telecom and raised barriers to new competition; and that only competition can ensure that Canada will have a telecommunications equipment industry dynamic enough to service its needs when communications are evolving rapidly. The study also claimed that because of its link with Bell Canada, Northern Telecom had to produce equipment of higher durability than necessary, had to sell to Bell at remarkably low prices and had to use American designs when Canadian innovations might have been better.

Hearings on the issue began in 1977. After the CRTC had recorded more than 5,000 pages of transcript, and citing the experience and waste relating to the 10-year, billion-dollar suit in the United States seeking to force a similar separation between AT&T and Western Electric, the telephone companies (not merely Bell) suggested to the Restrictive Trade Practices Commission that they had yet to hear a convincing argument to justify the requested divestiture of Northern Telecom.

In the interconnect case, CNCP applied for access to Bell Canada's switched telephone network. CNCP wanted to connect their customers to their intercity network through Bell Canada's local switched telephone network. CNCP have made it clear that if they are successful in their application to interconnect with Bell Canada equipment, they intend to try to gain access to the switched networks of *all* the other Canadian telephone companies right across the country. This would substantially improve CNCP's competitive position because they would then be able to provide services they previously could not offer.

The issue is whether or not there should be competition for profitable intercity telephone voice services that now support unprofitable local residential telephone services. To the extent that competition would have the certain result of reducing a substantial part of Bell's profitable intercity telephone revenues, Bell would have to generate additional revenues from other sources, or raise its existing residential telephone rates.

In 1975, *Public Utilities Fortnightly* published the results of an exhaustive study which focused on the impact of interconnection on a sizeable independent U.S. telephone company. It reported: "[Interconnection] will undoubtedly reduce the telecommunications costs of some of the business users and may lead to a more efficient allocation of economic resources, but it seems highly unlikely that any method of repricing telephone services in response to competition can avoid making some groups of subscribers worse off than they were before."

In May 1979, the CRTC granted the CNCP application. The decision, however, precluded direct CNCP competition in message toll service (MTS) and wide area telephone service (WATS). At the time of writing, Bell Canada and other TCTS members were still assessing the implications of the decision and considering what future action might be appropriate.

Regulatory bodies must also soon rule on a third matter of critical concern to the common carriers. The question is: Are the cable TV operators simply deliverers of programming material, or are they common carriers of telecommunications services and, therefore, free to carry such services into the home? The cable people appear to want to be allowed to provide such services to the home as electronic mail, shopping by phone, on-line banking, and all the other wired city, world-of-tomorrow services. Of course, it is partly a problem of competition relating to ownership and the possible establishment of parallel facilities, and partly a problem of determining who will or *should* provide data services. With new technological developments — such as fibre optics — it is certain that most Canadian homes will have a large channel capacity in the near future. The vacuum created by those unused channels will be filled — by cable TV carriers, or by others.

An old adage tells us that the more things change, the more they stay the same. The regulatory mood which prevails today is not much different, in many respects, from the one that prevailed at the turn of the century. Under the circumstances, it seems reasonable to conclude that regulation is here to stay.

2

Big Business
What's a telephone worth?

*In the view of the member companies of the TransCanada
Telephone System it is essential that the present
telecommunications carrier industry structure and
performance and the public's general acceptance of the
results produced, be examined carefully in order to retain the
benefits and build on the strengths of the existing system. In
this way, the public interest will be best served.*

"The TransCanada Telephone System" by N.C. Phemister, retired
secretary and director of
Government Relations and Public Affairs, TCTS (1977)

Like everywhere else in the world, telecommunications is big business in Canada. In 1978, total investment of TCTS members was well over the $15 billion mark and growing at a rate of nearly $2 billion a year. Total revenues from all sources were approximately $4.2 billion which, co-incidentally, is just about what AT&T earned as *net profit* in the United States for 1977. Approximately $2.4 billion of this was toll revenue. Over 94,000 people were employed by TCTS member companies in Canada and the annual payroll was approximately $1.5 billion.

Over Canada's 3,851,809 square miles of territory, the telecommunications industry has woven an enormous web of signals and voice. The network includes satellites high in the sky, cables deep on the ocean floors, telegraph and telephone lines, microwave systems and high frequency radio facilities. The network spreads across prairies, through forests, over mountain peaks and across jumbled packs of ice and snow — from the 49th parallel to the high Arctic, from Victoria to St.

John's — providing a flood of entertainment, and facilitating business and social intercourse.

Member companies of TCTS are responsible for the major part of this web of communication facilities. Of the roughly 14 - 15 million telephones in Canada at the end of 1977, TCTS member companies accounted for about 90 per cent of them — or approximately 13.9 million telephones. These represented a total investment in telephone plant of close to $15.1 billion with additional investment of $2 billion in new or improved plant, buildings, equipment, vehicles and other facilities.

Using these figures and a pocket calculator it is a simple matter to calculate the worth of a single telephone. Simply divide $15.1 billion by 13.9 million (telephones) and voilà, every single telephone in the system is worth $1,086.33! Add to this the $150 TCTS companies spend on each telephone every year to keep the system up-to-date, and we arrive at the grand total of $1,236.33.

Now consider this figure in relation to your annual telephone bill, then decide if the telephone people are justified in telling Canadians they are getting a bargain.

The TransCanada Telephone System *per se* owns nothing. It has no assets, no liabilities and no capital. As noted, it is *not* a corporate entity. Everything it uses on a day-to-day basis is provided one way or another by its member companies. The cost of capital items (such as furniture and equipment) is shared by the member companies through an account administered at TCTS headquarters in Ottawa. "Consumables," paid for through the administrative expense system, are also jointly shared by the member companies.

All TCTS headquarter staff members are on loan from, and are paid directly by, the member companies who claim those payments as TCTS expenses. Their salaries and expenses are shared by the member companies on the basis of the formula established to cover administrative costs.

By the end of 1978, Canadians were making nearly 20 billion telephone calls annually. Over a billion of these were long distance calls and more than six million were calls overseas.

The TCTS consortium handles roughly 90 per cent of all Canadian calls. It has over 86.6 million miles of wire circuits (including cable). Prince Edward Island alone has over 348,000 miles of wire; Newfoundland has over 1.6 million. The microwave system spans 124,901 route miles — 7,307 of which are in Saskatchewan alone.

Bell Canada, with 8.6 million telephones, is by far the largest and the dominant telephone company in Canada. Bell is also the country's largest utility company, standing fifth in terms of revenues (sales) among all Canadian industrial companies (behind Ford, General Motors, Imperial Oil and Canadian Pacific).

Employing over 52,000 people (better than half of all Canadians involved in telecommunications) Bell's total investment in telephone plant at the end of 1978 was slightly more than $8.7 billion. The company carries out the largest corporate construction programme in Canada — each year spending almost a billion dollars to expand and repair facilities and to relocate and build new ones.

Bell Canada has more shareholders than any other Canadian company. Nearly a quarter of a million Canadians hold shares in the company. At present about 99 per cent of Bell Canada shares are held in Canada.

Founded in 1882 by The Bell Telephone Company of Canada, the manufacturing arm of the company, now known as Northern Telecom Ltd., is still 60 per cent owned by Bell Canada. Northern Telecom revenues in 1978 passed the $1.5 billion mark; a goal of $3 billion in annual sales has been targeted within the next five years. The company is Canada's largest manufacturer of telecommunications equipment. It stands second in North America and ranks among the top five such manufacturers in the world. Northern Telecom is the largest private employer of scientists and technicians in Canada and has plants in the U.S., the Netherlands, Eire, Malaysia, Turkey and elsewhere.

In 1971, concerned that the Canadian market was entering a no-growth period, Northern Telecom decided to enter the huge U.S. market. (California alone has more telephones than all of Canada.) U.S. facilities were subsequently acquired, and by 1978, 29.8 per cent of the company's total sales were in and to the U.S. (Northern Telecom's total sales for 1978 were approximately $1.5 billion.)

Bell-Northern Research Limited is the research and development arm of Bell Canada (which owns 30 per cent) and Northern Telecom (which owns 70 per cent). It is a non-profit enterprise with a staff of over 2,400 which includes more than 1,550 engineers, scientists and technical personnel who, under the direction of Denis Hall, the company's young and dynamic president, carry on research, design, development, long-range planning and systems engineering in all fields of telecommunications.

Bell-Northern is also Canada's biggest private spender on research and development. Of the total national expenditure of $180 million in 1978, Bell-Northern by itself accounted for $100 million. (That year private industry was responsible for approximately 70 per cent of the total expenditure on R&D; government carried 30 per cent.)

Bell also has an interest in several of its TCTS associates. At the time of writing, Bell owned 67.0 per cent of Newfoundland Telephone Company Limited; 38.6 per cent of The New Brunswick Telephone Company, Limited; and 40 per cent of Maritime Telegraph and Telephone Company Limited, which in turn owns 44.4 per cent of The Island Telephone Company Limited serving Prince Edward Island.

Bell Canada-International Management Research and Consulting Ltd. was formed in 1976 to provide advice to international telecommunications companies. It is wholly-owned by Bell. Bell also holds a 30 per cent interest in Bell-Northern Software Research Inc., a company specializing in research and development of computer software (programming); BNR holds the other 70 per cent. Rival computer companies regard the organization of Bell-Northern Software Research Inc. as a strong potential competitor in their field.

Bell also controls Northern Telephone Co. in northern Ontario (99.7 per cent), Telébec Ltée, covering a wide area in Quebec (100 per cent) and The Capital Telephone Co., which, in turn owns Tele-Direct Ltd., a producer and distributor of telephone directories.

Around a million telephones are controlled by the 32 active members of the Canadian Independent Telephone Association, including companies such as edmonton Telephones (305,000), Thunder Bay Municipal Telephone Co. (88,000), Québec Téléphone (255,000) and approximately 700 smaller companies — of which more than 600 are in rural Saskatchewan — some with no more than a dozen subscribers.

General Telephone and Electronics Corporation of New York, through its subsidiary, Anglo-Canadian Telephone Company, controls British Columbia Telephone Company (50.14 per cent) and Québec Téléphone (54.2 per cent). Through B.C. Tel's ownership of Okanagan Telephones, GTE effectively controls that company, too. B.C. Tel is the second largest telephone company in Canada, with a total investment in telephone plant of $2.0 billion and 1.6 million telephones.

The three government-owned Prairie companies represent a combined total investment of $2.9 billion in telephone plant and approximately 2.2 million telephones. This represents 16.0 per cent of the national total.

In the Atlantic Provinces, MT&T is the largest company with plant valued at $500.0 million and 451,629 telephones; NBTel follows with plant valued at $415.9 million and 358,842 phones; then Newfoundland Telephone with $234.3 million in plant and 175,312 telephones; and finally, Island Tel with $57.5 million

240

in plant and 59,436 telephones.

Big business means big money and wherever there is big money one can be sure there are big taxes. The member companies of TCTS paid a combined total of over $532.4 million in taxes in 1978 — federal, provincial and municipal. The three Prairie companies got a break because as provincial Crown agencies they do not pay federal taxes. By comparison, taxes paid by SASK TEL ($1.4 million) accounted for only 1.2 per cent of its operating expenses in 1978, whereas taxes paid by Bell ($386.1 million) accounted for 21.6 per cent of its operating expenses. Even little Island Tel with operating expenses of 10.5 million paid $2.1 million, or 20.0 per cent of its operating expenses, in taxes.

Privately owned companies often have to answer complaints about over-charging. Customers in Halifax don't understand why they pay nearly twice as much as customers in Saskatoon for the same basic telephone service. There are several reasons, of course, which have to do with the fundamental differences between regions in Canada — economic as well as geographic — but taxes represent an important consideration everywhere.

When Basil Beneteau was a vice-president with B.C. Tel he suggested that telephone bills be designed to show precisely how the charges were broken down. The billing format he suggested took into account basic local and long-distance telephone rates and broke out all the tax charges that were current in B.C. at the time. The layout of the telephone bill was more or less as follows:

- Telephone service including sales tax on materials
  purchased $5.28
- Federal, provincial and municipal taxes   2.37
- 5 per cent provincial sales tax   .38
                                                        Total $8.03

Beneteau did not go so far as to suggest that the percentage of tax in relation to the total charges (in this case 24.25 per cent) be shown on the bill. Most government people didn't like the idea very much.

Throughout the world, especially in the developing Third World, the rush for modern communications systems is on. From Argentina to Zambia, there is scarcely a nation that does not have plans to develop a modern telecommunications system. Before the revolution in 1978, Iran alone planned to spend close to $15 billion on telecommunications over the next 10 years. While there is now serious doubt as to whether any part of that plan will be executed over the years ahead, the need for a modern system will continue.

Rising to meet this surging demand are the giants of telecommunications around the world: AT&T, ITT, Siemens A.G. of Germany, N.V. Philips Gloeilampenfabrieken of the Netherlands, L.M. Ericsson Telephone of Sweden, Japan's Nippon Electric, and Canada's Northern Telecom and Bell Canada. The catch lies in the fact that many of the countries bidding for telecommunication systems are including "civil works" considerations in their contracts — peripheral tasks such as road building, supply of water systems and building construction, all of which must be attended to before the telephone plant installation can even be started.

Robert Scrivener, chief executive officer of Northern Telecom, points out: "You're in 30 or 40 businesses. You may make a billion dollars, but you can also lose two billion, and it's impossible to tell in advance."

The mounting cost of research and development which is required to stay abreast of change has been enormous. Northern Telecom has already spent over $200 million in its labs on electronic switching. By itself the domestic home market cannot support such expenditures. Basil Beneteau, now president of Northern Telecom, says: "Canada alone cannot digest the technological banquet . . . you have to sell the world market to support that kind of R and D."

Once into the race for Third World business, the competing companies find they face infuriating and frustrating obstacles, unrealistic expectations, sheer incompetence, a burning desire to industrialize coupled with a reluctance to impose sound rate structures, and the darkest of local politics. Some countries have simply picked up every gadget available — Earth stations, microwave systems and even satellites — without any real idea of how to put them all together. When things don't work, the usual response of the local authorities is to take it out on the company contracted to install the system. Northern Telecom walked away from just such a situation in Nigeria a few years ago. Says Scrivener, "We don't go after the big spectaculars any more."

On December 15, 1977, however, Bell Canada, together with the L.M. Ericsson Company of Sweden and the Philips group from the Netherlands, landed a contract valued at $3.1 billion to modernize the telephone system in Saudi Arabia. Among other things, the project involves adding 470,000 automatic switched phone lines. The contract also means more than 600 jobs and about $165 million (net) for Bell over the five years of its agreement. Two of the unsuccessful bidders were ITT and Western Electric. We might safely assume, therefore, that Canada's performance over the next few years will be watched with keen interest.

As always in a monopoly situation, there are people who will consistently believe that big is bad. People from the telephone companies and organizations such as TCTS get blue in the face telling average Canadians that they are getting better service at less cost than their counterparts virtually anywhere else in the world. However, the facts don't always carry as much weight as they should; the general attitude toward big business these days is generally hostile.

Arnold Groleau, now a retired Bell executive vice-president, once stated the case this way:

> Some people say we want to be loved. That is not so, but we do want to be respected and we do want our accomplishments to be recognized and under-stood. We want people to be *aware*, if not to appreciate the fact — that they are getting good telephone service. It's discouraging to those of us who know what has been done over the years and who take pride in this business to hear and read in the newspapers about some of the things said during a rate hearing.
>
> The fact is that our service compares favourably with any in the world in terms of both cost and quality, and, except for the U.S., is so far ahead of any other country, that people in Canada don't know how lucky they are.*

Most telephone people are inclined to think Groleau's statement is as valid today as it was when he made it over a decade ago.

*Any comparison between Canadian and U.S. rates must take into account a fundamental difference in philosophy between telephone people in the two countries which is reflected in rate structuring. In Canada, the practice is to provide almost universal access to basic telephone service to encourage people to become telephone subscribers — and to subsidize local rates with higher long distance rates. In the U.S. the practice is to charge high local rates and substantially lower long distance rates — mainly to encourage people to use long distance.

3

Digital Magic
Computer Talk

No one took to the computer more eagerly or saw its usefulness more quickly than the businessman. Now, 24 years after General Electric became the first company to acquire a computer, these versatile machines have become the galley slaves of capitalism.

Time Magazine (1978)

In the 20 or so years since the computer emerged as a practical tool, it has revolutionized the methodology of management in business, government, industry, and academic and financial circles. Without the computer, life today would, of course, go on — but it would be immeasurably more difficult.

The full potential of the computer has only recently begun to be realized. In the time-frame of the past 10 years, the power of the computer has been increased enormously as a result of the ability to use it remotely — in effect, by wedding it to a system of telecommunications. Computer communications in Canada is increasing at the rate of approximately 25 per cent each year and is one of the most vital growth industries in the country today.

What does this have to do with you and me? Consider three examples:

Recently, a professor, at the University of Toronto required some specific information on the use of certain building materials in ancient Persia. To obtain it he referred to a "data base," which is the technical term for a place where information of a particular sort is "stored." In this case, the data base happened to be the National Research Council (NRC) in Ottawa, which has an enormous amount of information stored in its computers.

The professor "accessed" the NRC data base and was advised by the computer that it had 827 archaeological listings under the heading called up. Through a series of specific questions, the professor narrowed his inquiry down to a working list of 12 items. Finally, he asked the computer for a summary of these items, whereupon the computer provided him with a print-out of the titles of the 12 research papers available on the subject of his inquiry including bibliographic information, and a two- or three-line commentary summarizing each paper.

The professor, in relating his experience, explained that without the aid of the computer he would have had to spend weeks in the library searching for that information. He went on to say that his search turned up one vital publication written by an obscure Russian archaeologist which he might never have found had it not been for the help of the computer.

The entire procedure took less than 10 minutes, and it was conducted over the telephone.

As a shopper, you have almost certainly noticed the electronic cash registers which are now a common sight at most supermarket check-out counters and department stores. What these machines do for you mainly is speed up service and virtually eliminate error. What they do for the merchant/owner depends entirely upon what he decides he needs. The only real limits are imposed by what he is willing to pay for his computer programmes, equipment and services. His "package" can be designed to handle inventory control, reordering, and customer credit vertification. Customer purchases are recorded by means of the product codes they carry. Departmental and overall sales volume and inventory levels by product or department can be determined precisely at a moment's notice. Reorder information can also be easily obtained. Indeed, the register-computer can even be programmed to look after payroll, complicated accounting and personnel records. And while one might be impressed that the process is virtually instantaneous, it is even more striking to consider that the store may be part of a single system joining dozens of stores hundreds of miles apart by means of a telephone network.

Finally, suppose you need a pair of gloves but, for whatever reason, you cannot get to a store to buy them. With the electronic systems now available you can easily make your purchase using a catalogue from a store of your choice and a push-button telephone. Initially, you need only dial (punch) the number for the store and be put through to the computer ordering service. "Good morning," says the machine, "your telephone number, please". You respond by inputting your number (punching out the numbers on your telephone), which the computer verifies. "Your credit card number, please." The correct number provides the computer with another verification. Further coded numbers may also be required at this point to ensure that the caller is an accredited user.

You then refer to the catalogue and determine the codes for the brand, size and colour of the products you want. Following the instructions of the computer you merely punch these in as required on your telephone. The computer will then summarize your order to ensure that it is complete and correct. To finalize the order you merely push the octothorp (#) button on the telephone whereupon the computer will ask about delivery and payment. There are codes for each response and again you need only punch in the appropriate code on the telephone. When the order is completed the computer will sign off with a polite "Thank you for ordering from Superstore."

Andy McMahon, TCTS director of Computer Communications, points out that such telephone/computer services are both available and in use now. Although many future applications sound like something out of science-fiction, the fact is that the future use of computers and the services they will provide through the telephone network are limited only by the imaginations of men and, of course, the costs of development.

The TransCanada Telephone System has been involved in the data business virtually since its beginning. Data transmission really evolved from what was originally telegraph type transmission. The telegraph was, and still is, a very simple form of data transmitter. As modern networks evolved they could be used as easily for voice as for teletype and telegraph transmission; historically, the use of telegraph tended to fade into the background as the importance of voice and teletype transmission increased.

During the 1950s however, the North American business community began to have a requirement for what might be called a "message-record" — a communications facility used by businesses to confirm hotel reservations, real-estate arrangements, and so on. As a result, the use of private-line services such as teletype increased substantially. Although the technology goes back as far as the old days of the telegraph, it began to reach a sizeable market only during the 1950s, and essentially all of the subscribers used the telephone network as the medium.

As time passed, it became more and more important for computers to be able to communicate with other devices, particularly those in remote locations. If, for example, a company had its computer located somewhere outside the city away from its head office, that company would require adequate time arrangements to enable it to use its computer just as if it were next door. The communication linkage between a computer and its remote terminals — or between computers and other computers — came to be known as computer communications.

The early sixties also saw the emergence of computer service bureaus and the development of the "time-sharing" industry. These companies provide leased or shared computer capacity to a group of users or companies who individually are unable to have their own facilities. This development stimulated the growth of the computer and the communications industries in Canada by triggering a demand for the talents and skills of a host of people who might not otherwise be involved in computer communications, while at the same time making facilities available to users who would not otherwise be able to afford them.

One of the initial problems was a straightforward technical one; the normal telephone network was designed to handle voice — it was not designed to handle data. The human ear is a marvellously adaptable mechanism. It can tolerate noise on the line and adjust to little bleeps and blips that are caused by conditions somewhere in the network or along the line. But these same bleeps and blips play havoc with data. Computers cannot adjust to or tolerate such noise. The computer interprets anything on the line as a signal — so every distortion or little noise, however acceptable to the ear, can mess up data transmission beyond belief. Each blip becomes an error — and there is no market for data errors.

Obviously, a high quality voice network was not enough. In order to handle data transmission acceptably, the telecommunications network in Canada had to be upgraded. Before the mid-fifties no network was capable of handling all forms of computer communication accurately and economically. There were two clear-cut options: the construction of a completely new and distinctly separate network to handle data only; or the adaptation and refinement of the existing network. The option finally chosen was a compromise and represented an attempt to achieve the best of both alternatives. As a first stage, a type of hybrid network was developed using the existing telephone network, to which was added separate functional components designed exclusively for data transmission. The end result was a network that is functionally separated but physically integrated. A microwave tower, for example, carries both voice and data, buz within that particular structure the signals are segmented — one for data and one for voice.

The development of this network involved a fundamental technological change. Prior to the evolution of computer communications, nearly all of the telephone network was an analogue network — which very simply means that signals were transmitted in a form or wave pattern analogous to a voice signal or pattern. The signal varied continuously with time, in much the same way as the voice or speech patterns vary — hence the term "analogue." The major problem with an analogue system is that the signal tends to fade over distance as it moves along the network. The result is that the signal must be boosted or amplified along the line to compensate for loss of power (volume). As a matter of fact, all signals lose power over distance, but when an analogue signal is amplified, any noise (distortion) that it picks up or that is inherent in it is also amplified. By the time a signal travels from Ottawa to Vancouver, it has been amplified several times, and, therefore, the volume of extraneous noise travelling along with it can be very significant. Indeed, distortion can be so substantial as to make the signal useless for data transmission. A new technology — digital technology — had to be developed for data communication.

Most computers and business machines today handle information in a digital format. This is essentially a method by which a unit of information (it could be a voice signal from a computer) is "encoded" into a format that reduces the signal to a series of electrical pulses, represented by one of two states: "ON" or "OFF." By careful analysis of an analogue signal, that signal can be translated or encoded into a sequence of ON-OFF pulses, not unlike turning a light switch on and off very quickly. The beauty of a digital signal is that although it also fades over distance when it is transmitted, the pulse rate of the signal is not affected. Since there are only two states to be determined — ON and OFF — the signal is detected acd repeated in a *regenerated* form, rather than in an amplified form. When a digital signal is boosted, it has the vigour of a fresh signal. There is no accumulated distortion: hence, there is no error. The quality of transmission is thus substantially higher and more appropriate for data transmission — considerations which are very important to the users of large computer systems.

More signals can be funnelled down an equivalent capacity line or waveguide using digital transmission than using analogue transmission — another major advantage of digital technology. Use of a narrower frequency band is also possible because all that is required for digital transmission is the ability to distinguish between the two states, ON and OFF. In effect, being able to compact a signal carries with it real economies.

The first major digital system used for both *voice and data* was installed in Metropolitan Toronto in the mid-sixties to handle local requirements. Then in the early seventies, TCTS conducted a series of experiments in digital transmission which served as the basis for the development of a long-haul data network. That network, known as the Dataroute, became operational in 1973 and is one of the longest — if not the longest — exclusive digital data networks in the world.

During the period of experimentation with digital transmission, it became apparent to TCTS that a separate organization was needed to deal effectively with the new emerging market for data computer communications. The existing TCTS framework was ideally suited to deal with basic telephone service, but it was not structured to best serve what was a highly competitive marketplace requiring entirely new services, totally new kinds of responses to customers' needs and, in many cases, totally different technologies. In 1972, therefore, a new organization was established within TCTS — The Computer Communications group. The new group's function was to serve the needs of computer communication customers across Canada. Since its establishment, the group has contributed substantially to developments which have made Canada an acknowledged world leader in computer-telecommunications technology.

The CCG drew staff from TCTS member companies, but it also brought in outside specialists in sales and marketing, engineering and planning, design and installation, and maintenance. The CCG has served TCTS very well, and by being able to focus its specialized knowledge and attention on computer communications problems it has contributed to the growth of the Canadian market, which over the past seven years has been expanding at a phenomenal rate.

The Dataroute provides a basic digital network across Canada for both low-speed and high-speed data transmission operations. In the beginning, Dataroute was essentially a private line service providing a dedicated circuit between two customer locations. It was terminal to terminal; computer to computer; Toronto to Vancouver or wherever. In the long run that arrangement was inefficient for many kinds of data services. Dedicating the physical components of a network to a relatively few specialized or individual users does not make optimum use of that particular investment or facility. Clearly, there are many hours during a normal day when a customer or user is not transmitting data or otherwise using his circuit to full capacity. After-hours and at night the circuit lies idle — an investment not earning its keep.

Since 1973, the network has grown and has been updated and modified. Customer response has been excellent. The improved system not only raised the levels of performance and service, it also carried with it substantial customer savings through price reductions (as much as 90 per cent) because of improved efficiency. From TCTS's point of view, the network substantially reduced its requirements for additional capital because the System was able to achieve a much higher utilization of its facilities. Dataroute proved to be a major stepping stone in the development of the total TCTS digital system.

The obvious next step was in the direction of providing a system or network that would optimize facilities and, consequently, investment. This led to a "switched network" arrangement which, in simple terms, means a shared facility. When one customer is not using a particular facility, other customers can. A central switching office arranges this in much the same way as for a voice network. Every central switching office has for years operated on the premise that, at any point in time, only a certain percentage of customers will use the existing capacity, thus affording maximum utilization.

The next step was to develop a *public* switched data network across Canada. The intent was to build a network that would be as flexible, accessible and usable for the data user as the telephone network is for the telephone user. Again there were several options open. The one finally chosen is technically known as "packet switching," a system firmly based on digital transmission. In 1975 TCTS announced its plans to build such a public switched data network, to be called Datapac. Introduced in 1976, this system is now up and running. It is the first commercial packet switching network in the world operated by a common carrier. As a result of Datapac service, a telephone customer today can pick up his telephone and request a computer connection (using the required codes) anywhere in the world, just as a telephone customer can pick up his telephone and obtain a voice connection anywhere in the world.

Admittedly, the data business today is in the main related to the requirements of large businesses, industries and banks. On-line banking, for example, has a major requirement for this type of facility because most bank accounts are now stored in the banks' central computers. Very little information on individual accounts is kept in branch banks. When a customer visits his bank to make a deposit or withdrawal, the common practice today is to have the teller "access" a terminal, which is connected directly to the bank's central computer where all the records are stored. The customer's passbook is also updated automatically on the terminal connected to the data base. This is merely one application of the Datapac network. An electronic funds transfer system will likely evolve from it, reducing the use of cash and increasing further the use of credit cards. Simple purchases will be processed directly to a customer's bank account.

Andy McMahon suggests that in the near future a fully integrated digital transmission system will be built that will carry voice as well as data, and that will also involve significant improvements in transmission. In addition to enjoying higher quality voice transmission it will also be possible to carry more conversations over the same facilities, with obvious economies. As a matter of fact, there is considerably more to McMahon's suggestion than may be apparent at first glance, because TCTS is already planning to "go digital" for its voice network (switching and transmission). The financial implications of this are almost as far-reaching as the technological and service implications.

Like most communicators in the data business, the people at TCTS and elsewhere are very enthusiastic about the future of digital communications — but they are not starry-eyed. According to both Terry Heenan of TCTS and Denis Hall of Bell Northern Research, "Technology is not the barrier." What will happen depends entirely upon the kind of services people want; the market opportunity which, it is hoped, will be attractive enough to encourage people with money to invest in those services; and the regulatory conditions that will permit carriers to develop those facilities and services. What is certain at this point, however, is that a push-button type telephone, a television terminal and a few special adapters to connect these components are the main ingredients from the householder's standpoint. Some people consider the next step to be a giant one — integrating these components into a system that is then connected to the public switched network. Indeed, that connection through the ordinary telephone line may well provide anyone with a telephone and a TV set with access to any other telephone, data terminal or computer in the entire world! The only items that are not now in place are the data bases, which are needed to provide the information that would make such a home hookup worth-while.

Datapac, 1000, a nationwide network for data communications was first introduced to Canadians in 1974.

A new system called Viewdata, which is being developed in England, has some interesting applications that TCTS is watching. The system has been put together jointly by the General Post Office (which is responsible for telephones in Britain) and several manufacturers of television equipment and developers of information storage systems and data banks. They have built a very substantial data base containing a wealth of information across a broad spectrum of subject areas. Among the information stored, as an example, are complete run-downs on all automobiles manufactured and sold in England. A potential buyer can access the system simply by picking up his push-button phone and request the information he wants. Specifically, he can find out how much each model costs, details and prices of options, comparable gasoline mileage, maintenance experience on each make, trade-in value after two or three or however many years — everything he may want to know to help him make up his mind. Users are billed on the basis of the amount of information they call up from the computer plus a surcharge for connect time. That sort of service could catch on in Canada.

Of course, such service also requires a sizeable investment and can be made only by someone who is in a position to provide the data bank. The success of such an undertaking depends, moreover, upon how much the public is willing to pay for such a service. Producing a data bank could be compared to stocking a department store with a wide range of products. If no one wants the goods on the shelves (or the information in the memory bank), the store (or data bank) goes broke. But because of organizations like TCTS and its computer communications group, the public information data bank concept *is* being considered in North America, particularly in relation to its possible business applications.

As with most grand ideas this one begs the old questions of when is demand sufficient to justify investment in the scheme? What kind of data will users want, and what will they be prepared to pay? The average homeowner isn't going to spend $30 a month to access archaeological summaries from NRC. He'll get all he'll ever need in this connection from his library books. But promoters of the idea suggest customers may be willing to pay to access current price information at supermarkets or find out what's playing at downtown movie theatres — with prices, show times and ratings, of course. Customers may also want to peruse the menus of the restaurants in town, determine prices, find out what specials are offered and so on. Such services may be of interest to people and *may be* saleable. In the final analysis, it is a straightforward marketing problem.

When you come right down to it, Digital Magic really isn't magic at all. It is a reality which touches virtually everyone in North America every day. In fact, many of the benefits which we enjoy simply by living on this continent are the result of computer technology and the telecommunications system that is essential to it. The wired city will not descend upon us tomorrow — but by next week, anything may be possible!

4

Technology and the Telephone
The Wired City

*Bell's telephone has been a superb base for modern society
and it is hard to imagine that it will ever disappear, even when
unimaginable new developments come on the scene. . . . Bell
has been an astonishingly durable and potent influence on
science, business, government and society. And will, I think
still be so in the 21st century.*

The Future of the Telephone by John Kettle (1974)

The lure of prophecy has captured men's imaginations since the beginning of time.
Modern men are not immune and so politicians, scientists, technologists, writers
and imaginative readers everywhere all have visions of the Brave New World.
They may put the future into which they peer into different frameworks, but they
are alike in their fascination and delight with the crystal ball.

The telephone provides four great benefits: instant communication, two-way
communication, private communication and communication over distance.
Those who look ahead agree that the future efforts of telephone people should be
in the direction of perfecting each of these four areas. Outside of TCTS there are
substantial differences of opinion as to precisely how everyone should proceed to
achieve such perfection. At TCTS headquarters, however, there is consensus if not
unanimity at every level, and the considerations relating to future developments
are taken very seriously into account — particularly by the planning groups such

254

as the Operations and Network Planning group and the Business Development group. As a matter of fact, if any organization ever deserved the motto "Plan Ahead," it would be TCTS. *Everything* comes under planning scrutiny: finances, technical and engineering matters, staff requirements, equipment requirements, space requirements — the list could go on and on. What is signficant in this connection is that planning is absolutely crucial to the conduct of the business. *Nothing* is left to chance because the risks are simply too high. Tiny mistakes and errors of judgement can cost the member companies literally millions of dollars. And so great care is taken and projections are made on 1-, 5-, 10-, 25-, 30- and even 50-year bases.

Planning is hard work; speculating is a lot more fun — which is why Marcel Vincent must have enjoyed talking about the future one day back in 1964. At the time. Vincent was president and chief executive officer of the Bell Telephone Company of Canada; he was asked to describe his vision of life in the year 2064 — a 100-year projection. He qualified his remarks by observing that:

> The radical technological change now rushing through time will probably have gained such speed and momentum a century from now that even if one could accurately forecast conditions in 2064, those predictions would be obsolete by 2074.

Also acknowledging that he could only guess at unforeseeable break-throughs, Vincent replied:

> Whatever sort of world the year 2064 may bring, communications technology will help make it that way and communications development itself will be shaped by the needs of people that arise between now and then.

Vincent was fascinated by the tremendous changes in life-styles that communication advances might be expected to bring about and he envisioned someone at breakfast watching a wall-sized television newscast, then calling up a few sheets of news and features and other interpretative reports — all illustrated in full colour, of course — from a facsimile machine and studying them before heading to the office.

Almost characteristically, most visions of the future carry with them the tacit assumption that most, if not all, of our contemporary problems will be solved. Urban sprawl will be eliminated; no more traffic jams; and certainly no more pollution. Visions of a working future often concentrate on the freedom from the tyranny of the conventional office which future communications developments are expected to provide. And it is frequently implied that this will come about all as a result of carrying the job to the person rather than moving the person to the job. The image plainly suggests that once most work becomes innovative and creative it can be carried on as easily from the comfortable den of a West Vancouver mountainside home, or the study in a house facing a sandy Prince Edward Island beach, as it can from an office in a downtown building. Conventional behaviour patterns may, however, impose an inhibiting element. Some people may prefer the sociability of working with others to staying at home — however pleasant home may be.

At any rate, Mr. Vincent's executives have a choice — there is no longer any need to buck traffic into town or grab a commuter train. They can retire to an office at home, sit back in a contour chair and simply by touching buttons on the telephone terminal, in quick succession they can view the company's operations around the globe. After watching a scene in which a technician makes repairs that automatic equipment cannot handle, the executive and associates in other offices around the world can settle down to a televised conference call.

Today one must go back many, many generations to find anyone who had read "all" the books ever published in his own language. Indeed, it has been more than a half century since anyone in the professions could even claim to have read everything published in his field. We are being overwhelmed with information. There is more information on hand today than any one person can possibly cope with even in a lifetime. Some current publications are literally no more than lists of other publications; page after page of technical journals, articles and other documents — occasionally with abstracts — intended to short-circuit the task of potential readers and provide them with at least an overview of the flood of written and other material being produced. And once the problem of storage is truly solved, it will be impossible to keep up even with the mere listings.

The meshing of computers and telecommunications technology has produced an information explosion, an information revolution, an information age. Thus, future education will have to take on a new look. Vincent was therefore being no more than modestly imaginative when he suggested that he believed communications will play an important part in the learning process in 2064:

> The increase in the sheer volume of knowledge will be so rapid and so large that education will almost certainly have to continue throughout one's entire lifetime. The world's most brilliant and gifted teachers will lecture to students around the globe.
>
> I also foresee a far greater application of programmed learning techni-

ques with each pupil advancing at his own pace. Here again, communications facilities will carry programmes transmitted from a central point to the students' homes. This technique is already being developed and could be applied as easily to the needs of technologists, in terms of keeping them abreast of developments in their respective fields, as to the needs of very young people.

The cleavage between the physical sciences and the liberal arts will virtually have disappeared by the year 2064 and even those people with only a basic education will have a cultural background as well as a fundamental appreciation of the sciences.

Bell-Northern Research is the largest privately owned industrial research and development organization in Canada, and ranks among the top one per cent in North America. Hundreds of Bell-Northern's scientists are directly concerned with advancing the technology of tomorrow. Many major advances in world communications have been born in the Bell-Northern laboratories, among them electronic switchboards and systems. Such systems use computer technology and are more compact, efficient, speedy and economical than earlier types of switchers. Some of their components operate in billionths of a second. Many of these systems have been installed in Canada and the United States and have attracted world-wide attention. Some of them are so nearly self-sufficient that they have given rise to the following shaggy dog story: It is said that even the largest of these marvellous systems can be run by one man and a dog. The man's purpose is to feed the dog, and the dog's purpose is to make sure the man doesn't touch anything.

Vincent's prognosis of the likely future thrust of equipment and systems development in Canada was:

Continuing a trend that is already evident, much that is new in communications technology will be associated with space technology and exploration. The Telstar satellite of 1962 will seem an incredibly clumsy and primitive contraption to people four generations hence. Far more highly sophisticated satellites, packed with communications equipment, will orbit the earth while others may well have orbits in the solar system to provide a twenty-first century variety of long distance service — interplanetary communications.

I can see the trend toward miniaturization continuing indefinitely, until devices that we today consider to be ultramicrominiaturized will seem massive in 2064. We have electronic assemblies today which are no larger than a package of cigarettes but which 10 or 15 years ago would have required as much space as a mantel radio, and before World War II, would have filled a good-sized cabinet. Yet these assemblies are being replaced today by thin film devices on slides of glass or ceramic smaller than a business card and specialists in molecular electronics have already produced their equivalent in devices no larger than a pinhead. With this background it does not require a vivid imagination to foresee a computer not much larger than a wrist-watch a century from now.

The large computers of 2064 will probably have capacities for storing and processing data in quantities which are unbelievable by today's standards. Their memories may contain quadrillions of bits of information and significantly, they may well perform feats of logic that would dazzle the average person of 1964. These machines, linked by vast communications networks covering the Earth and extending well into space, will probably be actuated by the human voice as opposed to the computer-type instructions as represented by punched cards and magnetic tape today. They will also carry on conversations with each other as computers have already begun to do. Their calculations will free human minds for the more elegant tasks of scientific and philosophical speculation.

Unless an unforeseen breakthrough in scientific knowledge occurs, the laser, which is still undeveloped as a signficant communications element, could be the means by which vast amounts of information will be transmitted. When lasers become a practical means of transmitting information, they may well be used to carry the masses of data to feed the world's computers. Furthermore, they will carry voice and full-colour video pictures between persons anywhere in the solar system — a technician in a sea-floor apartment, a scientist on Mars, or a family in a tropical penthouse garden 745 stories high in a residential tower in the Canadian Arctic.

Wrist-watch style or necklace communication units could be worn by virtually everyone and could be all that is required to make contact with anyone in the solar system. Translation into any desired language will likely be automatic and instantaneous, and miniature video screens will show full-colour pictures. In homes and offices, wall-size television screens displaying three-dimensional images will probably be common. News, entertainment, private conversation and data will all pass over an integrated communications network which can be selected at will.

Push buttons will replace telephone dials in a few years and for some time thereafter service called 'touch tone' will be in general use. But I think that by 2064 we might also have 'voice dialing' — dialing, in effect, by speaking into the communications unit. Prototypes of such apparatus already exist in laboratories, but these will have to be refined substantially before they can be put into general use. . . .

Vincent ended his speculation by admitting that it would be naïve to expect that the year 2064 will see all the ills of mankind abolished and all problems solved. "However," he concluded, "I am hopeful that our descendants will have acquired a great deal more knowledge of human behaviour so that they may use their tremendously expanded powers with intelligence and wisdom."

Today, push-button telephones, where computerized switching has been installed, forward calls from one number to another automatically. Other "smart" telephones "memorize" frequently-used numbers and reach them for a caller with the touch of a single button. Telephones are even being used to turn lights and other electrical appliances on and off.

The scribble phone, too, is already available. It provides a telephone user with the facility of a video scratch pad on which he can write, sketch or draw diagrams as well as talk and listen, thus providing more "face-to-face" communication than the first video phones provided.

Not infrequently, technology races ahead of both need and desire. The picture phone or video phone was developed and put on the market in Canada in the late sixties. But people didn't want it, at least not at the price it was offered, and there is still considerable doubt as to whether anyone wants it at all. The complaints of those who tried it range from "picture too small" to "loss of privacy." However, the basic flaw, according to the communications philosophers who analysed the problem, was a lack of "shared visual space." The video phone did not permit or provide for any of the sorts of interaction as the scribble phone does. The experience was akin to talking to a television set over a telephone line.

Video conference calls are also already being conducted regularly out of specially-prepared conference rooms operating in five major Canadian centres. The conference participants all see one another, and their voices sound as if they are all in the same room. When one conferee finishes his part in the proceedings he can drop out if he wishes and his place can be taken by someone else. Any one of the conferees who wishes to make a particular point can use an electronic stylus to sketch a diagram on the display screen. Such illustrations appear on the screen as they are made, and if any of the participants wishes to secure a hard-copy of the item, he simply touches an appropriate button and it goes into an electronic memory bank. Conferees may from time to time also consult various computers for additional information.

The cost of this service is considerably less than the transportation expense involved in getting such a group together in one city, and the saving in time is even more impressive. However, as with the video phone, there are drawbacks and these have tended to inhibit the use of the system. Time zones create timing problems. Many people prefer the face-to-face synergism of a conference and the added privacy of a closed room. However, socially ingrained behaviour patterns are perhaps the greatest obstacle. In this connection most people in business enjoy a conference away from home — for whatever reason — and they will always rationalize such a business trip.

For a long time scientists and others in the communications field have talked glibly about the "wired city" — which at present is still a theoretical community, distinguished by having a total communications system in which the number of available services is limited only by the demand (desire backed by purchasing power) of subscribers.

For several years, wired-city experiments have been conducted at Erin Mills, just west of Toronto. The community developers there are determined to supply the most modern communications system possible to their homeowners and they are already providing services that include virtually all of the standard cable-television and telephone offerings. However, over 100 additional sophisticated services are also being considered. These will be introduced gradually as the community grows. Of course, all of the existing services are being monitored carefully and the results of the Erin Mills experience will no doubt be relied upon to provide guidance with respect to new services, as well as to provide information on how to proceed on larger scales. As the project develops further it will also provide an appraisal on the value and acceptance of such services by the members of the community.

One of the new services could be that of computerized shopping. Push-button telephones make this possible. In Toronto some catalogue shoppers are already beeping orders directly into a computer.

Access to film libraries has already been provided to Ottawa schools and it could be extended to individual subscribers. Banking can also be handled entirely by push-button access to computers with no cash handled and no cheques written by depositors. With the appropriate computer connections and a push-button (dial) system to handle transactions, customers would have only to pick up their telephones and make their purchases; the computers will execute all the necessary entries for both the store and the bank — in a matter of seconds.

Not all the wonders described by Marcel Vincent are by any means functions of the telephone as it is known today, but the one thing they all have in common is the requirement of a delivery system. Telephone companies are far ahead of anyone else in terms of providing such delivery networks. Denis Hall, president of Bell-Northern Research, considers Canada's existing network to be a national treasure — but a treasure that is grossly underutilized. It is not surprising, therefore, that while encouraging his research and development people to be bold in terms of new ideas and techniques, Hall also reminds them frequently to "concentrate on the wires that are already there."

To some scientists and technologists, the how of the delivery is often more exciting than the message itself. The technology of fibre optics, whereby light is transmitted through highly refined glass fibres — each one the diameter of a human hair — is the centre of considerable attention these days. Such fibres can be bundled into comparatively slim, flexible cables that are nearly impervious to environmental influences and that are capable of carrying thousands of voice channels, scores of television channels, and enormous amounts of video and digital traffic on a single cable. But even fibre optics are relegated to second place when the potential transmission ability of the laser beam, with perhaps *millions* of telephone circuits or their equivalent in data and television channels, is unlocked.

In both the Toronto and Calgary areas work is proceeding with construction of fibre optical transmission lines. Alberta Government Telephones vice-president Jack Childs says the new system being installed from Calgary to Cheadle on the TransCanada Telephone System is required to handle AGT's digital radio transmission network. It will be capable of transmitting more than 273 million units of information a second. Each optical fibre cable will handle the equivalent of more than 4,000 communication channels. The AGT system, which is expected to be on line in early 1980, will have the most extensive and most sophisticated application of fibre optics transmission at work anywhere. As Childs explains it, fibre optics transmission is akin to sending a pulse of light down a tunnel — which is reminiscent of the bemused layman over a hundred years ago who tried to explain the success of Alexander Graham Bell's device by suggesting that the voice travelled down a hole through the middle of the wire.

Of course the entire subject of optical communications is still a major field of study for telecommunications researchers. They have developed "light-emitting diodes" (LEDs) to replace the old flashlight-type bulbs used in switchboards and business telephones. Testing shows that under normal conditions LEDs can last a century or more without replacement. One scientist jokingly refers to them as "semi-infinite."

Laser transmission represents another possible giant leap forward with its potentially immense information carrying capacity — literally millions of television programmes or a billion telephone calls on a single light beam. Equally exciting is a recent proposal to use a beam of neutrino particles to send messages directly through the Earth! (The neutrino is a fundamental subatomic particle which carries no electrical charge and has virtually no mass, so it is able to pass through most matter without colliding with anything; hence, without slowing down or losing any appreciable part of its energy. Under certain conditions the neutrino can be manipulated so that in its passage from one point to another it emits both light and sound. It can also be measured with delicate instruments.) Such a system could be of tremendous importance if environmental changes, either natural or man-initiated, were to destroy the present system of radiowave telecommunication. The New York *Times* recently printed a story showing that such a system is possible within a year. One early application would be to send messages to submarines submerged deep in safe ocean retreats.

It is impossible to predict the future with any amount of certainty, but the message that seems to be coming through our crystal ball is that the wedding of the world's communications and information systems — with all of their ancillary support systems — has far-reaching implications for Canadians. Certainly, the availability of a low-priced switchable computer terminal, linked through the telephone network to service facilities and data banks around the globe, will eventually provide Canadian users with the greatest possible access to the world's accumulated knowledge. Canadians will have the benefit of the world's largest library, movie house, store, newspaper, radio and television station, museum, directory, art gallery or any other information source. Users will be able to obtain answers to every conceivable question from the state of one's bank account, or the date of a wedding anniversary or the time of a lunch date, to the specialties of all the French restaurants in Montreal or Paris or the Chinese restaurants in Vancouver or Hong Kong — with menus if required — along with addresses and phone numbers for reservations. Updated traffic and weather reports will be available as a matter of course and even medical and perhaps legal advice will be available. The integrated system of the future will be the repository for all sorts of information, which will be readily accessible and available to all.

Bell's Alex Lester once remarked that he hoped future generations wouldn't spend all their time communicating. In his view, it is going to be just as important then, as it is now, to spend some time thinking.

Probably more than any other group in Canada today, TCTS, through its member companies, is thinking about and shaping this country's telecommunications future. In a sense, the telecommunications symphony that future generations of Canadians will listen to is being scored now. And it is the *telephone* and the telephone carrier systems that are the featured instruments in the orchestration. The member companies of the TransCanada Telephone System have served notice that they firmly intend to try to supply the services Canadians want, or at the very least, provide the medium or media by which such services are conveyed. They are well-placed to do so because of their vast, already established networks connecting most homes and offices in Canada. The companies are already working with and carrying computer data; and they have perfected workable systems for renting equipment to the public at large, charging for services, maintaining complicated equipment, providing myriad support services and generally operating a large and complex facility at a high level of efficiency.

Communications and information are certain to become the two indispensable elements of life in tomorrow's world. The people at TCTS are equally certain that if they do not provide the essential framework and faciliites to accommodate these elements, the country will not only lose its pre-eminent position in the world-scheme of telecommunications, the average Canadian will also be the loser for decades to come.

5

Beyond Tomorrow
The Information Age

Past successes are seen only as the prologue to tomorrow by telecommunications scientists, whose focus is on the future. Their knowledge has been so expanded and technology has become so advanced in recent years that, to a large extent, they must choose from among numerous possible futures in deciding goals toward which their science, technology and innovative talent should be directed."
"*The Vital Link* – Telecommunications Serving Canada"

A cartoon in a recent issue of *The Financial Post* shows an executive addressing a roomful of employees. He is saying: "As of September first, I'm sorry to say, you will all be replaced by a tiny chip of silicon."

Which is all good and well if you happen to be one of the proponents of the wired-city concept of the future and you are certain that everyone will be working at home anyway. But as Vernon Leworthy points out, the notion of the wired city means different things to different people and not everyone, he suggests, will want to work at home no matter what advanced gadgetry is available to make it possible. He is supported in this view by Gordon Thompson, a senior scientist at Bell-Northern Research, one of a new breed of telecommunicators, who describes his job simply as "thinking."

In his office in Ottawa — a fascinating cubby-hole that looks as if he had just moved in from an office twice as big and brought everything with him, including a few trophies from his collegiate days along with some items he picked up at a recent science fair — Thompson suggests that the coming information age will and

264

must be completely different from the industrial era.

"If we try to deal with information technology the same way we do with industrial technology, we will be putting new wine into old skins," he warns.

Thompson believes that the TransCanada Telephone System has an important place in the new era and that like the bumblebee, TCTS will continue to fly. But he is also convinced that people of TCTS must recognize that the nature of their organization has been changing steadily since it was founded nearly 50 years ago and that over the years ahead their objectives will change more dramatically than ever in order to meet the changing needs of the people the organization is serving.

He agrees with science writer John Kettle who sees us already well into the information age. According to Kettle: "Our age, like all others before it, has a vision and a crusade which we pursue with religious ardour and devotion. The object of that crusade is information. For the twentieth century it is the equivalent of the Church, the Empire, and the Englightenment all rolled into one."

In Canada and the United States, a large part of the total work-force is already involved, in one way or another, in the "information" sector, but it receives very little recognition as a creator of wealth in our economic system. Only the industrial, service and agricultural sectors are recognized as legitimate creators of the GNP. In both Canada and the U.S., a strikingly high percentage of the total labour dollar goes into the pockets of researchers, journalists, educators, bureaucrats and others involved in various aspects of information. If this represents cause for concern it must be that productivity — notably in the government sector — is abysmally low."

In Thompson's opinion, if information is to be sold as a "commodity" in the technologically sophisticated marketplace of tomorrow, that information must be rich and varied. It must satisfy needs far more sophisticated than those which currently exist and which are now satisfied by — what he calls Big-Mac "infoburgers" — sold at newstands and available off the shelves of conventional libraries. He claims that in "tomorrow's information marketplace, ordinary people will have an opportunity to create capital by peddling their creations — music, essays, poems, stories, theses, games, jokes and other products generated from leisure-time diversions — to an enormous national or international communications bank. Users will have to plug into the system for the subject of their choice and pay a fee for audio recordings, video information and print-outs. Depositors would also pay a monthly fee for the privilege of having access to the system. If the depositors or "producers" fall behind on payments, or the demand for their products disappears, those products will be withdrawn.

The creation of information is an altogether different process from most technological processes. Obviously, writing a book is not the same as building an automobile. Composers and writers, for example, do not work in factories or large organizations. Most of them are "entrepreneurs" in their own right. Similarly, tomorrow's significant contributors to the information marketplace will be independent entrepreneurs. Their activities will be widely diffused throughout the population.

Thompson and other advocates of such information marketplaces are probably overstating the case somewhat when they suggest that the system they proclaim will free 50 to 80 per cent of tomorrow's Canadians from the bondage of wage earning; but such a system, nonetheless, could be a very useful mechanism for removing the barriers of costly, inefficient and antiquated methods of publication and distribution between information producers and consumers. Outmoded delivery systems could be easily replaced by the technologically superior systems and transmission facilities available from the TCTS group of companies. In real terms, such an arrangement is possible right now. The essential delivery network is already in place. Only the matters relating to producer "input" and consumer "takeout" have to be worked out.

Many data banks are already in place and are being expanded. A system in the U.S. called INFOMART offers access to over a score of other data bases including the index of the holdings in the Library of Congress — over two million books listed by author, title and subject! The New York *Times* information bank gives access to every article published in the *Times* over the past decade and is being expanded all the time to include not only earlier issues but many articles from other newspapers and publications. There are also dozens of data banks in Canada — for doctors, lawyers, oilmen, librarians, engineers, politicians, farmers and teachers. The Ontario city of Mississauga, just outside Toronto, is even building a data base for its firemen which will provide them with valuable fire-fighting information on every building in that city. Such information banks represent a beginning, but they are not as "convivial" (to use Thompson's terminology) as future systems will be.

The image that grips the imagination of thousands of people in the knowledge industry is that of a worldwide information grid which will allow everyone on the globe to reach every bit of knowledge — information — that has ever been produced: every book, newspaper article, speech in a legislature, movie and television programme, photograph or painting, airline schedule, catalogue or index, thesis and research study, lecture, radio programme, patent and all sorts of

266

The TransCanada Service Coordination Centre is the nerve centre of the
TCTS network. The illuminated display board gives an "at-a-glance"
reading of the status of the network.

other data — literally all the intelligence, thought and other recorded experience
of the human race.

Such a grid or system would be nothing less than a new mass medium which
could, if properly understood and used, revolutionize the world's economies and
our way of life. Facilities and services within the framework of such a system could
only be provided by an organization such as TCTS, which can take proper
advantage of the economies of scale, and which has the resources, the manpower,
the experience and the desire to tackle the job.

Such a system could have a far greater impact on the modern world than the
Industrial Revolution had on Europe 200 years ago — particularly if it is seen as a
totally new technology and not just as an add-on to industrial technology.
Improper, careless or thoughtless use of the new information technology will only
add to our current economic and social problems.

There are, of course, problems that have to be considered before deciding
finally on any plan of action. The problems are fundamental and it is therefore no
accident they are essentially the same as those troubling politicians, economists,
scientists and ordinary citizens all over the world today. In a sense, these problems
in combination are like the elephant that was examined by four blind men; each
man had good evidence to conclude that the animal is like a tree, a snake, a leaf
and a wall. Clearly, there are times when there is no substitute for "vision."

Thompson has identified five problem areas which relate specifically to the current state of industrial technology, and which are therefore central to any consdieration of a sytem that may displace that technology:

1) There must be a real growth in Gross National Product in order to keep industrial technology alive. There are not enough resources, however, to sustain such growth.

2) Industrial technology has become so complicated and so massive that it requires centralist control. In democratic societies, however, centralist controls are largely abhorred.

3) In today's society if a person has a job, he has a role. If one is a student *preparing* for a job he also has a role. But if a person is unemployed, he is a misfit. Efficient industrial technology is geared to eliminate jobs. How do we reconcile an expanding population with a technology that is dedicated to reducing the overall number of jobs?

4) Because consumption is one of the cornerstones of industrial technology, the system must stimulate demand by persuading consumers that goods are "scarce." But goods are not scarce; modern Western society is the most productive ever to exist.

5) The distribution of natural and other resources around the world is inequitable. Industrial technology pits the unacceptable cost of sharing the Earth's resources equally with the consequential cost of not sharing. As a result, the gap between rich and poor nations continues to widen.

Clearly, these problems are not going to be solved simply by the application of more of the same technology that created them in the first place. And indeed, they are not the only problems. But many people in the Canadian telecommunications business are beginning to believe that the new information technology, serviced by existing communications systems, could be an important part of the solution. The implication of this is a new telecommunications system that is literally a new mass medium. According to Thompson, there are three components: the information marketplace, the "serendipity machine," and ideographic writing.

The *information marketplace* is a system that treats information as a private "commodity" that can be exchanged in the marketplace the same way we buy and sell cars. This envisions a true private enterprise system in which "authors" are rewarded for the information or commodity they produce (which is input into the data banks of a computer system) in direct proportion to the usage of that information by "consumers." Each consumer would pay a fee to access any of the information held in any of the available data banks.

The *serendipity machine* is an adaption of the educational use of computers developed under a scheme known as Computer Aided Learning. The machine itself is essentially a video terminal that has a variety of capabilities. In computer-aided learning the user can determine the most appropriate type of information required at each successive learning stage. Kindred users can be identified and communication paths can be established between such users. It is this feature that gives the machine its name.

Ideographic writing is the use of symbols or pictures to communicate as opposed to a phonic alphabet. Chinese, Japanese and Ancient Egyptian writing are examples. The major constraint of a phonic alphabet is that because so much depends on context it is extremely difficult to apply simply and accurately. A relatively simple ideographic language has already been developed and is currently being taught — with exciting results — to verbally handicapped children. An ideograph keyboard and graphics display terminal along with the requisite computer-processing facilities are all that is needed. These items are already available at relatively low cost.

The information marketplace, given convenience and conviviality by communications networks, willl also compete with television for our time. In many respects, television as we know it today is an ephemeral medium. That is, the images are there — then gone. There is no opportunity to stop at any point; the individual viewer cannot recall any given programme or part of a programme (except by expensive and bulky video-taping equipment). The new medium, through the use of the home computer terminal, will be totally and easily recallable. Because television programming in the new medium will be controlled entirely by the producers who make the shows, the new medium will be paced by the user; instead of offering programmes designed to appeal essentially to mass viewing, the new medium will offer much more material suited to individual tastes. Users will be able to select programmes most in line with their individual tastes, inerests and language. In addition, the new medium will have the very important feature — like the telephone — of being usable by 'plain folks' with relatively little training.

"One of the paradoxes of the telephone business right now," according to Thompson, "is that we have been responsible for more technological development than most other industries on this continent. That means that we are very solidly placed in the technological environment which we are now trying to break out of. Our problem is our inability to use our existing communications media correctly to nurture new ideas. We already have most of the technology we need but, unfortuantely, we are wasting our money and our energy spinning our wheels. That, to my way of thinking, is the challenge to the TransCanada Telephone System — to get the Hell out where it is and quit fiddling around and invent the 'son of the telephone.' If the new information technology is properly structured, it will allow new ideas to flourish instead of killing them off; the new system offers every person the chance to write his own ticket.

"The widespread use of the 'new' technology of writing helped create the hundred golden years in Athens. The printing press helped produce the Renaissance. If communications innovations can trigger or stimulate such developments, then surely there is no better candidate than this new medium with its intelligent, almost universal network, and its intelligent terminals, to be the catalyst for yet another great age of Man."

Provider and User
As Close as a Dog is to its Tail

Telephony is the nervous system of our civilization and, like Ariadne's thread, assures modern man's survival in the immense labyrinth of our great urban centres.

In Search, by Jean-Pierre Plant (Department of Communications Publication, Summer 1974)

The story of the TransCanada Telephone System — that bumblebee of world telecommunications — traces a specific aspect of telephony in Canada: long distance. The early years were fraught with difficulty, not only in terms of hard times and war, but also in terms of the sheer geography of Canada and the disparate nature of its many regions. In retrospect, some people may consider it remarkable that TCTS was able to achieve anything at all, much less anything great! What is truly remarkable, however, is that as an organization TCTS has well-served the needs of its individual members and, in so doing, has provided an outstanding level of service to the Canadian public.

The original thread of copper that TCTS stretched across a continent nearly fifty years ago has been expanded to form a vast network of facilities that now connects virtually every home and business in Canada. As well as providing for the telecommunications needs of private citizens and Canadian business, that same network today carries a majority of the continent's radio and television programming and plays an important role in connection with many vital defence and research activities.

Co-ordinated research and planning, drawing upon many of the best minds in the country and using many of the latest technological developments, have enabled TCTS to combine many subsystems into an efficient, integrated network which functions under uniform standards and operating techniques and which co-ordinates perfectly with other continental and world-wide networks.

In real terms, the development of the TransCanada network has made a lasting and significant contribution to the economic, cultural, social and political life of Canada. In my view, that is an important contribution and one in which I believe the organization can genuinely take pride.

But what about tomorrow?

Although there is little agreement among scientific pundits as to precisely what will happen, prospects are nonetheless intriguing. Unquestionably, the world of the future will have the benefit of a long list of electronic conveniences which we can only marvel at now. The fact that some of those conveniences may carry with them concomitant losses in terms of individuality, personal privacy, taste and perhaps even decency, represents a problem which the architects of our future society will have to resolve.

TCTS has nearly 50 years of experience, knowledge and expertise to contribute toward the continuing growth and development of one of the best telecommunications systems in the world. The organization can offer its skills, provide most of the facilities, make alternatives known and hope that the "right" decisions are made. However, those decisions are largely the responsibility of the users of telecommunications services; it is up to them to decide what they want.

The technology developed and the services provided by TCTS will reflect the needs of users; usage will depend upon the technology developed. If that sounds like a dog chasing its own tail, the analogy is valid because the providers and the users of telecommunications services must stay about that close to each other.

The member companies of the TransCanada Telephone System are determined to use all the new and emerging technological developments to meet both existing and future telecommunications needs and to ensure that Canada's place is maintained in the forefront of world telecommunications. It is possible to achieve this, in part, by continuing the spirit of service and dedication which was exemplified by Charles Fleetford Sise. Sise carried high ideals of personal honour into the everyday business of building a telephone system in Canada. Like him, the leaders of TCTS hold that a great public service corporation should be a good public servant.

The telephone has been a precious boon to all mankind. For Canadians, who populate the second-largest country in the world, it has meant the virtual elimination of distance. If the telephone hasn't yet made neighbours of us all, it's not because the TransCanada Telephone System isn't trying!

Appendices

Chief Executives of TCTS
TCTS Organization Chart
The Policy of TCTS

Chief Executives of TCTS

P. A. McFarlane, Bell Canada
Chairman, 1932-1945

H. G. Young, Bell Canada
Chairman, 1958-1962

J. C. Carlile, B.C. Tel
President, 1971-1974

R. V. Macaulay, Bell Canada
Chairman, 1945-1951

T. W. Eadie, Bell Canada
Chairman, 1952-1958

A. J. Groleau, Bell Canada
Chairman, 1963

Z. H. Krupski, Bell Canada
Chairman, 1964-1971

E. D. Thompson, NBTel
President, 1974-1977

T. F. Heenan, B.C. Tel
President, 1978-

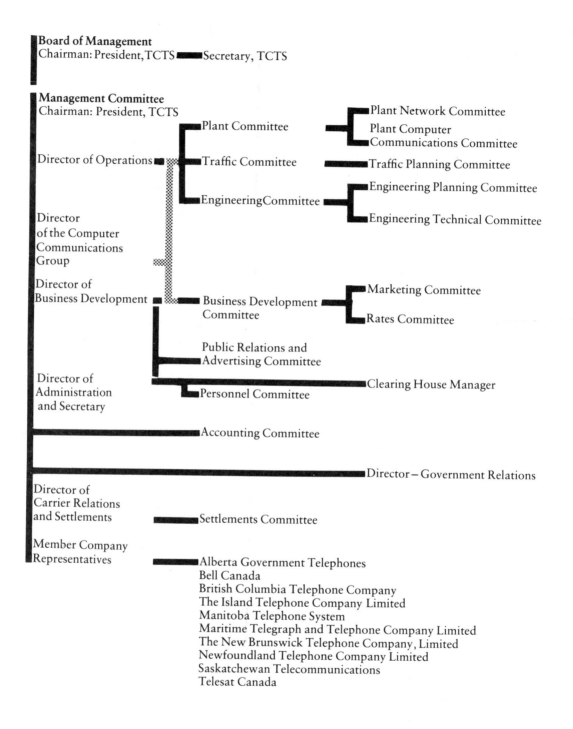

Board of Management
Chairman: President, TCTS ━━ Secretary, TCTS

Management Committee
Chairman: President, TCTS

Plant Committee
 ┏ Plant Network Committee
 ┗ Plant Computer Communications Committee

Director of Operations

Traffic Committee ━━ Traffic Planning Committee

EngineeringCommittee
 ┏ Engineering Planning Committee
 ┗ Engineering Technical Committee

Director of the Computer Communications Group

Director of Business Development

Business Development Committee
 ┏ Marketing Committee
 ┗ Rates Committee

Public Relations and Advertising Committee

Director of Administration and Secretary

Clearing House Manager

Personnel Committee

Accounting Committee

Director – Government Relations

Director of Carrier Relations and Settlements

Settlements Committee

Member Company Representatives

Alberta Government Telephones
Bell Canada
British Columbia Telephone Company
The Island Telephone Company Limited
Manitoba Telephone System
Maritime Telegraph and Telephone Company Limited
The New Brunswick Telephone Company, Limited
Newfoundland Telephone Company Limited
Saskatchewan Telecommunications
Telesat Canada

276

The Policy of TransCanada Telephone System

The TransCanada Telephone System is organized, by compact of its members, to provide Canadians with a full range of national telecommunications services. The System arranges to extend services beyond Canadian territory in conjunction with Teleglobe Canada or by direct negotiation as appropriate. Services under the functional jurisdiction of the System are designated by its Board of Management, and do not normally include services solely within a member's territory.

The purpose of the TransCanada Telephone System is to fulfil the national telecommunications requirements of the Canadian people and to work in the public interest by providing a comprehensive range of services of the highest quality at reasonable cost, consistent with the financial needs and obligations of its members.

Therefore, recognizing its economic and social obligations, the System will continue:

1. To make a broad range of high-quality services widely available throughout Canada at reasonable rates appropriate to the Canadian environment;
2. to foster and introduce technical innovation in a timely and economic manner so as to constantly improve the quality, reliability, scope and value of its services;
3. to assume its full responsibility for meeting telecommunications requirements for defence, national emergency and government services, including incorporation of a high degree of survivability into the network;
4. to provide people with telecommunications services of a type and scope that will assist in achieving national objectives;
5. to market its services actively in a manner which will benefit all users of telecommunications services;
6. to make facilities available for any specific telecommunications requirement, but in so doing, to jeopardize neither the technical or service excellence of the total network available to the public, nor the financial obligations of its members;
7. to make effective use of its resources to the fullest extent practicable, including the encouragement of Canadian research and development;
8. to expand and utilize the resources and technical competence of its members in order to achieve the efficiency and effectiveness necessary for competitive operation;
9. to optimize the financial return of each member over the long term in order to meet financial needs and obligations;
10. to divide jointly earned revenues through processes which, by agreement, are fair and equitable to each member;
11. to assist in the development of regulatory processes appropriate to the Canadian environment.

Chronology

1874

Invention of "the electric speaking-telephone" by Alexander Graham Bell at Tutelo Heights in Brantford, Ontario. (July 24)

1875

First telephone constructed and speech sounds heard on Gallows frame instrument. (June 2)

First draft of telephone patent specifications prepared by Bell. (September)

1876

U.S. patent number 174465 issued to Bell on his 29th birthday. (March 3)

First intelligible message transmitted over telephone — "Mr. Watson, come here. I want you." (March 10)

World's first long distance call made from Brantford to Paris, Ontario. (August 10)

1877

First lease of telephones made; to Hugh C. Baker, Charles D. Cory, Mrs. J.R. Thomson and T.C. Mewburn of Hamilton, Ontario, on August 29. Leases signed October 18.

1877

Two telephones leased to federal Government to connect Prime Minister Alexander Mackenzie and Governor-General, Lord Dufferin. Lease signed November 9, but backdated to September 21 by Professor Melville Bell so it could be designated the first telephone lease signed in Canada.

First permanent outdoor telephone line erected between Boston office of Charles Williams, electrical manufacturer and his home in Somerville, Massachusetts. (April 4)

First telephone rented for business purposes to two young lawyers connecting their Boston office and the home of one of them. (May 1)

First telephones used in a mine installed in Caledonia Colliery at Glace Bay (also first two telephones in Nova Scotia). (August)

Mine mechanic William Wall builds first telephones in British Columbia for use in coal mine near Nanaimo.

1878

First telephones installed in Manitoba by Horace McDougall connecting his Winnipeg home with the telegraph office where he worked. (March 1)

First two Bell telephones in Victoria, B.C. installed by R.B. McMicking. (March 22)

First two telephones installed in New Brunswick by G. & G. Flewwelling at Hampton. (March 1)

Postmaster-General John Delaney and meteorologist John Higgins connect homes with first two telephones in Newfoundland. (March 20)

First telephone exchange opened in the U.S. in New Haven, Conneticut. (January 28)

1879

National Bell Telephone Company in U.S. acquires Canadian rights to telephone from Bell family.

Canada's first long distance line erected between Hamilton and Dundas, Ontario, by Hamilton District Telephone Company.

First telephone exchange in Canada and the British Empire (ninth in the world) opened in Hamilton. (July 15)

1880

Bell Telephone Company of Canada incorporated. (April 29)

Victoria and Esquimalt Telephone Company incorporated just 10 days after Bell in Ontario, becoming the first telephone company in British Columbia and Western Canada. (May 8)

"Hello" adopted as official greeting at convention of Bell Telephone companies in Niagara Falls, New York. (September)

1882

The forerunner of today's Northern Telecom Limited established by the Bell Telephone Company of Canada as a manufacturing department to make telephone equipment. (July 24)

Ida Cates of Winnipeg hired as first female switchboard operator, in Manitoba.

1883
First private telephone lines installed on Prince Edward Island.

North West Mounted Police make first use of telephone, in Regina.

1885
The Telephone Company of Prince Edward Island founded. (July 8)

First Vancouver telephone exchange opened in Tilley's bookstore (in what was then known as Granville). (October 19)

1888
New Brunswick Telephone Company incorporated. (April 6)

First metallic circuit built; between Hamilton and Toronto.

1891
Vernon and Nelson Telephone Company incorporated. (April 20)

1892
Legislation passed by Canadian Government to ban raising of rates without Parliamentary approval.

1904
Name of Vernon and Nelson Telephone Company changed to British Columbia Telephone Company. (July 5)

1905
Select Committe of House of Commons investigates the Canadian telephone industry but declines to make recommendations. (Summer)

1906
Alberta Government Telephones incorporated. (May 8)

1907
First provincial regulatory legislation in Nova Scotia controlling telephone companies passed. (April 13)

1908
Manitoba interests of Bell Telephone Company bought out and Manitoba Telephone System incorporated. (January 15)

Department of Railways, Telegraph and Telephones created in Saskatchewan (changed to Saskatchewan Telecommunications in 1947). (June 12)

Takeover of Bell Telephone Company interests in Alberta by provincial government. (April 1)

1909
Takeover of Bell Telephone Company interests in Saskatchewan by provincial government. (January 15)

1910
Maritime Telegraph and Telephone Company buys The Prince Edward Island Telephone Company. (June 28)

1911
Nova Scotia Telephone Company bought by Maritime Telegraph and Telephone Company.

1912
First telephone employees' labour union formed by Telephone Workers Association of New Brunswick. (June 26)

1915
First transcontinental telephonic communication, between New York and San Francisco. (January 29)

1916
First transcontinental call in Canada, from Montreal to Vancouver, routed through U.S. (February 14)

Western Canada Telephone Company formed. (March 17)

1919
Avalon Telephone Company incorporated in Newfoundland (name changed to Newfoundland Telephone Company Limited in 1970). (December)

Name of Western Canada Telephone Company changed to British Columbia Telephone Company Limited. (December 23)

1920
Regular commercial service opened between Bell Telephone Company of Canada and the Atlantic provinces. (January)

Western Canadian Telephone convention held

at Winnipeg; forerunner of Telephone Association of Canada. (October 13-15)

1921

First meeting of Telephone Association of Canada held in Vancouver. Members agree to study "All-Red" toll route. (August 22-27)

1923

British Columbia Telephone Company acquires all assets of British Columbia Telephone Company Limited. (February 8)

Canada's first publicly owned radio station, CKY in Winnipeg, opened. (July)

Prairie provinces' telephone networks interconnected. (August 28)

Canada's first chain or network radio broadcast, sponsored by CNR between Ottawa and Montreal.

Installation of radios on CNR trains. (December)

1925

Alberta interconnected to U.S. continental network.

1926

Winnipeg connected to Fort William. (May 5)

Winnipeg and Manitoba linked with Chicago and U.S. network via U.S. continental network. (December 22)

1927

Canada united by cross-country radio, telegraph and telephone hookup for diamond jubilee. (July 1)

Calgary-Vancouver linked by telephone for first time. (November 6)

Controlling interest in British Columbia Telephone Company bought by Theodore Gary and Company interests of Kansas City (December)

1928

Winnipeg and Sudbury connected. (August 7)

Bell authorized by Telephone Association of Canada to prepare study on a coast-to-coast all-Canadian line, from Halifax to Vancouver. (August 24-28)

Quebec City, Quebec and Saint John, New Brunswick, connected. (December 16)

1929

North-West Telephone Company established in British Columbia to service northwest coastal area. (March 20)

Report on "All-Red" toll line submitted to and accepted by committee named by TAC to set up and co-ordinate construction. (August 31)

1931

Seven major Canadian telephone companies sign agreement creating the Trans-Canada Telephone System. (March 1)

Clearing house set up to handle distribution of revenue to Trans-Canada Telephone System members. (August 1)

Cross-country toll circuit completed; beginning of business for TCTS in September.

1932

TCTS cross-country line formally dedicated and declared open. (January 25)

Canadian Radio Broadcasting Commission established. (May 26)

1933

CNCP telegraph companies awarded radio transmission contracts. (April 1)

1936

Canadian Broadcasting Corporation established. (November 2)

1939

First Newfoundland radio-telephone hookup with mainland. (January 10)

TCTS equips royal train with telephone service for Royal Visit of King George and Queen Elizabeth. (May 17-June 10)

1941

Building of land line communication system for Alcan highway completed by Alberta Government Telephones with assistance from Bell Canada (2,830 miles of line erected in 8 months). (December 1)

1943-44

Château Frontenac and Citadel specially wired for Quebec Conference of wartime leaders with Churchill, Roosevelt and Mackenzie King.

1948

Prince Edward Island and Nova Scotia establish first Canadian microwave link. (November 19)

1953
TCTS invited to send token force to assist in construction of DEW Line.

1955
General Telephone and Electronics of U.S. acquires controlling interest in British Columbia Telephone Company. (October 31)

1956
Completion of first troposcatter system in the world, linking eastern Arctic with lower Canada. (October 31)

1957
Avalon Telephone joins TCTS. (June 3)
Completion of Mid-Canada Line. (June)

1958
New full division revenue settlement plan adopted by TCTS. (June 1)
Inauguration of new trans-Canada microwave network by TCTS makes possible coast-to-coast Canadian television in Canada. (July 1)

1961
CTV network opened.

1962
Launching of Alouette I, Canada's first artificial Earth satellite for experimental purposes.

1964
CNCP microwave network completed.

1969
Telesat Canada incorporated, first communications satellite system. (September 1)

1970
Launching of Anik I, Canada's first commercial domestic geostationary communications satellite. (November 9)

1972
Canadian Telecommunications Carriers Association formed. (February 8)

1973
Dataroute, world's first digital transmission network, established by TCTS. (February 21)
Anik II launched. (April 20)

1974
Global TV opens.

1975
Anik III launched. (May 7)
The Island Telephone Company Limited joins TCTS. (September 1)

1976
Datapac, the first switched network digital transmission, established by TCTS.

1977
Telesat Canada joins TCTS. (Janaury 1)
New revenue-sharing plan adopted by TCTS.

Glossary

Address: 1. In communication – the coded representation of the destination of a message. 2. In computing – the coded representation of the location of a set of data in storage.

Alphanumeric: Made up of letters (alphabetic) and numbers (numeric).

Alternating current (AC): An electrical current that reverses at regularly recurring intervals of time, and that has alternating positive and negative values.

AM: Amplitude modulation.

Amplifier: A unidirectional device which increases the power or amplitude of an electrical signal.

Amplitude modulation (AM): The process of modifying the amplitude of a carrier wave with a signal; e.g., AM radio.

Analogue: Pertaining to representation by means of continuously variable physical quantities.

Attenuation: The difference (loss) between transmitted and received power due to transmission loss through equipment, lines or other communications devices.

Audio: Frequencies which can be heard by the human ear (usually between 15,000 and 20,000 Hz).

Band: A range of frequencies between two defined limits; e.g., the voiceband in telephony is about 300 to 3,000 Hz.

Bandwidth: The difference between the upper and lower limits of a band; e.g., bandwidth of a voice channel is 3,000 (300 equals 2,700 Hz).

Bit: A contraction of the term binary digit. A bit can be either 0 or 1 and is the smallest possible unit of information.

Broadband: Refers to transmission facilities whose bandwidth (range of frequencies they will handle) is greater than that available on voice grade facilities. Also called wideband.

Broadcast: The ability to send messages or communicate with many or all points on a circuit simultaneously.

Cable: An assembly of one or more insulated wires in a common protective sheath.

Cable, coaxial: A cable consisting of one or more tubes, each of which has a wire contained within and insulated from a surrounding conductor. Large numbers of individual circuits can be derived from a coaxial cable by means of carrier and multiplexing techniques.

Carrier system: A method of obtaining or deriving several channels from one communication path by combining them at the originating end, transmitting a wideband or highspeed signal and then recovering the original information at the receiving end.

Carrier wave: A single frequency signal of constant amplitude which may be modulated or modified with respect to frequency, amplitude or phase for transportation over a wire, cable or radio facility.

Cathode ray tube (CRT): A television-like picture tube which on receipt of information bearing electronic signals produces a visual display of the information. *See visual display unit, Vucom.*

Central office: The location of telephone switching equipment where customers' lines are terminated and interconnected. Also called switching centre.

Centrex: A type of private branch exchange service where incoming calls may be dialed direct to extensions without operator assistance. Out-going and intercom calls are dialed by extension users.

Channel: An electrical transmission path between two or more stations. Channels may be furnished by wire, radio or a combination of both.

Circuit: A physical transmission path between two or more points.

Circuit switching: A method of communications where an electrical connection between calling and called stations is established on demand for exclusive use of the circuit until the connection is released.

Common carrier telecommunications: Telecommunications provided by an administration or private operating agency and intended mainly, in a public correspondence service, for the transmission, emission or reception of signs, signals, written images and sounds or intelligence of a nature by wire, radio, optical or other electromagnetic systems between specific points subject to appropriate remuneration. Common carrier telecommunications may include several branches; e.g., telegraph service, telephone service, data transmission service.

Computer: An automatic electronic machine capable of carrying out arithmetic or logic operations on data which are presented to it at the input and of providing numerical results or decisions at the output. Three types of computers may be distinguished. Analogue computers – the information is in analogue form and is processed in this form (a magnitude is represented by a voltage). Digital computers – the information is in binary form (series of zeros and ones). Hybrid computers – these combine the characteristics of the two previous types. A computer can also act as a communications terminal when it accepts or supplies data to remote terminals over a telecommunications line. Also there are many sizes of computers which differ in scope and price.

Connecting agreements: Agreements between two or more telecommunications carriers in which are specified the terms under which their respective physical facilities will be connected and the manner in which jointly earned revenues will be settled between them.

Cross arm: The horizontal bar on a telephone pole supporting the glass insulators to which telephone lines are attached.

Cross talk: Interference between two telephone channels arising from the coupling between them.

CRTC: Canadian Radio- television and Telecommunications Commission – the regulatory federal authority for commercial radio and TV broadcasters, cable system operators, and communications common carriers.

CTCA: Canadian Telecommunications Carriers Association – the body that represents the interests of Canada's communications common carriers.

Data base: A collection of data fundamental to an enterprise. A data base can be a file, computer, etc., i.e., any medium which contains in-

formation pertinent to an organization.

Data communications: The movement of encoded information by means of electrical transmission systems. The transfer of data between points of origin and reception, including all manual and machine operations necessary to transfer such data.

Datapac network: A nationwide, common-user, packet-switched data network provided by The Computer Communications Group of the TransCanada Telephone System.

Data Processing: The use of a computer for the processing of information. Processing involves the use of the computer for operations that include the functions of storing, retrieving, sorting, merging and calculating data according to programmed instructions.

Dataroute: A private line digital transmission system for data provided by The Computer Communications Group of the TransCanada Telephone System. It can be accessed via the DDD network and/or by analogue private line services.

Dial Up: The use of a rotary dial or Touch-Tone telephone to initiate a station-to-station telephone call.

Digital: Pertaining to digits or the representation of data or physical quantities by digits.

Digital multiplex switching system (DMS): A family of switching systems utilizing new technology that will provide digital circuit switched service for voice and data transmission. DMS is characterized by the use of pulse code modulation (PCM) and time division multiplexing (TDM) throughout the switched network. The system allows the direct switching of PCM signals used in transmission systems without their conversion to analogue format.

Digitize (digitalize): The process of converting analogue signals to digital form.

Direct connection: A facility which avoids the use of address selection signals on a packet switched data network. The network interprets the call request signal as an instruction to establish a connection with a single destination address previously designated by the user.

Direct distance dialing (DDD): A telephone service which enables users to directly dial telephones outside the user's local exchange area without the aid of an operator.

Direct inward dialing (DID): A feature of Centrex systems where incoming calls are completed to extensions without the need of an operator.

Extended area service (EAS): Telephone service that allows customers in an exchange to pay flat monthly or measured rates instead of long distance charges for calls to nearby exchange areas. Most exchanges in large metropolitan areas have EAS.

Facsimile: Transmission of pictures, maps, diagrams, etc. The image is scanned at the transmitter, reconstructed at the receiving station, and duplicated on some form of paper or film.

Faxcom: A facsimile communications service offered by the TransCanada Telephone System which allows for the transmission of graphics (written, drawn, typed) over the DDD network.

Fibre optics transmission system (FOTS): A transmission system utilizing small diameter glass fibres through which light is transmitted. Information is transferred by modulating the transmitted light. These modulated signals are detected by light-sensitive semiconductor devices (photodiode).

Flat rate service: A service which is provided for a fixed monthly charge regardless of usage.

Frequency modulation (FM): The process of modifying the frequency of a carrier wave in step with the amplitude variations of the signal to be transmitted; e.g., the 202 Series Data Sets are frequency modulated.

Giga: Greek word meaning one billion. Used as a prefix in the international system of measurements; e.g., gigahertz, that is one billion cycles per second.

Grade of service: A measurement of the quality of communications service in terms of the availability of circuits when calls are to be made. Grade of service is based on the busiest hour of the day and is measured in either per cent calls blocked for dial access situations, or average delay for manual situations.

Group, Channel: A unit or organization on telephone carrier (multiplex) systems. A full-group is a channel equivalent to 12 voice grade channels (48 kHz). A half-group has the equivalent bandwidth of six voice grade channels (24 kHz). When not subdivided into voice facilities, group channels can be used for high-speed data communication.

Hard copy: A printout of information on either plain paper or business forms. A permanent visible record of data as opposed to other forms of visual display which cannot be retained for future use.

Hard drawn copper wire: Copper wire annealed to increase its tensile strength.

Harmonic: Frequencies which are multiples of some fundamental frequency. The presence or absence of harmonic components in a signal changes both the shape of the AC wave and its tonal qualities. For example, 2,000 Hz is the second harmonic of 1,000 Hz.

Hertz: Internationally recognized unit of measure for electrical frequency. The number of cycles per second. Abbreviation is Hz.

Hollerith code: Code used to represent data on punched cards. Data is represented by holes punched in one or more of 12 positions in each column. The 12 positions are divided into two sections. One is numbered 1 to 9 and the other, 11 and 12, which may also be referred to as X and Y or zone punches. 0 can be either a numbered or zone punch.

Induction: The transfer of the flow of alternating current from one part of a circuit to another.

Information retrieval: A system or technique concerned with searching large quantities of stored information and making selected information available.

Integrated circuit: An electronic circuit or array of components etched into a single chip of silicon material. Used in third generation computers and other equipment to reduce size and increase speed and reliability.

Interface: A shared boundary. The connection point between two subsystems or devices. Typically, the connection between business machines and the data set, modem or communications channel.

J Carrier system: A broadband carrier system providing 12 channels and using frequencies up to 14 kHz.

Kilo: Greek word meaning 1,000. Used as a prefix in the international system of measurements; e.g., kiloHerz.

Lineman: A person who sets up or repairs communication lines.

Link: 1. A transmission path between two stations, channels or parts of communications system. 2. In telephony – a path which interconnects lines in a common control switching system.

Magicall: A telephone accessory which can store up to 400 telephone numbers and dial any of them automatically at the push of a button.

Message switching: The switching technique of receiving a message, storing it until the proper outgoing circuit and station are available, and then retransmitting it toward its destination. Also known as store-and-forward switching.

Micro: Greek word meaning one-millionth of a unit. Used as a prefix in the international system of measurements; e.g., microsecond, that is 0.000001 of a second. Commonly expressed as 10-6.

Microwave: A high capacity transmission system which transmits extremely high radio frequencies over line-of-sight distances between relay stations. Microwave provides very wide bandwidths at low interference levels.

Milli: Greek word meaning one-thousandth of a unit. Used as a prefix in the international system of measurements; e.g., millisecond, that is 0.001 of a second. Commonly expressed as 10-3.

Minicomputer: The class of stored programme digital computers which are suitable for general purpose applications but are smaller and cheaper and have less capacity than general purpose computers.

Modulation: A process whereby a signal is transformed from its original form into a signal that is more suitable for transmission over the medium between the transmitter and the receiver.

Multicom: An umbrella name for a number of switched communications services provided by The Computer Communications Group of the TransCanada Telephone System offering alternate voice and data transmissions at speeds up to 50 kbps.

Multiplexing: Techniques to combine several communications channels into one facility or transmission path.

Nano: Greek work meaning one-billionth of a unit. Used as a prefix in the international system of measurements; e.g. nanosecond, that is 0.000000001 of a second. Commonly expressed as 10-9.

Network: A series of points interconnected by communications channels, often on a switched basis. Networks are either common to all users (e.g., the DDD and multicom networks) or privately leased by a customer for his own use.

Operations research (OR): One branch of management science concerned with simulating, predicting, and optimizing the operation of a business or system or a portion thereof.

Optical character recognition (OCR): The machine identification of printed characters through use of light-sensitive devices.

Packet: A group of data with individual address and control signals in a specified format transferred as a whole within the data network.

Packet switching: The transfer of data by means of addressed packets whereby a channel is only occupied for the duration of transmission of the packet. The channel is then available for the transfer of other packets. In contrast with circuit switching, the data network determines the routing during, rather than prior to, the transfer of a packet.

Paper tape: A data recording medium consisting of a continuous length of paper or mylar tape typically 7/16″ wide or 1″ wide. Characters are recorded on the tape by punching holes across the width of the tape corresponding to the pattern of binary "ones" for that character in the code being used.

Plant: The land, buildings, machinery, apparatus and fixtures employed in carrying on trade or industrial business.

Pulse modulation: The modulation of the characteristics of a series of pulses in one of several ways to represent the information bearing signal. Typical methods involve modifying the amplitude (PAM), width or duration (PDM), position (PPM) or the duration of the pulse over time (PTM). The most common pulse modulation technique in telephone work is pulse code modulation (PCM). In PCM, the information signals are sampled at regular intervals and a series of pulses in coded form are transmitted, representing the amplitude of the information signal at that time.

Punched card: A data recording medium consisting of a stiff-paper card in which holes are punched to represent data in machine-readable format. In some systems each card contains one or more related data elements and is referred to as a unit record.

Pupin coil: A loading coil inserted in series with the conductors on a telephone line at regular intervals.

Pushbutton telephone: A telephone set or system in which each instrument has a series of buttons for selecting the line to be used, holding a line, or other functions. Does not refer to the technique used for dialing calls.

Rate centre: The telephone company location used for measuring mileages in the calculation of interexchange rates for measured and flat rate interexchange services.

Repeater: A bi-directional device used in channels to amplify or regenerate signals.

Semiconductor: Refers to the solid state components made of a semiconductor material (usually germanium or silicon) used in electronic circuitry. Transistors, diodes and integrated circuits are all classed as semiconductor devices.

Settlement summaries: Consolidated settlement information from all TCTS member companies.

Signal: A detectable impulse (voltage, current, magnetic field or light impulse) by which information is communicated through electronic or optical means over wire, cable, microwave or laser beams.

Tariff: The published volume of rates, rules and regulations concerning specific equipment and services provided by a communications common carrier.

Telecommunications: The aggregate of several modes of conveying information, signals or messages over a distance.

Telegraphy: A system of communication for the transmission of signals generated by a telegraph key.

Telemetry: The transmission of a measurement over long distances, usually by electromagnetic means. Includes the apparatus for measuring, formulating and recording the value of a measured quantity at a distance; e.g., waterlevel monitoring, flow rate metering.

Telenet: Telenet Communications Corp – a U.S. communications carrier offering packet switching transmission.

Telephone: A two-way device used mainly for voice communications which converts audible signals into electrical waves which can then be transmitted over communications channels.

Telephone, electronic: A telephone set which employs electronic circuitry to provide additional features and improved performance.

Telephony: The branch of telecommunications which has to do with transmission and reproduction of speech, and in some cases, other sounds; additional information may also be transferred.

Telephotography: Transmission of pictures over long distances by electrical means. Different from facsimile in the techniques used to scan and reproduce the picture.

Teletypewriter: A typewriter device capable of sending and receiving basically alphanumeric information over communications channels. Also known as a teleprinter.

Telex: An automatic dial-up teletypewriter switching service provided on a world-wide basis by various common carriers; e.g., within Canada CNCP Telecommunications provides Telex service, while in the United States, Western Union is the carrier.

Terminal: 1. A point at which information can enter or leave a communication network. 2. An input/output device designed to receive or send source data.

Time division multiplexing (TDM): A technique for combining one facility or transmission path in which each channel is allotted a specific position in the signal stream based upon time. Thus, the information on input channels is interleaved at higher speed on the main or multiplexed channel. At the receiving end, the signals are separated to reconstruct the individual or derived channels. The number of channels derived in this manner is dependent on the speed and bandwidth of the channels to be multiplexed and the speed of the high-speed channel.

Time Sharing: A method of operation in which a computer is shared by several users for different purposes at (apparently) the same time. Although the computer actually services each user in sequence for a short period of "time slice," the high speed of the computer makes it appear that all users are being handled simultaneously.

Toll call: Any call outside the defined local calling area, the income from which is credited to toll revenue.

Toll office: A switching centre where inter-city circuits terminate. Usually one office in a city is designated the toll office and is also used for mileage rate measurements.

Touch-Tone: A registered service mark of AT&T for pushbutton "dialing" service. Depressing a button on a Touch-Tone pad generates two (of a possible seven) tones which are recognized by the switching equipment as a specific digit. Because tones are used instead of DC pulses (as in rotary dialing), Touch-Tone service may be used for end-to-end signalling such as transmission of numeric data to a computer or other business machine.

Transceiver: A device capable of transmitting and receiving, not necessarily simultaneously.

Trunk: A circuit or channel connecting two exchanges or two switching devices. A circuit capable of being switched at both ends and provided with the necessary terminating and signalling equipment.

Visual display unit: A device which produces a visible read-out or display of data. Often equipped with a keyboard for interactive communication with a computer. Also referred to as a cathode ray tube (CRT) terminal. Visual display units are similar in appearance to television screens. A hard copy of the image may be produced for permanent record using a peripheral printer.

Voiceband: The band of frequencies permitting intelligible transmission of the human voice.

Vucom: A family of CRT terminals, intelligent and non-intelligent, provided by The Computer Communications Group of the TransCanada Telephone System.

WATS: Wide area telephone service.

Waveguide: A hollow metal pipe, rectangular or circular in cross-section but sometimes elliptical, which is precisely dimensioned to enable it to carry radio-frequency energy from one point to another. Used in microwave radio systems.

Bibliography

Public Documents

Bill C-24: An Act respecting Telecommunications in Canada. 1977.

Brief: for Commons Committee on Broadcasting re government bill to Establish a Communications Satellite Corporation.

Brief: for a Royal Commission on Canadian Economic Prospects, TCTS, January 1965.

Brief: for Special Parliamentary Committee on Radio, TCTS, Session 1936.

Brief: to Department of Commerce, TCTS, 1962.

Canada Yearbook, Ministry of Industry, Trade and Commerce, Section 16.1, 1974.

Debates: House of Commons, 1905, p. 2682.

Debates: House of Commons, July 8, 1959, p. 56998.

Huck, W.H. *Memorandum:* Department of Defence Production Assessment of Mid-Canada Line, private, 1959.

Public Notice: CRTC, Ottawa, August 4, 1978.

Submission: Regarding Bill C-43, the Telecommunications Act. CTCA, October 1977.

Submission: A Response to Proposals for a Communications and for a Computer Communications policy for Canada. Green Papers, May 1972, Bell Canada.

Telesat Canada Act, RS c T-4, 1971.

White Paper: On a Domestic Satellite Communications System for Canada, Ottawa: Queen's Printer, 1968.

Published Sources

"Aerial Tramways Used to Maintain Service on Alberta Unit of Microwave System," from *Within our Borders,* Edmonton, March 1958.

"Along the Tower Trail—to Winnipeg," *CBC Times,* September 30, 1956.

"Anik Calls Now Go Across Canada," *Bell News,* May 28, 1973.

Balfour, Clair "Grocery Shopping May Become Technology," *Globe & Mail,* August 2, 1972.

Bell News, Bell Canada, Montreal, issues 1964 to 1974.

Bell Quarterly, Bell Canada, Montreal, 1932 issues.

"Bell's Family Tree," *Financial Times,* May 2, 1977.

Blue Bell, Bell Canada, Montreal, issues 1920 to 1959.

Bliss, Chas. K. *Blissymbolics,* Sydney, Australia, 1970.

Bonneville, Sydney "The TransCanada Telephone System," *Bell Quarterly,* (undated).

Branch, Stephen and Chesholm, Laudine "Why the Railways Battle for Microwave Systems," *Financial Post,* March 24, 1962.

"Bridging the Communications Gap," *Financial Post,* December 11, 1975.

Brooks, John *Telephone, the First 100 Years,* New York: Harper & Row, 1975.

Brown, J.J. *Ideas in Exile,* Toronto: McClelland & Stewart, 1967.

"Canada's First Voice Highway in the Sky," *Blue Bell,* March 1953.

"The Case of Splitting Northern Telecom from its Parents Still Has to be Made," *Financial Post,* 1977.

Cashman, Tony *Singing Wires: The Telephone in Alberta,* Edmonton: Alberta Government Telephones, 1972.

Cashman, Tony and Jones, Yardley *AGT Presents the Telephone and What Difference Does It Make?* Edmonton, 1972.

Casson, Herbert N. *The History of the Telephone,* Chicago: A. C. McClurg, 1910.

Catto, C.E. *The Nova Scotia Project,* (undated).

Cavers, J.S. "The New TransCanada Telephone System," *The Telephone Echo,* March 1932.

"The Circuits Go Up, Part Two of a Quarter Century of TransContinental Telephone Service," *Bell Quarterly* January 1940.

Collins, Robert *A Voice from Afar,* Toronto: McGraw-Hill Ryerson, 1977.

"Computer Careers in Canada," *Telephony,* March 19, 1973.

"Computer Communications Group Formed," *Information Bulletin,* August 31, 1972.

"The Computer Horror," Victoria *Times,* May 13, 1978.

"The Computer Society," *Time* Magazine (special edition), February 20, 1978.

"Conversation with New York Costs Winnipeg Man $137.00," Winnipeg *Tribune,* January 6, 1957.

"CRTC Northern Hearings," *Inuit Taparisat,* Winter 1978.

Curran, Alex and Hamilton, Dave "The Evolution of Data Communications, a Canadian Experience," *Telesis,* Spring 1975.

Dalfen, Chas. M. *The Telesat, Canada's Domestic Communications Satellite System,* (undated).

"Data Speed System Opens," *Bell News,* November 1962.

"Datapac to Cut Costs 10-50%," *Bell News,* November 4, 1974.

"Direct Telephone Connection to Chicago Soon," Winnipeg *Tribune,* April 28, 1926.

"Direct Telephone Line now Links Chicago and Winnipeg," Winnipeg *Free Press,* December 24, 1926.

"Direct Telephone Line to British Columbia Open," Montreal *Gazette,* December 14,

Edinborough, Arnold "Story of Waste on the Mid-Canada Line," *Saturday Night,* March 14 and 28, 1959.

English, H. Edward *Telecommunications For Canada,* Toronto: Methuen, 1973.

"First Private Call Over Telephone Lines to Pacific Coast," Montreal *Star,* February 16, 1916.

From Sea to Sea, Formal Opening on July 1, 1958, of coast-to-coast microwave network of the TransCanada Telephone System, published on behalf of TCTS by Bell Telephone, Montreal, 1958.

Galbraith, J.K. *The Age of Uncertainty,* London: British Broadcasting Corporation: André Deutsch, 1977.

Goldman, Mark David "Information about Telephones You Can't Get by Dialing Information," *Weekend* Magazine, November 4, 1972.

Guzzardi, Walter, Jr., "The Great World Telephone War," *Fortune* Magazine, August 1977.

Hay, J.M. *Royal Train Story,* Bell Canada, Montreal.

"Hello, Montreal, Vancouver is Speaking," Vancouver *Province,* February 15, 1916.

Horton, David "The New Digital Network Speeds Canada's Data System," *Telesis,* Fall 1973.

"How Microwave Works," *Engineering Journal,* January 1962.

Hutcheson, Gordon D. "Revolution Coming in Telecommunications," *Financial Post,* July 8, 1972.

Hutcheson, Gordon, D. "Telesat Countdown Faces Cabinet," Ottawa *Journal,* September 10, 1971.

Jameson, Robert "Computerized Canada," *Financial Post,* June 10, 1978.

Johnson, Pat "Telephone Companies Getting Wagons In a Circle," Vancouver *Province,* March 11, 1978.

Kettle, John "The Information Society," *Computer Communications Group,* June 1977.

"The Future of the Telephone," *Canadian Communications Quarterly,* Summer 1974.

A Link of Empire, A record of the opening, by his excellency, the Earl of Bessborough, Governor General of Canada, on January 25, 1932, of the TransCanada Telephone System, Montreal: published privately by The Bell Telephone Company, February 1932.

Lowe, Frank and Beaver, Bert "Canada's Invisible Link," *Weekend* Magazine, September 29, 1956.

Mackay, Doug *The Honourable Company, A History of the Hudson's Bay Company,* Toronto: McClelland & Stewart, 1966.

"Maritime Linked to CBC-TV System," Montreal *Gazette,* February 1, 1958.

Meier, Albin R. "Canadian Communications Advance Rapidly," *Telephony, Journal of the Telecommunications Industry,* March 19, 1973.

"Microwave Goes Up Dog Mountain," *The Sun Telegram,* March 17, 1957.

"Microwave's Miracle Will Revolutionize Our Communications," Calgary *Herald,* February 2, 1957.

"Microwave Signals a Battle," Toronto *Telegram,* March 16, 1962.

"Microwaves Across Northumberland Strait," *Monthly Bulletin,* November 1948.

Mitchell, A.M. "A Dream Becomes a Reality," *The Silent Partner,* Telephone Association of Canada, February 1932.

"New Computer Communications Organization," Information *Bulletin* March 2, 1971.

"New Electronics Skyway for Private Canadian TV," *Bell News,* August 2, 1961.

"New Military Telephone Network for North American Air Defense," *Bell Lab Record,* March 1964.

"The New TransContinental Route is an Aid to Canada," *Telephone Talk,* December 1926.

Nicol, Eric Column in Vancouver *Province,* May 1978.

Oakley, Beatrice *History of Early Edmonton,* (undated)

Paine, Albert B. "In One Man's Life," a chapter from *The Personal and Business Career of T.N. Vail* New York: Harper Brothers, 1921.

"Participatory TV Tested," *TV Times,* April 28, 1978.

Patten, William, *Pioneering the Telephone in Canada,* Montreal: privately printed, 1926.

P.E.I. Leads World with New Phone System, (from undated news clippings).

"Phone Firms Nose out Rails in Bid for Radio Traffic," *Financial Post,* October 6, 1962.

Pilliod, J.J. "Twenty Years of Transcontinental Telephony," *Bell Quarterly,* October 1935.

"Regulating the Regulators," Vancouver *Province,* April 1978.

"Ringing Up Complaints," *Canadian Press,* May 1978.

Roberts, A.G. "Data Communications at the Crossroads, *Canadian Data Systems,* July 1970.

"Scientists Predict Sending Messages thru the Earth," *New York Times,* October 1977.

Seppala, Rafaela "French Can Dial a Call Girl—If They Can Find a Phone," *UPI,* 1978.

"Special Network for Grey Cup Telecast," Bell Canada, *Information Bulletin,* November 23, 1955.

TCTS and TAC Minutes of Combined Meeting, Montreal, 1931.

"Telecommunications in Canada," *The Telephone Journal* (special issue on Canada), March 1977.

Teleconferencing Project Report, January 1975.

Telephone Association of Canada, Minutes of Meetings and Proceedings, annual meetings, 1921 through 1931.

"Telephone Companies Wish Data Would Go Away," *Office Equipment and Methods,* November 1972.

Telephone Echo, issues 1921 to 1932.

"The Telephone 100 Years Later," *In Search, The Canadian Communications Quarterly* (special issue), Summer 1974.

Telephone Talk, B.C. Tel, Vancouver, issues 1921 to 1937.

The Telephone's Role in the History of Commonwealth Communications, a Brief Telephone History. (undated).

"Telephonic Connection, Fort William to Winnipeg Inaugurated," Winnipeg *Free Press,* May 6, 1926.

"Telesat's Decision to Join Phone System a Golden One?" *Financial Post,* May 28, 1977.

"Two-Way Conversation Carried out Successfully with Ottawa, Montreal and St. John's," Montreal *Gazette,* January 11, 1939.

Walters, D.W. "Computer Communications in Canada," *Telephony,* March 1973.

Weir, E. Austin *The Struggle for National Broadcasting in Canada,* Toronto: McClelland & Stewart, 1965.

White, Sean, "Northern Telecom Could Live Without Bells," *Financial Post,* 1977.

"The World's Telephones" (as of January 1, 1977), New York: *AT&T Long Lines.*

Ziegler, Rod "AGT to Use Fibre Optics," Edmonton *Journal,* May 1978.

Pamphlets, Brochures and Booklets

A *Technical Description of the Canadian Domestic Satellite Communications System,* Telesat Canada, Ottawa, 1974.

An Outline of the History of CP Telecommunications, Canadian Pacific, Montreal, 1972.

Alexander Graham Bell, booklet, Bell Canada, Montreal (undated).

Alexander Graham Bell National Historical Park, Brochure, National Park Service, Ottawa (undated).

Anikom Services, Brochure, Telesat Canada, Ottawa (undated).

Annual Reports: British Columbia Telephone Company; Bell Canada; Telesat Canada; Maritime Telegraph & Telephone Company Limited; Newfoundland Telephone Company Limited; The New Brunswick Telephone Company, Limited; Saskatchewan Telecommunications; Manitoba Telephone System; Alberta Government Telephones; The Island Telephone Company Limited; Teleglobe Canada, 1976 and 1977.

Bell Canada, booklet, Bell Canada, Montreal (undated).

Bell Homestead, Brochure, National Park Service, Ottawa (undated).

The Computer Communications Group, pamphlet, TCTS, Ottawa (undated).

Datapac Overview, CCG, Ottawa, (undated).

Growing Up With Newfoundland, information booklet, Newfoundland Telephone Company Limited (undated).

Hay, J.M. *Royal Train Story,* Montreal, 1939.

History of the Telephone in Saskatchewan, Saskatchewan Telecommunications, Regina (undated).

Let's Get Together; Brochure, Telesat Canada, Ottawa, (undated).

Minutes of Meeting, Telephone Association of Canada, annual conventions, 1921-1931 inclusive.

Minutes of Meeting, combined meeting TransCanada Telephone System and Telephone Association of Canada, May 1931.

Minutes of Meeting, Western Provincial Telephone Companies, 1920.

Status Report on Microwave Project, TCTS, Ottawa, November 25, 1956.

Telecommunications — the Telephone Plus, Booklet, Bell Canada, Montreal.

Telephones Through the Years, Bell Canada, Montreal (undated).

Thanks a Hundred, Mr. Bell, Bell Canada, Montreal, 1974.

TCTS, Bell Quarterly, July 1932.

TCTS Toll Settlement Arrangements, Alberta Government Telephones, Edmonton, April, 1977.

The Vital Link, Telecommunications Serving Canada, CTCA, Ottawa (undated).

Unpublished Sources

An Overview of the Telecommunications System in Newfoundland, Canadian National, commissioned study (undated).

Brice, G.E., *The TransCanada Telephone System,* an address, Alberta Government Telephones Marketing Symposium, Edmonton, November 15, 1969.

Britnell, G.E. *Public Ownership of Telephones in the PRAIRIE Provinces,* manuscript, (undated).

Bryant, J.F., Address by the Minister of Telephones, Saskatchewan government, Regina, January 28, 1932.

Chinnick, R.F. *Canadian Satellite Telecommunications Plans for the 1980s,* Paper for delivery, International Astronautical Federation, September 25, 1977.

Eadie, Thomas W., Press Conference, *Bell News,* Montreal, June 18, 1956.

Early Telephone Development in St. John, manuscript, Western Union and Dominion Telephone Companies (undated).

Groleau, Arnold, *Communications of the Future,* speech, March 6, 1963.

Groleau, Arnold, *The TransCanada Telephone System Programme,* speech, 1955.

Groleau, Arnold, *Ten Years of Progress,* address, Bell Canada, Montreal, (undated).

Growing Up with the Province, Slide Tape Presentation, Newfoundland Telephone Company Limited, St. John's, August 1977.

Hewat, W.B., *Data Communications, Current and Future,* address, March 1974.

History of the Telephone Company of Prince Edward Island, manuscript, The Island Telephone Company Limited (undated).

The Island Telephone Company, manuscript, The Island Telephone Company Limited (undated).

Kee, C.A. *History of The New Brunswick Telephone Company,* manuscript, The New Brunswick Telephone Company Limited, (undated).

Krupski, Z.H., *A Domestic Communications Satellite System, Its Integration with Terrestrial Communications,* speech, October 6, 1969.

Lester, A.G., *Reminiscences,* Bell Canada, Montreal (undated).

Leworthy, Verson J. *Applied Network Planning,* Discussion with the Hon. Eric Kierans, January 13, 1969.

McKay, A. Murray, *History of Maritime Telegraph and Telephone,* unfinished manuscript, 1978.

Mallet-Paret, Doug, *Evidence in Chief,* Regulation and Settlement AGT, Alberta Government Telephones, January 21, 1976.

Memorandum of Agreement, (between seven companies that formed TransCanada Telephone System), March 1931, TCTS, Ottawa.

Millidge, N.C. *TransCanada Telephone System: Its Purpose and Missions,* paper, Ottawa, July 7, 1977.

Muir, G.A., *A History of the Telephone in Manitoba,* manuscript, Winnipeg, (undated).

The New Brunswick Telephone Company, Limited, manuscript, The New Brunswick Telephone Company, Limited (undated).

Northern Electric Company, history, manuscript, Bell Canada, Montreal (undated).

Noseworthy, Sandra, *A Short History of the Newfoundland Telephone Company Limited,* manuscript, St. John's, 1977.

Noyes, J.W., Gaudet, G. and Bonneville, Sydney, *Development of Transcontinental communications in Canada,* paper presented to the American Institute of Electrical Engineers, New York, January 30, 1956.

Owen, H.G. *A Short History of the TransCanada Telephone System,* Volumes C and E, TCTS, Ottawa, 1974-75.

Owen, H.G., *What is the Mid-Canada Line,* paper, Bell Canada, Montreal (undated).

People of Service, a Brief History of the Manitoba Telephone System, Manitoba Telephone System, Winnipeg (undated).

Scrivener, R.C., *Datapac Overview,* address, Bell Canada, Montreal (undated).

Scrivener, R.C., speech at signing of Bell-Telesat contract, Frobisher Bay, October 13, 1972.

Teleconferencing Project Report, TCTS, Ottawa, January 1975.

Thompson, Gordon B. *Muloch or Aquarius?* Bell Northern Research, manuscript, Ottawa, (date coming).

Thompson, Gordon. B. *Memo from Mercury, the Role of Communications in a Socioeconomic system in Transit,* Bell Northern Research, manuscript, Ottawa, 1978.

Warren, W.H. Letter to R.V. Macaulay, TCTS, Ottawa (undated).

Wilkinson, Elfleda, *British Columbia Telephones,* unfinished manuscript, British Columbia Telephone Company, 1978.

Interviews

BY THE AUTHOR

Ades, Gordon, president, Alberta Government Telephones, August 1977.

Archibald, Donald, manager general services, Maritime Telegraph and Telephone Company Limited, November 1977.

Archibald, Gordon, chairman board of directors, Maritime Telegraph and Telephone Company Limited, November 1977.

Auld, Walter, vice-president, The New Brunswick Telephone Company, Limited, November 1977.

Brait, A.A. president, Newfoundland Telephone Company Limited, November 1977.

Chinnick, Robert F., vice-president, Telesat Canada, January 1978.

Cox, Kenneth V., president, The New Brunswick Telephone Company, Limited, November 1977.

Eadie, Thomas W., president, Bell Canada (ret), chairman TCTS, (1952-1958) March 1978.

Edmonds, Duncan, adviser to Joe Clark, March 1978.

Graham, Ed, vice-president, planning, The New Brunswick Telephone Company, Limited, January 1978.

Heenan, Terence, president, TCTS, January 1978.

Hierlihy, Oscar, Newfoundland Telephone Company Limited, November 1977.

Krupski, Z.H., chairman, TCTS, (1964-1977) January 1978.

Leworthy, J. Vernon, vice-president, Bell Canada, (ret) September 1977.

Mackay, Dr. A. Murray, chairman, board of directors, Maritime Telegraph and Telephone Company Limited, (ret) September 1977.

McMahon, Andrew, director, The Computer Communications Group, November 1977.

Millidge, N.C. secretary and director of administration, TCTS, February 1978.

Phemister, N.R. TCTS (ret), February 1978.

Robertson, Struan, president, Maritime Telegraph and Telephone Company Limited, November 1977.

Thompson, Gordon, vice-president, Bell Northern Research, February 1978.

BY TONY CASHMAN, Alberta Government Telephones historian

Baker, Ted, Alberta Government Telephones, July 1972.

Bearman, Ross, Saskatchewan Telecommunications, April 1976.

Bishop, Harold, December 1975.

Bonneville, Sydney, TCTS, April 1976.

Bourne, Harold, British Columbia Telephone Company, April 1975.

Carlile, Jack, British Columbia Telephone Company, April 1976.

Collins, Bert, British Columbia Telephone Company, August 1975, January 1976.

Dickie, Gerald, Alberta Government Telephones, March 1972.

Farrell, Gordon, president, British Columbia Telephone Company (ret) August 1975.

Fenton, Jim, Manitoba Telephone System, (ret), July 1975.

Johnston, Jack, Saskatchewan Telecommunications, April 1976.

Jones, Walter, British Columbia Telephone Company, August 1975.

Kennedy, Gil, British Columbia Telephone Company, October 1975.

Mallet-Paret, Doug, Alberta Government Telephones, March 1972.

McLean, Cyrus, British Columbia Telephone Company (ret), August 1975.

Mills, Jim, Manitoba Telephone System, October 1975.

Milne, Gordon, Saskatchewan Telecommunications, April 1976.

Muirhead, Stuart, Saskatchewan Telecommunications, September 1975.

Peddle, Ron, Saskatchewan Telecommunications, April 1976.

Pipes, Winfield, British Columbia Telephone Company, August 1975.

Smail, Herb, Saskatchewan Telecommunications, April 1976.

Strachan, Al, British Columbia Telephone Company, August 1976.

Taylor, Gordon, former Alberta Minister of Railways and Telephones, April 1972.

Thomson, Harry, Alberta Government Telephones, July 1972.

Williams, Larry, British Columbia Telephone Company, October 1977.

Wolokoff, Frank, British Columbia Telephone Company, September 1977.

BY R.H. SPENCER, Bell Canada historian (ret)

Eadie, Thomas W. president, Bell Canada and chairman, TCTS, (ret), March 17, 1977.
Groleau, Arnold, Bell Canada, November 1978.
Lester, Alex, G., Bell Canada, November 1978.

BY R.H. SPENCER AND H.G. OWEN, Bell Canada

Noyes, Jack, Bell Canada, May 1976.

BY FURBER MARSHALL, historian, Maritime Telegraph and Telephone Company Limited

Bunker, Harry, The New Brunswick Telephone Company, Limited, February 1975.
Grant, J. Havard, The New Brunswick Telephone Company, Limited, February 1975.
Lutes, John N., The New Brunswick Telephone Company, Limited, March 1975.
Nickerson, Allan, Maritime Telegraph and Telephone Company Limited, March 1975.

BY ELFLEDA WILKINSON AND HAROLD BOURNE, historians,
British Columbia Telephone Company

Farrell, Gordon, president, British Columbia Telephone Company, (ret) March 1970.

BY ED MATHESON, TCTS history project coordinator

Hall, Denis, president, Bell Northern Research, June 1978.

296

Index

Picture Credits

Alberta Government Telephones 75, 127, 141; Bell Canada, Historical Collection 23, 26, 28, 29, 32, 38, 39, 40, 43, 45, 47, 55, 59, 67, 83, 96, 187, 196, 201, 205; British Columbia Telephone Company and Brown Photographers 152, Dominion Photo 155 and B.C. Jennings Ltd 76, Glenbow Alberta Institute 128; Oscar Hierlihy 116; The Island Telephone Company Limited 111, 207; Manitoba Telephone System 89, 125, 131; Maritime Telegraph and Telephone Company Limited 118, 119, 120; The New Brunswick Telephone Company, Limited 85, 107, 109, 115; Newfoundland Telephone Company Limited 209; Saskatchewan Telecommunications 132, 139, 142, 145; Telesat Canada 161, 164, 167; The TransCanada Telephone System 251, 267. The photograph of Alexander Graham Bell, page 23 is © Library of Congress, Washington, U.S.A. and the Bell family.

TransCanada Telephone System